D1199465

MATHEMATICAL LOGIC

A First Course

UNIVERSITY MATHEMATICS SERIES

Fred Brauer and John A. Nohel, Editors
University of Wisconsin

ELEMENTARY DIFFERENTIAL EQUATIONS: PRINCIPLES, PROBLEMS, AND SOLUTIONS

Fred Brauer and John A. Nohel, University of Wisconsin

ORDINARY DIFFERENTIAL EQUATIONS: A FIRST COURSE

Fred Brauer and John A. Nohel, University of Wisconsin

THE QUALITATIVE THEORY OF ORDINARY DIFFERENTIAL EQUATIONS

Fred Brauer and John A. Nohel, University of Wisconsin

MATHEMATICAL LOGIC: A FIRST COURSE

Joel W. Robbin, University of Wisconsin

MATHEMATICAL LOGIC:

A FIRST COURSE

Joel W. Robbin

University of Wisconsin

W. A. BENJAMIN, INC., *New York · Amsterdam · 1969*

MATHEMATICAL LOGIC: *A First Course*

Library of Congress Catalog Card Number 69-15423
Manufactured in the United States of America

12345K32109

The manuscript was put into production August 21, 1968
This volume was published on May 1, 1969

W. A. BENJAMIN, INC., *New York, New York* 10016

PREFACE

Today, many universities offer an advanced undergraduate–graduate course in mathematical logic. Such a course is normally taught by either the philosophy department or the mathematics department, but it usually attracts students from diverse fields and varying backgrounds. A typical class may contain students of mathematics, philosophy, linguistics, computer science, and engineering. Some of these students will eventually specialize in mathematical logic; others only want to relate the subject to problems in their own fields of interest. Some will be completely at ease with mathematical jargon; others will be unfamiliar with the notions of set theory or the concept of mathematical proof. This textbook attempts to meet the needs of such a course.

Chapters 1 and 2 provide enough material for a leisurely one-semester course. The exercises are sufficiently challenging to keep the better students from getting bored. A less leisurely one-semester course which omits the completeness theorem in favor of the incompleteness theorem would omit §§16–18 and include Chapters 3 and 4 and §37 plus as much of the remainder of Chapter 5 as time permits. The whole book (with the exercises) contains sufficient material for a year course, but it is probably better to leave Chapter 6 for independent study and use the time to introduce the student to either recursive function theory or set theory. A graduate course or a course containing only mathematics students should be able to cover a substantial part of the first five chapters in one semester.

The book contains a wide selection of exercises. Unstarred exercises test understanding of the text and are generally relatively easy. Starred exercises (*) treat topics not dealt with in the text and are often extremely difficult. Solutions to some of the exercises are given (in varying detail) in the section at the back of the book entitled "Answers to Selected Exercises."

Only rarely does part of the text depend on the result of an earlier exercise. When this is the case, the answer to that exercise is given in the "Answers to Selected Exercises."

There is an appendix on basic set theory intended for students with little or no mathematical background. This appendix makes the book self-contained. In principle, a person could read the book without any previous knowledge or outside help. In practice, the subject matter is quite difficult and only students who have attained a high level of mathematical maturity could be expected to get through the book without the help of a teacher.

I have generally followed the notational conventions of S. C. Kleene's *Introduction to Metamathematics*. Lightface Roman type is used for particular expressions in the formal language, boldface Roman type is used for syntactical variables (i.e., variables in English ranging over expressions in a formal language), and italic type is used for semantical variables (i.e., variables in English ranging over mathematical objects other than the expressions of a formal language). In Chapter 2 I have also followed A. Robinson in not distinguishing between individual constants and the individuals which they denote. An index of symbols, including a more detailed explanation of the notational conventions, is given at the back of the book.

Theorem proving in the formal language is left almost entirely to the student; only metatheorems are proved in detail. A proof in a formal language will have little value to a student unless he can reconstruct it himself. Experience shows that students respond well to this challenge.

I have used the Halmos bar (▌) to indicate the end of a proof. I also use iff as an abbreviation for "if and only if" in definitions. Also I always indicate a definition by placing the definiens in **boldface** or *italics*. In Chapter 4 the usual mathematical symbol $\Leftrightarrow$ is also used as an abbreviation for "if and only if."

The present book obviously owes much to Alonzo Church's *Introduction to Mathematical Logic* (Princeton University Press, 1956) and I recommend Church's book as collateral reading for those students interested in the philosophical fine points of the subject. In addition, Chapter 6 contains material which I learned from Professor Church's lectures in a graduate course in logic which he used to teach regularly at Princeton.

I should like to express my thanks to Margaret Blumberg for typing the manuscript, Diane Rinehart and Audell Adkins for their secretarial assistance, and W. A. Benjamin, Inc., for production of the book.

JOEL W. ROBBIN

Madison, Wisconsin
September 1968

CONTENTS

NOTE TO THE STUDENT

Mathematical logic may be defined as the study of formal languages. Like ordinary languages, formal languages have a *syntax* (i.e. a grammar) and a *semantics* (i.e. a theory of meaning or truth); the most interesting parts of mathematical logic deal with the interplay between these two aspects of language. In principle, there is no reason why a formal language could not be used as a vehicle for communication like an ordinary language, but it is probably better to view formal languages as mathematical structures which mirror some of the properties of ordinary language.

The study of any formal language always proceeds in three steps. First, the syntax of the language is given. This is done by listing the alphabet (called the *primitive symbols*) of the language, and then specifying which finite sequences of these symbols constitute grammatically correct sentences (called the *well-formed formulas* or *wffs* of the language). The rules of proof of a language are also part of its syntax. Those sentences of the language which can be proven according to these rules are called its *theorems*. Syntactical questions (such as whether a particular sentence is a theorem) are always independent of any meaning or interpretation which the language might be given, and should be answered without reference to such meaning. Thus from the point of view of syntax, mathematical logic is a *meaningless game with symbols*.

Second, the semantics of the formal language is given. This consists in specifying the admissible interpretations of the language (in the case of the propositional calculus studied in Chapter 1 these are called *valuations*, and in the case of the first-order languages studied in Chapter 2 these are called *models*), and then specifying which sentences are *true* in a given interpretation. Sentences which are true in every admissible interpretation are called *valid* or *tautologous*.

Third, the relation between the syntax and the semantics is studied. The two principal questions here are the question of *soundness* (Is every theorem valid?) and the question of *completeness* (Is every valid sentence a theorem?).

It is anticipated that some of the readers of this book will have little or no mathematical experience. If you are one of these, study the appendix (particularly §A1 and §A2) in order to gain familiarity with the jargon of *set theory* and *mathematical induction*.

Any mathematical book should be read slowly; do not proceed to a new topic until you have thoroughly grasped the preceding topics. Look up unfamiliar symbols in the index or the index of symbols at the back of the book. Work as many of the unstarred exercises as are necessary to insure that you understand the text. Many of the answers are given at the end of the book, but you should always attempt the exercise before looking up the answer. The starred exercises develop material not covered in the text and are often very difficult; do not be discouraged if you cannot do them.

Chapter 1 THE PROPOSITIONAL CALCULUS

In this book we shall study certain *formal languages* each of which abstracts from ordinary mathematical language (and, to a lesser extent, everyday English) some aspects of its logical structure. Formal languages differ from informal languages in that the syntax of a formal language is precisely given. This is not the case with informal languages like English; authorities often disagree as to whether a given English sentence is grammatically correct. The study of formal languages is the content of that branch of mathematics known as *mathematical logic*. Mathematical logic has important applications in such diverse fields as electrical engineering, computer science, and philosophy and, in addition, yields much insight into the structure of language in general.

In this chapter we study a formal language called the *propositional calculus*. The purpose of this formal language is to abstract from ordinary language the properties of certain *sentential connectives* (commonly called "conjunctions" by grammarians). Among these are "not", "and", "or", "if", and "if and only if". We study only those connectives which are *extensional* in the sense that the truth value of a compound sentence built up from these connectives depends only on the truth values of the component simple sentences. (The conjunction "because" is not extensional in this sense. See Exercise 1.) Furthermore, we are concerned only with the meanings that common mathematical usage gives to these words; this is sometimes slightly different from their meanings in everyday language. We now explain the meanings of these connectives.

1. If P is a sentence, then the sentence "not P" is true exactly when P is false. The symbol used in mathematical logic for "not" is $\sim$. Thus, of the two sentences

$$\sim 2+2=4$$
$$\sim 2+2=5$$

the first is false while the second is true.

2. If P and Q are sentences, the sentence "P or Q" is true exactly when either P is true or Q is true (or both). The symbol for "or" is $\vee$. Thus, of the four sentences

$$2+2=4 \vee 2+3=5$$
$$2+2=4 \vee 2+3=7$$
$$2+2=7 \vee 2+3=5$$
$$2+2=7 \vee 2+3=7$$

the first three all are true, while the last is false.

Occasionally, the sentence "P or Q" has a different meaning in everyday life from the one given above. Thus, when a restaurant menu contains the phrase "soup or salad included with the dinner" it means that soup or salad, but not both, are included with the dinner. This usage of the word "or" is called the *exclusive or* (because it excludes the case that both components are true). Mathematicians generally use the *inclusive or* explained above; when they wish to use the exclusive or, they generally say "P or Q but not both."

3. If P and Q are sentences, then the sentence "P and Q" is true exactly when both P and Q are true. The mathematical symbol for "and" is $\wedge$. Thus, of the four sentences

$$2+2=4 \wedge 3+3=6$$
$$2+2=4 \wedge 3+3=7$$
$$2+2=5 \wedge 3+3=6$$
$$2+2=5 \wedge 3+3=7$$

the first is true while the others are false.

For the mathematician the sentences "P and Q" and "P but Q" have the same meaning. In everyday English this seems not to be the case, but the difference is primarily psychological rather than logical.

4. If P and Q are sentences, then the sentences "If P, then Q", "Q, if P", "P implies Q", "P, only if Q", and "Q whenever P" all have the same meaning for the mathematician: "P implies Q" is false when P is true and Q is false and true otherwise. The mathematical symbol for "implies" is $\supset$. Thus, of the four sentences

$$2+2=4 \supset 3+3=6$$
$$2+2=4 \supset 3+3=7$$
$$2+2=5 \supset 3+3=6$$
$$2+2=5 \supset 3+3=7$$

the second is false while the remaining three all are true.

This usage is in sharp contrast to the usage in everyday language. Usually a sentence of the form "If P, then Q" suggests a kind of necessity, that is, Q "necessarily follows from" P. For example, consider the sentence

"If Columbus discovered America, then Aristotle was a Greek."

Since Aristotle was indeed a Greek, this sentence (according to our meaning of the word "if") is true regardless of whether or not Columbus was the discoverer of America. However, common usage would judge this sentence to be either false or nonsensical since there is no apparent connection between Columbus' discovering America and Aristotle's being a Greek. To distinguish the meaning of "implies" given in our context from other possible meanings, logicians called implication according to the former meaning *material implication*. Material implication is extensional in the sense that the truth value of "P materially implies Q" depends only on the truth values of P and Q; other kinds of implication are not extensional in this sense. In this book, implication always means material implication.

5. If P and Q are sentences, then the sentences "P if and only if Q", "P is equivalent to Q", and "P exactly when Q" all have the same meaning for the mathematician: they are true when P and Q have the same truth value and are false in the contrary case. The symbol for equivalence is $\equiv$. Thus, of the four sentences

$$2+2=4 \equiv 3+3=6$$

$$2+2=4 \equiv 3+3=7$$

$$2+2=5 \equiv 3+3=6$$

$$2+2=5 \equiv 3+3=7$$

the first and last are true while the other two are false.

Evidently "P if and only if Q" has the same meaning as "If P, then Q, and if Q, then P". Hence equivalence has divergent meanings in everyday language just as implication has. To distinguish the meaning given in our context, it is referred to by logicians as *material equivalence* and this is the only meaning which we shall consider in this book. Material equivalence is the "equality" of the logic of propositions.

Now several of these connectives can be defined in terms of the others. For example, "P implies Q" means the same as "either not P or Q" and "P or Q" means the same as "not both not P and not Q". Thus, in our formal language we may take some of the connectives to be undefined and define the others in terms of these. The undefined symbols of a language are called its *primitive symbols*. We shall take $\supset$ and $\mathfrak{f}$ as primitive and define the other connectives in terms of $\supset$ and $\mathfrak{f}$. Here $\mathfrak{f}$ stands for some false sentence such as $0=1$.

EXERCISES

1. Give examples of three true English sentences P, Q, and R such that the sentence "P because Q" is true, but the sentence "P because R" is false. Conclude that "because" is not an extensional connective.

2. Find everyday usages of the connectives mentioned in the text whose meanings differ from the meanings given in the text.

3. In the land of Og, there are only two kinds of people: peasants, who speak only the truth, and princes, who always lie. Furthermore, all citizens of Og, peasant or prince, will answer exactly one question asked by a traveler. A traveler in Og comes to a fork in the road; he wants to journey to the capital, but does not know which road is correct. He meets a citizen of Og. What question should he ask? (All questions should be of the type that can be answered by "yes" or "no.")

4. In the land of Gog princes always lie, peasants always tell the truth, while merchants sometimes tell the truth and sometimes lie. A tourist is enjoying an afternoon refreshment in one of the local pubs when the bartender (who always tells the truth) says to him: "Do you see those three men over there? One is a peasant, another a prince, and the third a merchant. You may ask them three questions, always indicating which man you wish should answer. If, after asking these three questions, you correctly identify the peasant, prince, and merchant, they will buy you a drink." The tourist is indeed very thirsty. What questions should he ask?

   Hint: Locate the merchant with two questions. (All questions should be of the type which can be answered by "yes" or "no.")

5. Express the connective "neither P nor Q" in terms of the connectives mentioned in the text.

§1 Formation Rules for P

In this section we begin our study of the formal language P which is called the **propositional calculus**. The **primitive symbols of** P are the following:

1. the infinite list of symbols $p_1, p_2, p_3, \ldots$ called **proposition letters**;

2. the symbol $\supset$ called the **implication sign**;

3. the symbol $\mathfrak{f}$ called the **falsity sign**;

4. the symbols [and] called respectively the **left bracket** and the **right bracket**.

Any finite sequence of primitive symbols is called a *formula*. The class of **well-formed formulas of the propositional calculus or wffs of** P is defined inductively by the following rules:

(W1) Any proposition letter standing alone is a wff;

(W2) $\mathfrak{f}$ is a wff;

(W3) If **A** and **B** are wffs, then $[\mathbf{A} \supset \mathbf{B}]$ is a wff;

(W4) A formula is a wff only if it is required to be a wff by rules (W1), (W2), and (W3).

To make formulas more readable we adopt several *conventions* concerning the omission of brackets:

1. The outermost brackets on a formula are omitted. Thus we write

$$p_3 \supset [\mathfrak{f} \supset p_1]$$

rather than

$$[p_3 \supset [\mathfrak{f} \supset p_1]].$$

2. A dot to the immediate right of an implication sign indicates that a left bracket should replace the dot and a right bracket should appear at the end of the formula. Thus we write

$$p_2 \supset \centerdot\, \mathfrak{f} \supset p_1$$

instead of

$$p_2 \supset [\mathfrak{f} \supset p_1].$$

3. A dot to the immediate left of an implication sign indicates that a right bracket should replace the dot and a left bracket should appear at the beginning of the formula. Thus we write

$$p_2 \supset \mathfrak{f} \centerdot \supset p_1$$

instead of

$$[p_2 \supset \mathfrak{f}] \supset p_1$$

and

$$p_3 \supset [p_1 \supset p_2] \centerdot \supset \centerdot\, [p_3 \supset p_1] \supset [p_3 \supset p_2]$$

instead of

$$[p_3 \supset [p_1 \supset p_2]] \supset [[p_3 \supset p_1] \supset [p_3 \supset p_2]].$$

We also introduce several *abbreviations*. The sign

$\rightsquigarrow$

is used to introduce abbreviations; it is read "is an abbreviation for."

(D1) $\sim\mathbf{A} \rightsquigarrow [\mathbf{A} \supset \mathfrak{f}]$

The sign only $\sim$ is called the **negation sign**.

(D2) $\mathbf{A} \vee \mathbf{B} \rightsquigarrow \sim\mathbf{A} \supset \mathbf{B}$

The sign $\vee$ is called the **disjunction sign**.

(D3) $\mathbf{A} \wedge \mathbf{B} \rightsquigarrow \sim[\sim\mathbf{A} \vee \sim\mathbf{B}]$

The sign $\wedge$ is called the **conjunction sign**.

(D4) $\mathbf{A} \equiv \mathbf{B} \rightsquigarrow [\mathbf{A} \supset \mathbf{B}] \wedge [\mathbf{B} \supset \mathbf{A}]$

The sign $\equiv$ is called the **equivalence sign**.

An expression containing these signs should be thought of as an abbreviation for the corresponding formula of the propositional calculus.

When interpreting negation signs in an abbreviation the convention is that the right bracket is added at the leftmost position which makes the whole formula well formed. Thus, we write[1]

$$\sim\mathbf{A} \supset \mathbf{B}$$

instead of

$$[[\mathbf{A} \supset \mathfrak{f}] \supset \mathbf{B}]$$

and do not confuse it with

$$\sim[\mathbf{A} \supset \mathbf{B}]$$

which stands for

$$[[\mathbf{A} \supset \mathbf{B}] \supset \mathfrak{f}].$$

---

[1] The boldface capital letters **A**, **B**, . . . stand for arbitrary wffs, while the letters p_1, p_2, . . . denote particular proposition letters. In this book we will for the most part be making statements about all the wffs (or all the wffs of a certain form) and hence we will usually use boldface capitals. In giving examples, however, we will usually give particular formulas (and hence use p_1, p_2, . . .). In this section we use both notations in order to familiarize the reader with them.

The convention about brackets and dots apply to the other signs as well. Thus, we write

$$p_3 \vee \centerdot p_1 \vee p_2$$

instead of

$$[p_3 \vee [p_1 \vee p_2]]$$

and

$$p_4 \vee p_1 \centerdot \equiv \centerdot p_4 \wedge p_2$$

instead of

$$[[p_4 \vee p_1] \equiv [p_4 \wedge p_2]].$$

Furthermore, a dot to the immediate right of a negation sign indicates that a left bracket should replace the dot and a right bracket should appear at the end of the formula. Thus we write

$$\sim \centerdot \mathbf{A} \supset \mathbf{B}$$

instead of

$$\sim[\mathbf{A} \supset \mathbf{B}].$$

Finally, we sometimes omit subscripts on proposition letters:

$$p \rightsquigarrow p_1;$$

$$q \rightsquigarrow p_2;$$

$$r \rightsquigarrow p_3;$$

$$s \rightsquigarrow p_4.$$

In any wff or abbreviation for a wff the connective which corresponds to the outermost brackets (which are usually omitted) is called the **principal connective**. Thus in the formula

$$p_1 \supset [p_2 \vee p_1]$$

the implication sign is the principal connective while in

$$[p_1 \supset p_2] \vee p_1$$

the disjunction sign is the principal connective.

EXERCISES

1. Which of the following formulas are wffs or abbreviations for wffs? Which stand for the same wff? Indicate the principal connective in each wff.

(1) $\mathfrak{f}$
(2) $\mathfrak{f} \supset$
(3) p
(4) $[\mathrm{f} \supset \mathrm{f}]$
(5) $[\mathrm{p}_1 \supset \mathrm{p}_2 \mathfrak{f}$
(6) $\mathrm{p}_1 \supset\!\centerdot\ \mathrm{p}_2$
(7) $\mathrm{p} \supset\!\centerdot\ \mathrm{q} \supset\!\centerdot\ \mathrm{p} \supset \mathrm{q}$
(8) $\sim [\mathrm{p} \supset \mathrm{q}]$
(9) $\sim \mathrm{p} \supset \mathrm{q}$
(10) $\sim\centerdot\ \mathrm{p} \supset \mathrm{q}$
(11) $[\sim \mathrm{p}] \supset \mathrm{q}$
(12) $\mathrm{p} \supset \mathrm{q}\ \centerdot\!\equiv \mathrm{p}$
(13) $\mathrm{p} \vee \mathrm{q}$
(14) $\sim\centerdot \sim\sim \mathrm{p} \supset \sim \mathrm{q}$
(15) $\mathrm{p} \wedge \mathrm{q}$
(16) $\mathrm{p} \equiv \mathrm{q}$
(17) $\sim\centerdot \sim\sim [\mathrm{p} \supset \mathrm{q}] \supset \sim [\mathrm{q} \supset \mathrm{p}]$

2. Show that if **A** is a wff, then the number of right brackets in **A**, the number of left brackets in **A**, and the number of implication signs in **A** are all equal.

§2 Formal Semantics of P

There are precisely two **truth values**: **truth** and **falsity**. The truth value truth is denoted by the symbol 1 and the truth value falsity is denoted by the symbol 0.

A **valuation** is a function v from the set $\{\mathrm{p}_1, \mathrm{p}_2, \ldots\}$ of proposition letters to the set $\{0, 1\}$ of truth values. Thus v assigns to each proposition letter p_n $(n = 1, 2, \ldots)$ a truth value $v(\mathrm{p}_n)$: $v(\mathrm{p}_n) = 0$ or $v(\mathrm{p}_n) = 1$.

Given a valuation v we may extend it to the set of all wffs via the following inductive definition:

(V1) $v(\mathrm{p}_n)$ is already defined $(n = 1, 2, \ldots)$;

(V2) $v(\mathfrak{f}) = 0$;

(V3) $v(\mathbf{A} \supset \mathbf{B}) = 0$ if $v(\mathbf{A}) = 1$ and $v(\mathbf{B}) = 0$;
$= 1$ otherwise.

Thus a truth value $v(\mathbf{A})$ is determined for each wff **A** once truth values $v(\mathrm{p}_n)$ have been determined for the proposition letters $\mathrm{p}_1, \mathrm{p}_2, \ldots$. A wff **A** is a **tautology** iff $v(\mathbf{A}) = 1$ for *every* valuation v.

We illustrate with an example.

Proposition. If **A** and **B** are any wffs, then the wff $[\mathbf{A} \supset \mathbf{B}] \supset \mathfrak{f}\ \centerdot\!\supset\!\centerdot\ \mathbf{B} \supset \mathfrak{f}$ is a tautology.

PROOF. We must show

$$v([\mathbf{A} \supset \mathbf{B}] \supset \mathfrak{f} \,.\!\supset\!.\, \mathbf{B} \supset \mathfrak{f}) = 1$$

for every valuation v. Choose an arbitrary valuation v. There are four cases:

CASE 1. $v(\mathbf{A}) = v(\mathbf{B}) = 1$. Then $v(\mathbf{A} \supset \mathbf{B}) = 1$. Since $v(\mathfrak{f}) = 0$, $v([\mathbf{A} \supset \mathbf{B}] \supset \mathfrak{f}) = 0$. Hence $v([\mathbf{A} \supset \mathbf{B}] \supset \mathfrak{f} \,.\!\supset\!.\, \mathbf{B} \supset \mathfrak{f}) = 1$.

CASE 2. $v(\mathbf{A}) = 1$, $v(\mathbf{B}) = 0$. Then $v(\mathbf{B} \supset \mathfrak{f}) = 1$ and hence $v([\mathbf{A} \supset \mathbf{B}] \supset \mathfrak{f} \,.\!\supset\!.\, \mathbf{B} \supset \mathfrak{f}) = 1$.

CASE 3. $v(\mathbf{A}) = 0$, $v(\mathbf{B}) = 1$. Then $v(\mathbf{A} \supset \mathbf{B}) = 1$ and $v([\mathbf{A} \supset \mathbf{B}] \supset \mathfrak{f}) = 0$. Hence $v([\mathbf{A} \supset \mathbf{B}] \supset \mathfrak{f} \,.\!\supset\!.\, \mathbf{B} \supset \mathfrak{f}) = 1$.

CASE 4. $v(\mathbf{A}) = v(\mathbf{B}) = 0$. Then $v(\mathbf{A} \supset \mathbf{B}) = 1$ and so $v([\mathbf{A} \supset \mathbf{B}] \supset \mathfrak{f}) = 0$. Hence $v([\mathbf{A} \supset \mathbf{B}] \supset \mathfrak{f} \,.\!\supset\!.\, \mathbf{B} \supset \mathfrak{f}) = 1$. ∎

This proves the proposition. We now give a shorter way of presenting this argument. The four cases may be arranged in a table:

$\mathbf{A}$	$\mathbf{B}$	$\mathbf{A} \supset \mathbf{B}$	$[\mathbf{A} \supset \mathbf{B}] \supset \mathfrak{f}$	$\mathbf{B} \supset \mathfrak{f}$	$[\mathbf{A} \supset \mathbf{B}] \supset \mathfrak{f} \,.\!\supset\!.\, \mathbf{B} \supset \mathfrak{f}$
1	1	1	0	0	1
1	0	0	1	1	1
0	1	1	0	0	1
0	0	1	0	1	1

Each row in the table corresponds to one of the four cases preceding. A given entry in one of the four columns on the right is computed from entries to its left in the same row by rule (V3). This table is called a *truth table*. The truth table may be more compactly written by placing the truth value under the principal connective, thus:

$[\mathbf{A}$	$\supset$	$\mathbf{B}]$	$\supset$	$\mathfrak{f}$	$.\!\supset\!.$	$\mathbf{B}$	$\supset$	$\mathfrak{f}$
1	1	1	0	0	**1**	1	0	0
1	0	0	1	0	**1**	0	1	0
0	1	1	0	0	**1**	1	0	0
0	1	0	0	0	**1**	0	1	0

The boxed column is the one under the principal connective of the whole formula and gives the truth values of the whole formula in the various cases.

The shortest way to show that the formula is a tautology is to argue indirectly as follows:

If $v([\mathbf{A} \supset \mathbf{B}] \supset \mathfrak{f} \,.\!\supset\!.\, \mathbf{B} \supset \mathfrak{f}) = 0$, then $v([\mathbf{A} \supset \mathbf{B}] \supset \mathfrak{f}) = 1$ and $v(\mathbf{B} \supset \mathfrak{f}) = 0$. Hence $v(\mathbf{B}) = 1$. Then $v(\mathbf{A} \supset \mathbf{B}) = 1$ so that $v([\mathbf{A} \supset \mathbf{B}] \supset \mathfrak{f}) = 0$, a contradiction.

We now compute several truth tables of simple formulas.

(TT1) The truth table of $\mathbf{A} \supset \mathbf{B}$ is

A	**B**	**A ⊃ B**
1	1	1
1	0	0
0	1	1
0	0	1

This is simply the definition (V3). Thus $\mathbf{A} \supset \mathbf{B}$ is true exactly when the truth of **A** (materially) implies the truth of **B**.

(TT2) The truth table of $\sim\mathbf{A}$ is

A	**∼A**
1	0
0	1

Thus $\sim\mathbf{A}$ is true exactly when **A** is false. To verify this truth table we recall that $\sim\mathbf{A}$ stands for $\mathbf{A} \supset \mathfrak{f}$ [see (D1)]. Then using truth table (TT1):

A	⊃	𝔣
1	0	0
0	1	0

(TT3) The truth table of $\mathbf{A} \vee \mathbf{B}$ is

A	**B**	**A ∨ B**
1	1	1
1	0	1
0	1	1
0	0	0

Thus $\mathbf{A} \vee \mathbf{B}$ is true exactly when **A** is true or **B** is true (or both). To verify this truth table we recall that $\mathbf{A} \vee \mathbf{B}$ stands for $\sim\mathbf{A} \supset \mathbf{B}$ [see (D2)]. Then using truth tables (TT1) and (TT2):

~	**A**	⊃	**B**
0	1	1	1
0	1	1	0
1	0	1	1
1	0	0	0

(TT4) The truth table of $\mathbf{A} \wedge \mathbf{B}$ is

A	**B**	**A ∧ B**
1	1	1
1	0	0
0	1	0
0	0	0

Thus $\mathbf{A} \wedge \mathbf{B}$ is true exactly when both **A** and **B** are true. To verify this table recall that $\mathbf{A} \wedge \mathbf{B}$ stands for $\sim[\sim\mathbf{A} \vee \sim\mathbf{B}]$ [see (D3)]. Then by Tables (TT2) and (TT3):

~	[~	**A**	∨	~	**B**]
1	0	1	0	0	1
0	0	1	1	1	0
0	1	0	1	0	1
0	1	0	1	1	0

(TT5) The truth table of $\mathbf{A} \equiv \mathbf{B}$ is

$\mathbf{A}$	$\mathbf{B}$	$\mathbf{A} \equiv \mathbf{B}$
1	1	1
1	0	0
0	1	0
0	0	1

Thus $\mathbf{A} \equiv \mathbf{B}$ is true exactly when the truth of **A** is (materially) equivalent to the truth of **B**. To verify this table recall that $\mathbf{A} \equiv \mathbf{B}$ stands for $[\mathbf{A} \supset \mathbf{B}] \wedge [\mathbf{B} \supset \mathbf{A}]$ [see (D4)]. Then by tables (TT1) and (TT4):

$[\mathbf{A} \supset \mathbf{B}]$	$\wedge$	$[\mathbf{B} \supset \mathbf{A}]$
1 1 1	1	1 1 1
1 0 0	0	0 1 1
0 1 1	0	1 0 0
0 1 0	1	0 1 0

Remember that a truth table is only a convenient way for summarizing case analyses. For example, the second line of truth table (TT5) tells us that for any wffs **A** and **B** and any valuation v, if $v(\mathbf{A}) = 1$ and $v(\mathbf{B}) = 0$, then $v(\mathbf{A} \equiv \mathbf{B}) = 0$. For particular wffs **A** and **B** this particular case in the analysis may be vacuous. For example if **B** is a tautology (for example, if **B** is $p \supset p$), then it never happens that $v(\mathbf{B}) = 0$; thus we would never use the second line of truth table (TT5) to compute $v(\mathbf{A} \equiv \mathbf{B})$ no matter what $v(p)$ is. See Exercise 2 below.

EXERCISES

1. Show that the following are tautologies. (**A**, **B**, and **C** are arbitrary wffs.)

(1) $\sim [\mathbf{A} \supset \mathbf{B}] \supset \mathbf{A}$

(2) $\mathbf{A} \supset . \mathbf{B} \supset \mathbf{A}$

(3) $\sim\sim \mathbf{A} \equiv \mathbf{A}$

(4) $\mathbf{A} \supset [\mathbf{B} \supset \mathbf{C}] . \supset . [\mathbf{A} \supset \mathbf{B}] \supset [\mathbf{A} \supset \mathbf{C}]$

(5) $[\mathbf{A} \vee \mathbf{B}] \vee \mathbf{C} \,.\!\equiv\!.\, \mathbf{A} \vee [\mathbf{B} \vee \mathbf{C}]$

(6) $[\mathbf{A} \wedge \mathbf{B}] \wedge \mathbf{C} \,.\!\equiv\!.\, \mathbf{A} \wedge [\mathbf{B} \wedge \mathbf{C}]$

(7) $\sim [\mathbf{A} \wedge \mathbf{B}] \equiv . \sim \mathbf{A} \vee \sim \mathbf{B}$

(8) $\sim [\mathbf{A} \vee \mathbf{B}] \equiv . \sim \mathbf{A} \wedge \sim \mathbf{B}$

(9) $\mathbf{A} \wedge [\mathbf{B} \vee \mathbf{C}] \,.\!\equiv\!.\, [\mathbf{A} \wedge \mathbf{B}] \vee [\mathbf{A} \wedge \mathbf{C}]$

(10) $\mathbf{A} \vee [\mathbf{B} \wedge \mathbf{C}] \,.\!\equiv\!.\, [\mathbf{A} \vee \mathbf{B}] \wedge [\mathbf{A} \vee \mathbf{C}]$

(11) $\mathbf{A} \vee \mathbf{B} \,.\!\equiv\!.\, \mathbf{B} \vee \mathbf{A}$

(12) $\mathbf{A} \wedge \mathbf{B} \,.\!\equiv\!.\, \mathbf{B} \wedge \mathbf{A}$

(13) $\sim \mathbf{A} \supset \sim \mathbf{B} \,.\!\equiv\!.\, \mathbf{B} \supset \mathbf{A}$

(14) $\mathbf{A} \supset \mathbf{B} \,.\!\supset\! \mathbf{A} \,.\!\supset\! \mathbf{A}$

(15) $\mathbf{A} \supset \mathbf{B} \,.\!\supset\!.\, [\mathbf{B} \supset \mathbf{C}] \supset [\mathbf{A} \supset \mathbf{C}]$

REMARKS. Most of these tautologies have names: (2) is called the *law of affirmation of the consequent*; (3) is the *law of double negation*; (4) is the *self distributive law for implication*; (5) and (6) are *associative laws*; (7) and (8) are called *De Morgan's laws*; (9) and (10) are *distributive laws*; (11) and (12) are *commutative laws*; (13) is called the *law of contraposition*; (14) is *Peirce's law*; (15) is the *transitive law for implication.*

2. Show that $[\mathbf{A} \supset \mathbf{B}] \supset \mathbf{A}$ is a tautology if $\mathbf{A}$ is $p \supset p$ and $\mathbf{B}$ is q. Show that $[\mathbf{A} \supset \mathbf{B}] \supset \mathbf{A}$ is not a tautology if $\mathbf{A}$ is $p \supset q$ and $\mathbf{B}$ is $p \supset q$.

3. Show that if $\mathbf{A}$ is a tautology and $\mathbf{A} \supset \mathbf{B}$ is a tautology, then $\mathbf{B}$ is a tautology.

★4. Suppose the wff $\mathbf{B}$ results from the wff $\mathbf{A}$ by replacing one or more occurrences of the proposition letter $\mathbf{p}$ in $\mathbf{A}$ by the proposition letter $\mathbf{q}$. Show that $\mathbf{p} \equiv \mathbf{q} \,.\!\supset\!.\, \mathbf{A} \equiv \mathbf{B}$ is a tautology.

★5. Let $\mathbf{p}_1, \mathbf{p}_2, \ldots, \mathbf{p}_n$ be distinct proposition letters. A *monomial* in $\mathbf{p}_1, \mathbf{p}_2, \ldots, \mathbf{p}_n$ is a formula of the form

$$\mathbf{q}_1 \wedge \mathbf{q}_2 \wedge \ldots \wedge \mathbf{q}_n$$

where each $\mathbf{q}_i$ ($i = 1, 2, \ldots, n$) is either $\mathbf{p}_i$ or $\sim \mathbf{p}_i$. Describe the truth table of a monomial.

★6. A wff is in *full disjunctive normal form* iff it is either $\mathfrak{f}$ or else has the form

$$\mathbf{M}_1 \vee \mathbf{M}_2 \vee \ldots \vee \mathbf{M}_k$$

where $\mathbf{M}_1, \mathbf{M}_2, \ldots, \mathbf{M}_k$ are monomials. Describe the truth table of a wff in full disjunctive normal form. Show that for every wff $\mathbf{A}$ there is a wff $\mathbf{B}$ in full disjunctive normal form such that $\mathbf{A} \equiv \mathbf{B}$ is a tautology. Show that for every truth table there is a wff which has that table as its truth table.

7. Let $\mathbf{A}$ be a wff and v_1 and v_2 two valuations such that $v_1(\mathbf{p}) = v_2(\mathbf{p})$ for every proposition letter $\mathbf{p}$ which actually occurs in $\mathbf{A}$. Show that $v_1(\mathbf{A}) = v_2(\mathbf{A})$.

§3 Axiomatization of P

Any wff of P in one of the following three forms is called an **axiom** of the propositional calculus (or simply, an **axiom** of P).

3.1 $\mathbf{A} \supset . \mathbf{B} \supset \mathbf{A}$

3.2 $\mathbf{A} \supset [\mathbf{B} \supset \mathbf{C}] . \supset . [\mathbf{A} \supset \mathbf{B}] \supset [\mathbf{A} \supset \mathbf{C}]$

3.3 $\sim\sim \mathbf{A} \supset \mathbf{A}$

The **rule of inference** of the propositional calculus is

3.4 From **A** and $\mathbf{A} \supset \mathbf{B}$ to infer **B** (*modus ponens*).

We say that **B** *results* from **A** and $\mathbf{A} \supset \mathbf{B}$ by 3.4 (or by *modus ponens*).

A sequence of wffs of P, $\mathbf{B}_1, \mathbf{B}_2, \ldots, \mathbf{B}_m$ is called a **deduction** (of $\mathbf{B}_m$) in the propositional calculus iff for each $k = 1, 2, \ldots, m$, *either*

(DD1) $\mathbf{B}_k$ is an axiom (that is, $\mathbf{B}_k$ is of one of the forms 3.1, 3.2, or 3.3); *or*

(DD2) for some $i, j < k$, $\mathbf{B}_k$ results from $\mathbf{B}_i$ and $\mathbf{B}_j$ by the rule of inference 3.4 (that is, there is an $i < k$ and a $j < k$ such that $\mathbf{B}_j$ is $\mathbf{B}_i \supset \mathbf{B}_k$).

We say **B** is a **theorem** of the propositional calculus (or a **theorem** of P) iff there is a deduction $\mathbf{B}_1, \mathbf{B}_2, \ldots, \mathbf{B}_m$ such that $\mathbf{B}_m$ is **B**. The notation

$$\vdash \mathbf{B}$$

means that **B** is a theorem of P.

REMARKS. Forms 3.1, 3.2, and 3.3 are called **axiom schemas** or (for purists) **axiom schemata.** Each of these represents an infinite set of axioms. For example, the five formulas

$$p \supset . q \supset p$$
$$p \supset . p \supset p$$
$$p \supset p . \supset . \mathfrak{f} \supset [p \supset p]$$
$$p \supset \mathfrak{f} . \supset . [\mathfrak{f} \wedge q] \supset [p \supset \mathfrak{f}]$$
$$p \vee p . \supset . [p \supset p] \supset [p \vee p]$$

are all axioms; each of them is an *instance* of 3.1.

Remember also that 3.3 is an abbreviation for

$$[[\mathbf{A} \supset \mathfrak{f}] \supset \mathfrak{f}] \supset \mathbf{A}.$$

Notice that the symbol $\vdash$ is not a primitive symbol of the propositional calculus nor is it part of an abbreviation. It is a symbol in the *metalanguage* (in this case mathematical English); that is, the language in which we talk about the propositional calculus. The sequence of symbols $[\mathfrak{f} \supset p_1]$ is a wff in the propositional calculus, and $\mathfrak{f} \wedge p$ and $\sim p \vee p$ are abbreviations for wffs of the propositional calculus. However the sequence of symbols $\vdash [\mathfrak{f} \supset p_1]$ is neither a wff nor an abbreviation for a wff. Rather, it is an abbreviation for the English sentence "The sequence of symbols $[\mathfrak{f} \supset p_1]$ is a theorem of propositional calculus". This sentence, in turn, has the meaning explained in the preceding definition.

The following sequence of formulas is an example of a deduction:

(1) $p \supset [q \supset p] \cdot\supset\cdot [p \supset q] \supset [p \supset p]$

(2) $p \supset\cdot q \supset p$

(3) $p \supset q \cdot\supset\cdot p \supset p$

(4) $[p \supset q] \supset [p \supset p] \cdot\supset\cdot \mathfrak{f} \supset [[p \supset q] \supset [p \supset p]]$

(5) $\mathfrak{f} \supset\cdot [p \supset q] \supset [p \supset p]$

Step (1) is an instance of 3.2. Steps (2) and (4) are instances of 3.1. Step (3) results from steps (2) and (1) by 3.4. Step (5) results from steps (3) and (4) by 3.4. Thus we have proven

$$\vdash \mathfrak{f} \supset\cdot [p \supset q] \supset [p \supset p].$$

Now, in the above deduction we could replace each instance of p by a wff **A** and each instance of q by a wff **B**. We then would have shown,

> "If **A** and **B** are (arbitrary) wffs of the propositional calculus, then $\vdash \mathfrak{f} \supset\cdot [\mathbf{A} \supset \mathbf{B}] \supset [\mathbf{A} \supset \mathbf{A}]$".

This is called a **theorem schema**; it asserts that a certain infinite set of wffs are all theorems. For example,

$$\vdash \mathfrak{f} \supset\cdot [p \supset q] \supset [p \supset p]$$

$$\vdash \mathfrak{f} \supset\cdot [\mathfrak{f} \supset [\mathfrak{f} \supset \mathfrak{f}]] \supset [\mathfrak{f} \supset \mathfrak{f}]$$

and

$$\vdash \mathfrak{f} \supset\cdot [[p \vee q] \supset [p \supset r]] \supset [[p \vee q] \supset [p \vee q]]$$

are all instances of this theorem schema and are thus all theorems of the propositional calculus.

The following is a more useful example of a theorem schema.

If **A** is any wff, then

3.5 $\vdash \mathbf{A} \supset \mathbf{A}$.

The proof is given in the answers to selected exercises at the end of the book, but the student should try to work it out for himself. *Hint:* Read **A** for **A**, $\mathbf{A} \supset \mathbf{A}$ for **B** and **A** for **C** in 3.2.

EXERCISE

1. Let the wff **B** result from the wff **A** by means of replacing each occurrence of a proposition letter **p** in **A** by a wff **C**. Show that if ⊢ **A**, then ⊢ **B**.

§4 The Deduction Theorem

The axiom 3.1–3.4 is designed so that the deduction theorem (stated below) is especially easy to prove. In turn, the deduction theorem makes theorem proving in the system easy.

Let $\mathbf{A}_1, \mathbf{A}_2, \ldots, \mathbf{A}_n$ be a finite sequence of wffs of the propositional calculus. A finite sequence $\mathbf{B}_1, \mathbf{B}_2, \ldots, \mathbf{B}_m$ of wffs is called a **deduction from the hypotheses** $\mathbf{A}_1, \ldots, \mathbf{A}_n$ iff for each $k = 1, 2, \ldots, m$ *either*

(DH1) $\mathbf{B}_k$ is one of the formulas $\mathbf{A}_j$ $(j = 1, \ldots, n)$; *or*

(DH2) $\mathbf{B}_k$ is an axiom of the propositional calculus (that is, $\mathbf{B}_k$ has one of the forms 3.1, 3.2, or 3.3); *or*

(DH3) for some $i, j < k$, $\mathbf{B}_k$ results from $\mathbf{B}_i$ and $\mathbf{B}_j$ by *modus ponens* (rule 3.4) (that is, there are $i, j < k$ such that $\mathbf{B}_j$ is $\mathbf{B}_i \supset \mathbf{B}_k$).

Such a finite sequence $\mathbf{B}_1, \mathbf{B}_2, \ldots, \mathbf{B}_m$ is called a **deduction of $\mathbf{B}_m$ from the hypotheses $\mathbf{A}_1, \mathbf{A}_2, \ldots, \mathbf{A}_n$**. The notation

$$\mathbf{A}_1, \mathbf{A}_2, \ldots, \mathbf{A}_n \vdash \mathbf{B}_m$$

means: there is a deduction of $\mathbf{B}_m$ from the hypotheses $\mathbf{A}_1, \mathbf{A}_2, \ldots, \mathbf{A}_n$.

The use of the sign ⊢ in §3 is a special case of the above, namely the case $n = 0$. Indeed, a deduction of **B** from the empty set of hypotheses is precisely the same thing as a deduction of **B**.

The intuitive meaning of $\mathbf{A}_1, \mathbf{A}_2, \ldots, \mathbf{A}_n \vdash \mathbf{B}$ is that **B** can be proved under the assumption that $\mathbf{A}_1, \mathbf{A}_2, \ldots, \mathbf{A}_n$ all are true. On the other hand, in an informal language one proves a statement of form $\mathbf{A} \supset \mathbf{B}$ (if **A**, then **B**) by first assuming **A** and then proving **B**. This is the motivation for the following:

4.1 The Deduction Theorem for the Propositional Calculus. If $\mathbf{A}_1, \mathbf{A}_2, \ldots, \mathbf{A}_n \vdash \mathbf{B}$, then $\mathbf{A}_1, \mathbf{A}_2, \ldots, \mathbf{A}_{n-1} \vdash \mathbf{A}_n \supset \mathbf{B}$.

Before proving 4.1 we first prove the following:

4.2 Lemma. If $\mathbf{A}_1, \mathbf{A}_2, \ldots, \mathbf{A}_n \vdash \mathbf{B}$ and $\mathbf{A}_1, \mathbf{A}_2, \ldots, \mathbf{A}_n \vdash \mathbf{B} \supset \mathbf{C}$, then $\mathbf{A}_1, \mathbf{A}_2, \ldots, \mathbf{A}_n \vdash \mathbf{C}$.

Proof of 4.2. Assume $\mathbf{A}_1, \mathbf{A}_2, \ldots, \mathbf{A}_n \vdash \mathbf{B}$ and $\mathbf{A}_1, \mathbf{A}_2, \ldots, \mathbf{A}_n \vdash \mathbf{B} \supset \mathbf{C}$. Then there is a deduction $\mathbf{B}_1, \ldots, \mathbf{B}_m$ of **B** from $\mathbf{A}_1, \mathbf{A}_2, \ldots, \mathbf{A}_n$ ($\mathbf{B}_m$ is **B**) and a deduction $\mathbf{C}_1, \mathbf{C}_2, \ldots, \mathbf{C}_k$ of $\mathbf{B} \supset \mathbf{C}$ from $\mathbf{A}_1, \mathbf{A}_2, \ldots, \mathbf{A}_n$ ($\mathbf{C}_k$ is $\mathbf{B} \supset \mathbf{C}$). Then the sequence

$$\mathbf{B}_1, \mathbf{B}_2, \ldots, \mathbf{B}_m, \mathbf{C}_1, \mathbf{C}_2, \ldots, \mathbf{C}_k, \mathbf{C}$$

is a deduction of $\mathbf{C}$ from $\mathbf{A}_1, \mathbf{A}_2, \ldots, \mathbf{A}_n$ (since $\mathbf{C}$ results from $\mathbf{B}_m$ and $\mathbf{C}_k$ by *modus ponens* (3.4)). ▮

PROOF OF 4.1. Assume $\mathbf{A}_1, \mathbf{A}_2, \ldots, \mathbf{A}_n \vdash \mathbf{B}$. Then there is a deduction $\mathbf{B}_1, \mathbf{B}_2, \ldots, \mathbf{B}_m$ of $\mathbf{B}$ from $\mathbf{A}_1, \mathbf{A}_2, \ldots, \mathbf{A}_n$ ($\mathbf{B}$ is $\mathbf{B}_m$). We shall prove

$$(*) \qquad \mathbf{A}_1, \mathbf{A}_2, \ldots, \mathbf{A}_{n-1} \vdash \mathbf{A}_n \supset \mathbf{B}_k$$

for $k = 1, 2, \ldots, m$. Then taking $k = m$ in (*) we have 4.1.

We prove (*) by induction on k. Thus we assume as hypothesis of induction that (*) holds for all values of k that are less than some fixed value of k and prove (*) for that fixed value of k.

CASE 1. The wff $\mathbf{B}_k$ satisfies (DH1) in the definition of deduction from hypotheses. Then $\mathbf{B}_k$ is $\mathbf{A}_j$ for some $j = 1, 2, \ldots, n$.

Subcase 1*a*. Assume $j = 1, 2, \ldots, n - 1$. Then by (DH1)

$$\mathbf{A}_1, \mathbf{A}_2, \ldots, \mathbf{A}_{n-1} \vdash \mathbf{A}_j.$$

That is,

$$\mathbf{A}_1, \mathbf{A}_2, \ldots, \mathbf{A}_{n-1} \vdash \mathbf{B}_k.$$

By 3.1

$$\mathbf{A}_1, \mathbf{A}_2, \ldots, \mathbf{A}_{n-1} \vdash \mathbf{B}_k \supset . \mathbf{A}_n \supset \mathbf{B}_k.$$

Hence by Lemma 4.2

$$\mathbf{A}_1, \mathbf{A}_2, \ldots, \mathbf{A}_{n-1} \vdash \mathbf{A}_n \supset \mathbf{B}_k.$$

Subcase 1*b*. Assume $j = n$. Then $\mathbf{A}_n \supset \mathbf{B}_k$ is $\mathbf{A}_n \supset \mathbf{A}_n$. Hence $\mathbf{A}_1, \mathbf{A}_2, \ldots, \mathbf{A}_{n-1} \vdash \mathbf{A}_n \supset \mathbf{B}_k$ by 3.5. (Schema 3.5 says that $\vdash \mathbf{A}_n \supset \mathbf{A}_n$. This certainly implies that $\mathbf{A}_1, \mathbf{A}_2, \ldots, \mathbf{A}_{n-1} \vdash \mathbf{A}_n \supset \mathbf{A}_n$ for a deduction from no hypotheses is a fortiori a deduction from hypotheses.)

CASE 2. The wff $\mathbf{B}_k$ satisfies (DH2) in the definition of deduction from hypotheses. Then $\mathbf{B}_k$ is an axiom of the propositional calculus. Hence

$$\mathbf{A}_1, \mathbf{A}_2, \ldots, \mathbf{A}_{n-1} \vdash \mathbf{B}_k.$$

By 3.1

$$\mathbf{A}_1, \mathbf{A}_2, \ldots, \mathbf{A}_{n-1} \vdash \mathbf{B}_k \supset . \mathbf{A}_n \supset \mathbf{B}_k.$$

Hence by 4.2

$$\mathbf{A}_1, \mathbf{A}_2, \ldots, \mathbf{A}_{n-1} \vdash \mathbf{A}_n \supset \mathbf{B}_k.$$

CASE 3. The wff $\mathbf{B}_k$ satisfies (DH3) in the definition of deduction from hypotheses. Then there are $i, j < k$ such that $\mathbf{B}_j$ is $\mathbf{B}_i \supset \mathbf{B}_k$. By the induction hypothesis

(†) $\mathbf{A}_1, \mathbf{A}_2, \ldots, \mathbf{A}_{n-1} \vdash \mathbf{A}_n \supset \mathbf{B}_i$

and

$$\mathbf{A}_1, \mathbf{A}_2, \ldots, \mathbf{A}_{n-1} \vdash \mathbf{A}_n \supset \mathbf{B}_j.$$

That is,

(††) $\mathbf{A}_1, \mathbf{A}_2, \ldots, \mathbf{A}_{n-1} \vdash \mathbf{A}_n \supset [\mathbf{B}_i \supset \mathbf{B}_k].$

By 3.2

(†††) $\mathbf{A}_1, \mathbf{A}_2, \ldots, \mathbf{A}_{n-1} \vdash \mathbf{A}_n \supset [\mathbf{B}_i \supset \mathbf{B}_k] \centerdot \supset \centerdot [\mathbf{A}_n \supset \mathbf{B}_i] \supset [\mathbf{A}_n \supset \mathbf{B}_k].$

By (††), (†††), and 4.2

$$\mathbf{A}_1, \mathbf{A}_2, \ldots, \mathbf{A}_{n-1} \vdash \mathbf{A}_n \supset \mathbf{B}_i \centerdot \supset \centerdot \mathbf{A}_n \supset \mathbf{B}_k$$

whence by (†) and 4.2

$$\mathbf{A}_1, \mathbf{A}_2, \ldots, \mathbf{A}_{n-1} \vdash \mathbf{A}_n \supset \mathbf{B}_k.$$

This completes the proof of 4.1. ▮

Now that we have proved the deduction theorem we gain some insight into the axiom system 3.1–3.4. Axiom schema 3.1 (together with 3.4) enables us to put an arbitrary wff in front of a wff which we have already proved, that is, to infer $\vdash \mathbf{B} \supset \mathbf{A}$ from $\vdash \mathbf{A}$. This is precisely what we need for Subcase 1a and Case 2. Axiom schema 3.2 is precisely what we need for Case 3.

Notice that the proof of 4.1 is *effective*. This means that the proof tells us how, given a deduction of $\mathbf{B}$ from $\mathbf{A}_1, \mathbf{A}_2, \ldots, \mathbf{A}_n$, we may construct from it a deduction of $\mathbf{A}_n \supset \mathbf{B}$ from $\mathbf{A}_1, \mathbf{A}_2, \ldots, \mathbf{A}_{n-1}$. We illustrate this with an example.

The sequence of formulas p, p ⊃ q, q is a deduction of q from p, p ⊃ q. We represent this by

(1) $p, p \supset q \vdash p$

(2) $p, p \supset q \vdash p \supset q$

(3) $p, p \supset q \vdash q.$

Now the proof of the deduction theorem shows us how to change this deduction into a deduction of $[p \supset q] \supset q$ from p. Namely:

$$p \vdash p$$

$$p \vdash p \supset \centerdot\, [p \supset q] \supset p$$

$$(1') \quad p \vdash [p \supset q] \supset p$$

$$\vdots$$

$$(2') \quad p \vdash [p \supset q] \supset [p \supset q]$$

$$p \vdash [p \supset q] \supset [p \supset q] \centerdot \supset \centerdot\, [[p \supset q] \supset p] \supset [[p \supset q] \supset q]$$

$$p \vdash [[p \supset q] \supset p] \supset [[p \supset q] \supset q]$$

$$(3') \quad p \vdash [p \supset q] \supset q$$

The dots between the lines (1′) and (2′) stand for a deduction of $[p \supset q] \supset [p \supset q]$ which is obtained from 3.5. Assume $n = 2$, $m = 3$, $\mathbf{A}_1$ is p, $\mathbf{A}_2$ is $p \supset q$, $\mathbf{B}_1$ is p, $\mathbf{B}_2$ is $p \supset q$, and $\mathbf{B}_3$ is q. The lines (1′), (2′), and (3′) are $\mathbf{A}_1 \vdash \mathbf{A}_2 \supset \mathbf{B}_1$, $\mathbf{A}_1 \vdash \mathbf{A}_2 \supset \mathbf{B}_2$ and $\mathbf{A}_1 \vdash \mathbf{A}_2 \supset \mathbf{B}_3$ respectively. The line before (1′) is an instance of 3.1 (as indicated in Subcase 1a of the proof). The line after (2′) is an instance of 3.2 (as indicated in Case 3 of the proof) and the remaining lines follow from previous lines by *modus ponens* (3.4).

The deduction theorem greatly facilitates theorem proving in **P**. This is because a deduction from hypotheses is much easier to construct than a deduction (without hypotheses). Thus to prove a theorem of form $\vdash \mathbf{A} \supset \mathbf{B}$ it suffices to prove $\mathbf{A} \vdash \mathbf{B}$, and if $\mathbf{B}$ is of form $\mathbf{B}_1 \supset \mathbf{B}_2$, it suffices to prove $\mathbf{A}$, $\mathbf{B}_1 \vdash \mathbf{B}_2$, and so on.

We illustrate this by proving that $\vdash \mathbf{A} \supset \mathbf{B} \centerdot \supset \centerdot\, [\mathbf{B} \supset \mathbf{C}] \supset [\mathbf{A} \supset \mathbf{C}]$ for any wffs **A**, **B**, and **C**. The proof is as follows:

$$\mathbf{A} \supset \mathbf{B}, \mathbf{B} \supset \mathbf{C}, \mathbf{A} \vdash \mathbf{A} \supset \mathbf{B}$$

$$\mathbf{A} \supset \mathbf{B}, \mathbf{B} \supset \mathbf{C}, \mathbf{A} \vdash \mathbf{A}$$

$$\mathbf{A} \supset \mathbf{B}, \mathbf{B} \supset \mathbf{C}, \mathbf{A} \vdash \mathbf{B}$$

$$\mathbf{A} \supset \mathbf{B}, \mathbf{B} \supset \mathbf{C}, \mathbf{A} \vdash \mathbf{B} \supset \mathbf{C}$$

$$\mathbf{A} \supset \mathbf{B}, \mathbf{B} \supset \mathbf{C}, \mathbf{A} \vdash \mathbf{C}$$

$$\mathbf{A} \supset \mathbf{B}, \mathbf{B} \supset \mathbf{C}, \vdash \mathbf{A} \supset \mathbf{C}$$

$$\mathbf{A} \supset \mathbf{B} \vdash \mathbf{B} \supset \mathbf{C} \centerdot \supset \centerdot\, \mathbf{A} \supset \mathbf{C}$$

$$\vdash \mathbf{A} \supset \mathbf{B} \centerdot \supset \centerdot\, [\mathbf{B} \supset \mathbf{C}] \supset [\mathbf{A} \supset \mathbf{C}]. \quad \blacksquare$$

Lines 1, 2, and 4 are hypotheses, lines 3 and 5 follow by *modus ponens* applied to earlier lines (see Lemma 4.2) and the last three lines are applications of the deduction theorem (4.1).

EXERCISES

1. Which of the following are always true?

 (1) If $\vdash \mathbf{B}$, then $\mathbf{A}_1, \mathbf{A}_2, \ldots, \mathbf{A}_n \vdash \mathbf{B}$.

 (2) If $\mathbf{A}_1, \mathbf{A}_2, \ldots, \mathbf{A}_n \vdash \mathbf{B}$, then $\vdash \mathbf{B}$.

 (3) If $\mathbf{A}_1, \mathbf{A}_2 \vdash \mathbf{B}$, then $\mathbf{A}_2, \mathbf{A}_1 \vdash \mathbf{B}$.

 (4) If $\mathbf{A}_1, \mathbf{A}_2 \vdash \mathbf{B} \supset \mathbf{C}$ and $\mathbf{A}_1, \mathbf{A}_2 \vdash \mathbf{B}$, then $\mathbf{A}_1, \mathbf{A}_2 \vdash \mathbf{C}$.

 (5) If $\mathbf{A}_1, \mathbf{A}_2 \vdash \mathbf{B} \supset \mathbf{C}$ and $\mathbf{A}_1 \vdash \mathbf{B}$, then $\mathbf{A}_1, \mathbf{A}_2 \vdash \mathbf{C}$.

 (6) If $\mathbf{A}_1, \mathbf{A}_2 \vdash \mathbf{B} \supset \mathbf{C}$ and $\mathbf{A}_1 \vdash \mathbf{B}$, then $\mathbf{A}_1 \vdash \mathbf{C}$.

 (7) If $\vdash \mathbf{B} \supset \mathbf{C}$ and $\mathbf{A} \vdash \mathbf{B}$, then $\vdash \mathbf{C}$.

 (8) If $\mathbf{A}_1 \vdash \mathbf{B} \supset \mathbf{C}$ and $\mathbf{A}_2 \vdash \mathbf{B}$ then $\mathbf{A}_1, \mathbf{A}_2 \vdash \mathbf{C}$.

 (9) If $\mathbf{A}, \mathbf{A} \vdash \mathbf{B}$, then $\mathbf{A} \vdash \mathbf{B}$.

 (10) If $\mathbf{A} \vdash \mathbf{B}$, then $\mathbf{A}, \mathbf{A} \vdash \mathbf{B}$.

2. Use the proof of the deduction theorem to construct a deduction of $p \supset \centerdot [p \supset q] \supset q$ from the deduction of $[p \supset q] \supset q$ from p given above.

§5 Some Theorem Schemas of P

In this section **A** and **B** denote arbitrary wffs of P. The proofs of all the theorem schemas in this section are left as exercises for the reader. Although many of the proofs are given in the section entitled "Answers to Selected Exercises" at the back of the book, the reader is advised to try to prove them himself. The only theorem schemas necessary for the completeness theorem (6.2) are 5.2–5.5 and 5.7.

5.1 $\vdash \mathfrak{f} \supset \mathbf{A}$

Hint: Use 3.1 to show $\mathfrak{f} \vdash [\mathbf{A} \supset \mathfrak{f}] \supset \mathfrak{f}$. Then use 3.3 to show $\mathfrak{f} \vdash \mathbf{A}$. Then use the deduction theorem.

The meaning of 5.1 is that "from a false proposition, anything follows." Note that 3.3 is used to obtain a "proof by contradiction." This is a useful trick. For example, to prove an assertion of form $\vdash \mathbf{A} \supset \mathbf{B}$ we first may try to prove $\mathbf{A}, \sim\mathbf{B} \vdash \mathfrak{f}$. If we succeed in this we may then argue as follows: By the deduction theorem $\mathbf{A} \vdash \sim\sim\mathbf{B}$ (D1), whence by 3.3 and *modus ponens* $\mathbf{A} \vdash \mathbf{B}$, whence by the deduction theorem again $\vdash \mathbf{A} \supset \mathbf{B}$.

5.2 $\vdash \mathbf{A} \supset \centerdot \mathbf{B} \supset \centerdot \mathbf{A} \supset \mathbf{B}$

5.3 $\vdash \mathbf{A} \supset \centerdot \sim\mathbf{B} \supset \centerdot \sim[\mathbf{A} \supset \mathbf{B}]$

5.4 $\vdash \sim\mathbf{A} \supset \centerdot \mathbf{B} \supset \centerdot \mathbf{A} \supset \mathbf{B}$

5.5 $\vdash \sim\mathbf{A} \supset \centerdot \sim\mathbf{B} \supset \centerdot \mathbf{A} \supset \mathbf{B}$

The theorem schemas 5.2–5.5 correspond to the four lines in the truth table for $\mathbf{A} \supset \mathbf{B}$ (TT1); for example, 5.3 says "if **A** is true and **B** is false, then $\mathbf{A} \supset \mathbf{B}$ is false."

Hint for the proof of 5.2: Show $\mathbf{A}, \mathbf{B} \vdash \mathbf{A} \supset \mathbf{B}$ using 3.1. Then use the deduction theorem.

Hint for the proof of 5.3: Show $\mathbf{A}, \sim\mathbf{B}, \mathbf{A} \supset \mathbf{B} \vdash \mathfrak{f}$ and use the deduction theorem three times.

5.6 $\vdash \mathbf{A} \supset \mathbf{B} \,.\!\supset.\, \sim\mathbf{B} \supset \sim\mathbf{A}$

Hint: Show $\mathbf{A} \supset \mathbf{B}, \sim\mathbf{B}, \mathbf{A} \vdash \mathfrak{f}$.

5.7 $\vdash \mathbf{A} \supset \mathbf{B} \,.\!\supset.\, [\sim\mathbf{A} \supset \mathbf{B}] \supset \mathbf{B}$

Hint: Use 5.6 to get $\mathbf{A} \supset \mathbf{B}, \sim\mathbf{A} \supset \mathbf{B}, \sim\mathbf{B} \vdash \sim\mathbf{A}$ and then prove $\mathbf{A} \supset \mathbf{B}, \sim\mathbf{A} \supset \mathbf{B}, \sim\mathbf{B} \vdash \mathfrak{f}$. Then use 3.3, the deduction theorem, and (D1).

5.8 $\vdash \mathbf{A} \supset \mathbf{B} \,.\!\supset.\, [\mathbf{B} \supset \mathbf{C}] \supset [\mathbf{A} \supset \mathbf{C}]$

5.9 $\vdash \sim\mathbf{B} \supset \sim\mathbf{A} \,.\!\supset.\, \mathbf{A} \supset \mathbf{B}$

5.10 $\vdash \mathbf{A} \supset \sim\sim\mathbf{A}$

5.11 $\vdash \mathbf{A} \supset.\, \mathbf{B} \supset.\, \mathbf{A} \wedge \mathbf{B}$

Hint: $\mathbf{A} \wedge \mathbf{B}$ is $\sim[\sim\sim\mathbf{A} \supset \sim\mathbf{B}]$ by (D3) and (D2).

5.12 $\vdash \mathbf{A} \equiv \sim\sim\mathbf{A}$

Hint: Use 5.11, 3.3, 5.10, and (D4).

5.13 $\vdash \mathbf{A} \supset \mathbf{B} \,.\!\equiv.\, \sim\mathbf{B} \supset \sim\mathbf{A}$

Hint: Use 5.6, 5.9, and 5.11.

5.14 $\vdash \sim\mathbf{A} \supset.\, \mathbf{A} \supset \mathbf{B}$

Hint: Use 5.1.

5.15 $\vdash \sim\mathbf{A} \supset \mathbf{B} \,.\!\supset.\, \sim\mathbf{B} \supset \mathbf{A}$

5.16 $\vdash \sim[\mathbf{A} \supset \mathbf{B}] \supset \mathbf{A}$

Hint: Use 5.14 and 5.15.

5.17 $\vdash \sim[\mathbf{A} \supset \mathbf{B}] \supset \sim\mathbf{B}$

Hint: Use 3.1 and 5.6.

5.18 $\vdash [[\mathbf{A} \supset \mathbf{B}] \supset \mathbf{A}] \supset \mathbf{A}$

Hint: Show $[\mathbf{A} \supset \mathbf{B}] \supset \mathbf{A}, \sim\mathbf{A} \vdash \mathfrak{f}$.

5.19 $\vdash \mathbf{A} \vee \mathbf{B} \,.\!\supset\!.\, \mathbf{B} \vee \mathbf{A}$

Hint: By (D2), $\mathbf{A} \vee \mathbf{B}$ is $\sim \mathbf{A} \supset \mathbf{B}$.

5.20 $\vdash \mathbf{A} \wedge \mathbf{B} \,.\!\supset\!.\, \mathbf{B} \wedge \mathbf{A}$

5.21 $\vdash \mathbf{A} \wedge \mathbf{B} \,.\!\supset \mathbf{A}$

5.22 $\vdash \sim \mathbf{A} \supset \mathbf{B} \,.\!\equiv\!.\, \sim \mathbf{B} \supset \mathbf{A}$

5.23 $\vdash \mathbf{A} \supset \sim \mathbf{B} \,.\!\equiv\!.\, \mathbf{B} \supset \sim \mathbf{A}$

EXERCISES

1. Let P^1 be the formal language which is the same as P except that axiom schema 3.3 is replaced by the schema $\sim \mathbf{A} \supset \sim \mathbf{B} \,.\!\supset\!.\, \mathbf{B} \supset \mathbf{A}$. Show that P^1 and P are equivalent in the sense that they have exactly the same theorems. *Hint:* It suffices to show that $\sim \mathbf{A} \supset \sim \mathbf{B} \,.\!\supset\!.\, \mathbf{B} \supset \mathbf{A}$ is a theorem schema of P and 3.3 is a theorem schema of P^1; the former assertion implies that every theorem of P^1 is a theorem of P and the latter assertion implies that every theorem of P is a theorem of P^1.

2. Let P^2 be the formal language which is the same as P except that axiom schema 3.3 is replaced by the schema $\sim \mathbf{A} \supset \mathbf{B} \,.\!\supset\!.\, \sim \mathbf{B} \supset \mathbf{A}$. Show that P^2 and P have exactly the same theorems.

3. Let P^3 be the formal language which is the same as P except that axiom schema 3.3 is replaced by the two schemas $\mathfrak{f} \supset \mathbf{A}$ and $\mathbf{A} \supset \mathbf{B} \,.\!\supset \mathbf{A} \,.\!\supset \mathbf{A}$ (Peirce's law). Show that P^3 and P have exactly the same theorems.

§6 Completeness

The following theorem should come as no surprise.

6.1 Soundness Theorem. If $\vdash \mathbf{B}$, then $\mathbf{B}$ is a tautology.

PROOF. Suppose $\vdash \mathbf{B}$. Then there is a deduction $\mathbf{B}_1, \mathbf{B}_2, \ldots, \mathbf{B}_m$ where $\mathbf{B}_m$ is $\mathbf{B}$. We show that each $\mathbf{B}_k$ is a tautology by induction on k. There are precisely two cases.

CASE 1. Assume $\mathbf{B}_k$ is an axiom; that is, $\mathbf{B}_k$ is an instance of 3.1, 3.2, or 3.3. The reader may verify by either the truth table method or the indirect method described in §2 that each axiom is a tautology.

CASE 2. Assume $\mathbf{B}_k$ is obtained from $\mathbf{B}_i$ and $\mathbf{B}_j$ $(i, j < k)$ by 3.4 (*modus ponens*). Then $\mathbf{B}_j$ is $\mathbf{B}_i \supset \mathbf{B}_k$. By the induction hypothesis $\mathbf{B}_i$ and $\mathbf{B}_j$ are tautologies; that is, $v(\mathbf{B}_i) = 1$ and $v(\mathbf{B}_j) = v(\mathbf{B}_i \supset \mathbf{B}_k) = 1$ for every valuation v. But if $v(\mathbf{B}_i) = v(\mathbf{B}_i \supset \mathbf{B}_k) = 1$, then $v(\mathbf{B}_k) = 1$. Hence $v(\mathbf{B}_k) = 1$ for every valuation v; that is, $\mathbf{B}_k$ is a tautology. ▌

The completeness theorem is the converse of 6.1. We first prove the following lemma.

6.2 Lemma. Let v be a valuation. For each wff $\mathbf{A}$ let $\mathbf{A}'$ be the wff $\mathbf{A}$ in case $v(\mathbf{A}) = 1$ and let $\mathbf{A}'$ be the wff $\sim\mathbf{A}$ in case $v(\mathbf{A}) = 0$. Suppose $\mathbf{B}$ is a wff such that every proposition letter occurring in $\mathbf{B}$ appears in the list $\mathbf{p}_1, \mathbf{p}_2, \ldots, \mathbf{p}_n$ of proposition letters. Then $\mathbf{p}_1', \mathbf{p}_2', \ldots, \mathbf{p}_n' \vdash \mathbf{B}'$.

PROOF. By induction on the number of occurrences of $\supset$ in $\mathbf{B}$.

CASE 1. Assume $\mathbf{B}$ is a proposition letter. Then $\mathbf{B}$ is some $\mathbf{p}_i$ $(i = 1, 2, \ldots, n)$. Hence $\mathbf{B}'$ is $\mathbf{p}_i'$, and the theorem follows since

$$\mathbf{p}_1', \mathbf{p}_2', \ldots, \mathbf{p}_n' \vdash \mathbf{p}_i'.$$

CASE 2. Assume $\mathbf{B}$ is $\mathfrak{f}$. Then $\mathbf{B}'$ is $\sim\mathfrak{f}$; that is, $\mathbf{B}'$ is $\mathfrak{f} \supset \mathfrak{f}$. But $\vdash \mathfrak{f} \supset \mathfrak{f}$ by 3.5.

CASE 3. Assume $\mathbf{B}$ is $\mathbf{A}_1 \supset \mathbf{A}_2$. By the induction hypothesis (since both $\mathbf{A}_1$ and $\mathbf{A}_2$ have at least one less occurrence of $\supset$ than $\mathbf{B}$) we have

$$\mathbf{p}_1', \mathbf{p}_2', \ldots, \mathbf{p}_n' \vdash \mathbf{A}_1' \qquad \text{and} \qquad \mathbf{p}_1', \mathbf{p}_2', \ldots, \mathbf{p}_n' \vdash \mathbf{A}_2'.$$

By the appropriate instance of 5.2–5.5

$$\vdash \mathbf{A}_1' \supset \mathbf{.}\ \mathbf{A}_2' \supset \mathbf{B}'.$$

Hence

$$\mathbf{p}_1', \mathbf{p}_2', \ldots, \mathbf{p}_n' \vdash \mathbf{B}'$$

follows by two applications of *modus ponens* (3.4). ▌

6.3 The Completeness Theorem. If $\mathbf{B}$ is a tautology, then $\vdash \mathbf{B}$.

PROOF. Let $\mathbf{p}_1, \mathbf{p}_2, \ldots, \mathbf{p}_n$ be the list of all variables which appear in $\mathbf{B}$. Then for any sequence $\mathbf{p}_1', \mathbf{p}_2', \ldots, \mathbf{p}_n'$ where each $\mathbf{p}_i'$ is either $\mathbf{p}_i$ or $\sim\mathbf{p}_i$ we have by Lemma 6.2

$$\mathbf{p}_1', \mathbf{p}_2', \ldots, \mathbf{p}_n' \vdash \mathbf{B}.$$

Hence in particular

$$\mathbf{p}_1', \mathbf{p}_2', \ldots, \mathbf{p}_{n-1}', \mathbf{p}_n \vdash \mathbf{B}$$

and

$$\mathbf{p}_1', \mathbf{p}_2', \ldots, \mathbf{p}_{n-1}', \sim \mathbf{p}_n \vdash \mathbf{B}.$$

By the deduction theorem (4.1)

$$\mathbf{p}_1', \mathbf{p}_2', \ldots, \mathbf{p}_{n-1}' \vdash \mathbf{p}_n \supset \mathbf{B}$$

and

$$\mathbf{p}_1', \mathbf{p}_2', \ldots, \mathbf{p}_{n-1}' \vdash \sim \mathbf{p}_n \supset \mathbf{B}.$$

But by 5.7

$$\mathbf{p}_1', \mathbf{p}_2', \ldots, \mathbf{p}_{n-1}' \vdash \mathbf{p}_n \supset \mathbf{B} \,.\!\supset\!.\, [\sim \mathbf{p}_n \supset \mathbf{B}] \supset \mathbf{B}.$$

Hence by *modus ponens* (3.4) twice,

$$\mathbf{p}_1', \mathbf{p}_2', \ldots, \mathbf{p}_{n-1}' \vdash \mathbf{B}.$$

We have eliminated one hypothesis. By repeating this argument we can eliminate $\mathbf{p}_{n-1}'$, $\mathbf{p}_{n-2}'$, and so on until all the hypotheses are eliminated. ▌

Notice that the proof of the completeness theorem, like the proof of the deduction theorem, is effective. It gives us a method or an *algorithm* which we may apply to any tautology to construct a deduction of it.

We have also solved the *decision problem* for the propositional calculus; that is, we can give an algorithm for deciding if a given wff is a theorem. Indeed, a wff is a theorem if and only if it is a tautology and the method of truth tables constitutes an algorithm for deciding if a wff is a tautology.

EXERCISES

1. Let **A** be a wff which contains no proposition letter. Show that either $\vdash \mathbf{A}$ or $\vdash \sim \mathbf{A}$. Is this true if **A** does contain proposition letters?

2. Try this exercise only after you have studied Chapter 2.

   Let $\mathbf{\Gamma}$ be a set of wffs of P. The expression $\mathbf{\Gamma} \vdash \mathbf{B}$ means there exist wffs $\mathbf{A}_1, \mathbf{A}_2, \ldots, \mathbf{A}_n$ in $\mathbf{\Gamma}$ such that $\mathbf{A}_1, \mathbf{A}_2, \ldots, \mathbf{A}_n \vdash \mathbf{B}$. The set $\mathbf{\Gamma}$ is **inconsistent** iff $\mathbf{\Gamma} \vdash \mathfrak{f}$ and **consistent** otherwise.

   Show that if $\mathbf{\Gamma}$ is consistent, then there is a valuation v (see §2) such that $v(\mathbf{A}) = 1$ for every **A** in $\mathbf{\Gamma}$. Derive 6.3 as a corollary.

*3. The formal language P_I is obtained from the formal language P by deleting $\mathfrak{f}$ from the set of primitive symbols and deleting rule (W2) (which says that $\mathfrak{f}$ is a wff) in the definition of wff. The axiom schemas for P_I are 3.1, 3.2, and

$\mathbf{A \supset B \,.\!\supset A \,.\!\supset A}$ (Peirce's law), and the rule of inference of $\mathbf{P_I}$ is *modus ponens*. The definitions of deduction in $\mathbf{P_I}$, deduction from hypotheses in $\mathbf{P_I}$, and theorem of $\mathbf{P_I}$ are *mutatis mutandis* the same as for **P**. The notation $\vdash_I \mathbf{A}$ means **A** is a theorem of $\mathbf{P_I}$, and **QA** is an abbreviation for $[\mathbf{A \supset Q}]$. In unabbreviating an expression which uses this abbreviation more than once use association to the right; that is, **QQA** stands for $\mathbf{QA \supset Q}$ rather than $\mathbf{A \supset QQ}$.

Show that the deduction theorem holds for $\mathbf{P_I}$ and prove the following theorem schemas.

(1) $\vdash_I \mathbf{A \supset B \,.\!\supset\!.\, [B \supset C] \supset [A \supset C]}$

(2) $\vdash_I \mathbf{A \supset B \,.\!\supset\!.\, QB \supset QA}$

(3) $\vdash_I \mathbf{A \supset QQA}$

(4) $\vdash_I \mathbf{QQQA \supset QA}$

(5) $\vdash_I \mathbf{QQB \supset QQ[A \supset B]}$

(6) $\vdash_I \mathbf{QQA \supset\!.\, QB \supset Q[A \supset B]}$

(7) $\vdash_I \mathbf{QA \supset QQ[A \supset B]}$

(8) $\vdash_I \mathbf{QA \supset B \,.\!\supset\!.\, [QQA \supset B] \supset QQB}$

Hint: Only (7) requires Peirce's law. To prove (7) show that $\mathbf{QA} \vdash_I \mathbf{Q \supset B \,.\!\supset\!.\, A \supset B}$ [using (2) reading **B** for **Q**, **A** for **A**, and **Q** for **B**]. Hence using (1) obtain $\mathbf{QA, Q[A \supset B]} \vdash_I \mathbf{Q \supset B \,.\!\supset Q}$. Then by Peirce's law $\mathbf{QA, Q[A \supset B]} \vdash_I \mathbf{Q}$ and use the deduction theorem.

Notice that the wff **QA** behaves very much like the wff $\sim \mathbf{A}$.

*4. Let **Q** be some wff of $\mathbf{P_I}$ and v be a valuation. For each wff **A** of $\mathbf{P_I}$ let $\mathbf{A'}$ be **QQA** in case $v(\mathbf{A}) = 1$ and **QA** in case $v(\mathbf{A}) = 0$. Prove the following analog of Lemma 6.2: If **B** is a wff of $\mathbf{P_I}$ such that every proposition letter of **B** appears in the list $\mathbf{p}_1, \mathbf{p}_2, \ldots, \mathbf{p}_n$, then $\mathbf{p}_1', \mathbf{p}_2', \ldots, \mathbf{p}_n' \vdash_I \mathbf{B'}$.

*5. Let **A** and **Q** be wffs of $\mathbf{P_I}$. Show that if **A** is a tautology, then $\vdash_I \mathbf{QQA}$ and hence (since **Q** is arbitrary) $\vdash_I \mathbf{A}$. *Hint:* For the second assertion take $\mathbf{Q} = \mathbf{A}$.

REMARK. The language $\mathbf{P_I}$ is interesting in that the wffs of $\mathbf{P_I}$ are not sufficient to give all truth tables, for example, there is no wff **A** of $\mathbf{P_I}$ such that $v(\mathbf{A}) = 0$ for every valuation v. Compare with Exercise 6, §2.

*6. The formal language $\mathbf{P_1}$ results from **P** by making the following changes: (1) delete $\mathfrak{f}$ as a primitive symbol and add $\sim$ as a primitive symbol; (2) replace the formation rule (W2) (which says that $\mathfrak{f}$ is a wff) by the rule that if **A** is a wff of $\mathbf{P_1}$ then so is $\sim \mathbf{A}$; (3) replace the semantical rule (V2) (which says that $v(\mathfrak{f}) = 0$ for each valuation v) by the rule $v(\sim\mathbf{A}) = 0$ if $v(\mathbf{A}) = 1$ and $v(\sim\mathbf{A}) = 1$ if $v(\mathbf{A}) = 0$. The axiom schemas for $\mathbf{P_1}$ are 3.1, 3.2, and in addition the schema $\mathbf{\sim A \supset \sim B \,.\!\supset\!.\, B \supset A}$. The rule of inference is *modus ponens* and the definitions of deduction in $\mathbf{P_1}$, deduction from hypotheses, tautology, and theorem of P_1 are *mutatis mutandis* the same as for **P**. Show that a wff **A** of P_1 is a tautology if and only if it is a theorem of P_1. *Hint:* Prove the deduction theorem for P_1 and the theorem schemas 5.2–5.5 and 5.7. These are the only facts used in §6. Before proving 5.2–5.5 and 5.7, prove $\vdash \sim\sim \mathbf{A} \supset \mathbf{A}$ and $\vdash \mathbf{A} \supset \sim\sim \mathbf{A}$. The latter follows from the former as $\vdash \sim\sim\sim \mathbf{A} \supset \sim \mathbf{A}$ is an instance of the former. To prove the former show $\sim\sim \mathbf{A} \vdash \sim \mathbf{A} \supset \sim [p \supset p]$.

★7. The formal language P_1' results from P_1 by replacing the axion schema $\sim \mathbf{A} \supset \sim \mathbf{B} \,.\!\supset\!.\, \mathbf{B} \supset \mathbf{A}$ by the schema $\sim\sim \mathbf{A} \supset \mathbf{A}$. Show that P_1' is not complete; in particular, that $\sim p \supset \sim q \,.\!\supset\!.\, q \supset p$ is not a theorem of P_1' (although it is, of course, a theorem of P_1). *Hint:* Extend each valuation v of the proposition letters to a "nonstandard" valuation v' of all the wffs by using the following "nonstandard" truth tables (that is, semantical rules):

(v′1) If **p** is a proposition letter, $v'(\mathbf{p}) = v(\mathbf{p})$.

(v′2) $v'(\sim \mathbf{A}) = v'(\mathbf{A})$.

(v′3) $v'(\mathbf{A} \supset \mathbf{B}) = 0$ if $v'(\mathbf{A}) = 1$ and $v'(\mathbf{B}) = 0$; $v'(\mathbf{A} \supset \mathbf{B}) = 1$ otherwise.

Show that if **A** is a theorem of P_1' then $v'(\mathbf{A}) = 1$ for every v. For a suitable v, $v'(\mathbf{A}) = 0$ if **A** is $\sim p \supset \sim q \,.\!\supset\!.\, q \supset p$; hence this wff is not a theorem of P_1'.

This result is somewhat curious in that the axiom schemas of P_1' and of **P** are the same except that in the former case $\sim$ is a primitive symbol and in the latter case it is introduced by a definition schema.

★8. Hilbert's formulation of the propositional calculus does not employ the definition schemas (D1)–(D4). This formal language is called P_H and is obtained from **P** by making the following changes: (a) delete f as a primitive symbol; (b) add $\sim$, $\vee$, $\wedge$, and $\equiv$ as primitive symbols; (c) delete the formation rule (W2); (d) modify the formation rule (W3) to read as follows: if **A** and **B** are wffs of P_H, then so are $\sim \mathbf{A}$, $[\mathbf{A} \supset \mathbf{B}]$, $[\mathbf{A} \vee \mathbf{B}]$, $[\mathbf{A} \wedge \mathbf{B}]$, and $[\mathbf{A} \equiv \mathbf{B}]$; (e) delete the semantical rule (V2); (f) add the following semantical rules:

(i) $v(\sim \mathbf{A}) = 0$ if $v(\mathbf{A}) = 1$ and $v(\sim \mathbf{A}) = 1$ if $v(\mathbf{A}) = 0$;

(ii) $v(\mathbf{A} \vee \mathbf{B}) = 0$ if $v(\mathbf{A}) = v(\mathbf{B}) = 0$ and $v(\mathbf{A} \vee \mathbf{B}) = 1$ otherwise;

(iii) $v(\mathbf{A} \wedge \mathbf{B}) = 1$ if $v(\mathbf{A}) = v(\mathbf{B}) = 1$ and $v(\mathbf{A} \wedge \mathbf{B}) = 0$ otherwise;

(iv) $v(\mathbf{A} \equiv \mathbf{B}) = 1$ if $v(\mathbf{A}) = v(\mathbf{B})$ and $v(\mathbf{A} \equiv \mathbf{B}) = 0$ otherwise.

The axiom schemas for P_H are the following:

(1) $\mathbf{A} \supset\!.\, \mathbf{B} \supset \mathbf{A}$

(2) $\mathbf{A} \supset [\mathbf{B} \supset \mathbf{C}] \,.\!\supset\!.\, [\mathbf{A} \supset \mathbf{B}] \supset [\mathbf{A} \supset \mathbf{C}]$

(3) $\mathbf{A} \wedge \mathbf{B} \,.\!\supset \mathbf{A}$

(4) $\mathbf{A} \wedge \mathbf{B} \,.\!\supset \mathbf{B}$

(5) $\mathbf{A} \supset\!.\, \mathbf{B} \supset\!.\, \mathbf{A} \wedge \mathbf{B}$

(6) $\mathbf{A} \supset\!.\, \mathbf{A} \vee \mathbf{B}$

(7) $\mathbf{B \supset . A \vee B}$

(8) $\mathbf{[A \supset C] \supset . [B \supset C] \supset . [A \vee B] \supset C}$

(9) $\mathbf{A \equiv B . \supset . A \supset B}$

(10) $\mathbf{A \equiv B . \supset . B \supset A}$

(11) $\mathbf{[A \supset B] \supset . [B \supset A] \supset [A \equiv B]}$

(12) $\mathbf{\sim A \supset \sim B . \supset . B \supset A}$.

Notice that (1), (2), and (12) are the axiom schemas of the (complete) formal language P_1 of Exercise 6. The rule of inference of P_H is *modus ponens* and the various other definitions (for example, tautology, theorem of P_H) are *mutatis mutandis* the same as for P.

Show that P_H is sound and complete: that is, a wff of P_H is a theorem of P_H if and only if it is a tautology. *Hint:* the work of §6 may be modified so as to apply here. Another (and perhaps more instructive) approach is to prove the following: For every wff **A** of P_H there is a wff **A*** of P_1 such that $\mathbf{A \equiv A^*}$ is a theorem of P_H. The desired result follows immediately from Exercise 6.

*9. The *intuitionistic propositional calculus* is the formal language P_i obtained from P by adding $\vee$ and $\wedge$ as primitive symbols and modifying the formation rule (W3) to read as follows: If **A** and **B** are wffs of P_i, then so are $\mathbf{[A \supset B]}$, $\mathbf{[A \wedge B]}$, and $\mathbf{[A \vee B]}$. The axiom schemas of P_i are schemas (1)–(8) of the previous exercise plus the schema $\mathfrak{f} \supset \mathbf{A}$. The rule of inference is *modus ponens* and the definition of deduction, theorem, and so on is *mutatis mutandis* the same as for P. The definition schemas $\mathbf{\sim A} \rightsquigarrow \mathbf{A} \supset \mathfrak{f}$ and $\mathbf{A \equiv B} \rightsquigarrow \mathbf{[A \supset B] \wedge [B \supset A]}$ are also employed in this formal language. The notation $\vdash_i \mathbf{A}$ means A is a theorem of P_i.

Show that the deduction theorem holds for P_i and prove the following theorem schemas

(1) $\vdash_i \mathbf{[A \supset B] \supset . [A \supset \sim B] \supset \sim A}$

(2) $\vdash_i \mathbf{A \supset \sim\sim A}$

(3) $\vdash_i \mathbf{\sim\sim\sim A \supset \sim A}$

(4) $\vdash_i \mathbf{A \supset B . \supset . \sim B \supset \sim A}$

(5) $\vdash_i \mathbf{\sim\sim . A \vee \sim A}$

(6) $\vdash_i \mathbf{\sim . A \wedge \sim A}$

*10. Show that every theorem of P_i is a tautology in the sense of Exercise 8. Show that if any one of the following schemas is added to P_i as an axiom schema then the resulting language is complete in the sense that every tautology is a theorem.

(1) $\mathbf{A \vee \sim A}$

(2) $\mathbf{\sim\sim A \supset A}$

(3) $\mathbf{\sim A \supset \sim B . \supset . B \supset A}$

(4) $\mathbf{A} \supset \mathbf{B} \,.\!\supset \mathbf{A} \,.\!\supset \mathbf{A}$ (Peirce's law)

(5) $[\sim \mathbf{A} \supset \mathbf{B}] \supset. [\sim \mathbf{A} \supset \sim \mathbf{B}] \supset \mathbf{A}$

*11. Let V be a nonempty set. A *V valuation* is a function v which assigns to every proposition letter $\mathbf{p}$ a value $v(\mathbf{p})$ in V. A *system of truth values for* P_i consists of a nonempty set V (called the *truth values*), a nonempty subset D of V (called the *designated truth values*) and a set R of rules for extending each V valuation to the set of all wffs of P_i. If (V, D, R) is such a system a wff $\mathbf{A}$ is called a *tautology in* (V, D, R) iff $v(\mathbf{A})$ is in D for each V valuation v.
Consider the following system of truth values:

(1) V is the set of natural numbers $0, 1, 2, \ldots, n$.

(2) D is the set consisting of the single natural number n.

(3) For each V valuation v:

(R1) $v(\mathrm{f}) = 0$

(R2) $v(\mathbf{A} \vee \mathbf{B})$ = the larger of $v(\mathbf{A})$ and $v(\mathbf{B})$.

(R3) $v(\mathbf{A} \wedge \mathbf{B})$ = the smaller of $v(\mathbf{A})$ and $v(\mathbf{B})$.

(R4) $v(\mathbf{A} \supset \mathbf{B}) = n$ if $v(\mathbf{A}) \leqslant v(\mathbf{B})$ and $v(\mathbf{A} \supset \mathbf{B}) = v(\mathbf{B})$ if $v(\mathbf{B}) < v(\mathbf{A})$.

Show that each theorem $\mathbf{A}$ of P_i is a tautology in the above system of truth values (that is, if $\vdash_i \mathbf{A}$, then $v(\mathbf{A}) = n$ for every V valuation v).

*12. If $n = 2$ in the system of truth values of the last exercise show that the following are not tautologies:

(1) $\mathrm{p} \vee \sim \mathrm{p}$

(2) $\sim\sim \mathrm{p} \supset \mathrm{p}$

(3) $\sim \mathrm{p} \supset \sim \mathrm{q} \,.\!\supset. \mathrm{q} \supset \mathrm{p}$

(4) $\mathrm{p} \supset \mathrm{q} \,.\!\supset \mathrm{p} \,.\!\supset \mathrm{p}$

(5) $[\sim \mathrm{p} \supset \mathrm{q}] \supset. [\sim \mathrm{p} \supset \sim \mathrm{q}] \supset \mathrm{p}$

Conclude that they are not theorems of P_i.

*13. Use the system of truth values of Exercise 11 to show that

$$[\mathrm{p}_1 \equiv \mathrm{p}_2] \vee [\mathrm{p}_1 \equiv \mathrm{p}_3] \vee \ldots \vee [\mathrm{p}_1 \equiv \mathrm{p}_n] \vee [\mathrm{p}_2 \equiv \mathrm{p}_3] \vee [\mathrm{p}_2 \equiv \mathrm{p}_4] \vee \ldots \vee [\mathrm{p}_2 \equiv \mathrm{p}_n] \vee \ldots \vee [\mathrm{p}_{n-2} \equiv \mathrm{p}_{n-1}] \vee [\mathrm{p}_{n-2} \equiv \mathrm{p}_n] \vee [\mathrm{p}_{n-1} \equiv \mathrm{p}_n]$$

is not a theorem of P_i (for each n). This wff becomes a theorem of P_i on identification of two of its proposition letters. Hence conclude that there is no system of finitely many truth values whose tautologies are precisely the theorems of P_i.

*14. Prove 6.2 for P_i.

*15. Let **A** be a wff of $\mathbf{P_i}$. Show that if **A** is a tautology, then $\vdash \sim\sim \mathbf{A}$. *Hint:* Use Exercise 14. Hence if $\sim \mathbf{A}$ is a tautology, then $\vdash_i \sim \mathbf{A}$.

*16. Let **A** be a wff such that every well-formed part of **A** is a proposition letter, $\mathfrak{f}$, or of one of the forms $\mathbf{B} \wedge \mathbf{C}$ or $\sim \mathbf{B}$. Show that if **A** is a tautology, then $\vdash_i \mathbf{A}$.

*17. Let $\mathbf{A}^*$ result from **A** by replacing each proposition letter **p** by $\sim\sim \mathbf{p}$. Show that if **A** is a theorem of **P**, then $\vdash_i \mathbf{A}^*$. *Hint:* Apply * to each line in a deduction of **A** in **P**.

Exercises 18 and 24 are similar in spirit to Exercise 2. Do not attempt them until after you have studied §17.

*18. Let **A** be a wff of $\mathbf{P_i}$ and $\mathbf{\Gamma}$ be a set of wffs of $\mathbf{P_i}$. The set $\mathbf{\Gamma}$ is **A inconsistent** iff $\mathbf{\Gamma} \vdash_i \mathbf{A}$; otherwise, $\mathbf{\Gamma}$ is **A consistent.** The set $\mathbf{\Gamma}$ is **closed** iff $\mathbf{B} \in \mathbf{\Gamma}$ whenever $\mathbf{\Gamma} \vdash_i \mathbf{B}$. The set $\mathbf{\Gamma}$ is **disjunctive** iff either $\mathbf{B} \in \mathbf{\Gamma}$ or $\mathbf{C} \in \mathbf{\Gamma}$ whenever $\mathbf{B} \vee \mathbf{C} \in \mathbf{\Gamma}$. The set $\mathbf{\Gamma}$ is **A complete** iff for every wff **B**, either $\mathbf{B} \in \mathbf{\Gamma}$ or $\mathbf{B} \supset \mathbf{A} \in \mathbf{\Gamma}$. The set $\mathbf{\Gamma}$ is **regular** iff it is $\mathfrak{f}$ consistent, closed, and disjunctive.

Prove that

(1) If $\mathbf{\Gamma}$ is **A** consistent and **A** complete, then $\mathbf{\Gamma}$ is regular.

(2) If $\mathbf{\Gamma}$ is **A** consistent, then there is an **A**-consistent, **A** complete set $\mathbf{\Delta}$ with $\mathbf{\Gamma} \subseteq \mathbf{\Delta}$.

(3) If $\mathbf{\Gamma}$ is regular, then

(3a) $\mathbf{A} \wedge \mathbf{B} \in \mathbf{\Gamma}$ if and only if $\mathbf{A} \in \mathbf{\Gamma}$ and $\mathbf{B} \in \mathbf{\Gamma}$

(3b) $\mathbf{A} \vee \mathbf{B} \in \mathbf{\Gamma}$ if and only if $\mathbf{A} \in \mathbf{\Gamma}$ or $\mathbf{B} \in \mathbf{\Gamma}$

(3c) $\mathbf{A} \supset \mathbf{B} \in \mathbf{\Gamma}$ if and only if for every regular $\mathbf{\Delta}$ such that $\mathbf{\Gamma} \subset \mathbf{\Delta}$, if $\mathbf{A} \in \mathbf{\Delta}$, then $\mathbf{B} \in \mathbf{\Delta}$. *Hint for* 3*c:* If $\mathbf{A} \supset \mathbf{B} \notin \mathbf{\Gamma}$ then $\mathbf{\Gamma} \cup \{\mathbf{A}\}$ is **B** consistent.

*19. A **Kripke model** is a quadruple $\mathfrak{M} = (\Omega, \leqslant, \mathrm{S})$ where Ω is a nonempty set, $\leqslant$ is a binary relation on Ω, and S is a function which assigns to each $\alpha \in \Omega$ a set $\mathrm{S}(\alpha)$ of proposition letters of $\mathbf{P_i}$, and satisfying the following conditions for $\alpha, \beta, \gamma \in \Omega$:

(1) $\alpha \leqslant \alpha$

(2) if $\alpha \leqslant \beta$ and $\beta \leqslant \gamma$, then $\alpha \leqslant \gamma$

(3) if $\alpha \leqslant \beta$, then $\mathrm{S}(\alpha) \subseteq \mathrm{S}(\beta)$

For such a Kripke model $\mathfrak{M}$ and for $\alpha \in \Omega$ and a wff **A** of $\mathbf{P_i}$, the relation $\mathfrak{M} \vDash_\alpha \mathbf{A}$ (read **A** holds in $\mathfrak{M}$ at α) is defined inductively as follows:

(K1) $\mathfrak{M} \vDash_\alpha \mathbf{p}$ iff $\mathbf{p} \in \mathrm{S}(\alpha)$ if **p** is a proposition letter

(K2) not $\mathfrak{M} \vDash_\alpha \mathfrak{f}$

(K3) $\mathfrak{M} \models_\alpha \mathbf{A} \wedge \mathbf{B}$ iff $\mathfrak{M} \models_\alpha \mathbf{A}$ and $\mathfrak{M} \models_\alpha \mathbf{B}$

(K4) $\mathfrak{M} \models_\alpha \mathbf{A} \vee \mathbf{B}$ iff $\mathfrak{M} \models_\alpha \mathbf{A}$ or $\mathfrak{M} \models_\alpha \mathbf{B}$

(K5) $\mathfrak{M} \models_\alpha \mathbf{A} \supset \mathbf{B}$ iff for every $\beta \geqslant \alpha$, if $\mathfrak{M} \models_\beta \mathbf{A}$, then $\mathfrak{M} \models_\beta \mathbf{B}$.

(Here $\beta \geqslant \alpha$ means $\alpha \leqslant \beta$.) Show that $\mathfrak{M} \models_\alpha \sim \mathbf{A}$ if and only if for all $\beta \geqslant \alpha$, $\mathfrak{M} \not\models_\alpha \mathbf{A}$. (Here $\mathfrak{M} \not\models_\alpha \mathbf{A}$ means not $\mathfrak{M} \models_\alpha \mathbf{A}$.) Show that if $\mathfrak{M} \models_\alpha \mathbf{A}$ and $\alpha \leqslant \beta$, then $\mathfrak{M} \models_\beta \mathbf{A}$.

A wff is **intuitionistically valid** iff $\mathfrak{M} \models_\alpha \mathbf{A}$ for every $\mathfrak{M}$ and every α. Show that every theorem of $\mathbf{P_i}$ is intuitionistically valid.

*20. Consider the Kripke model $\mathfrak{M} = (\Omega, \leqslant, S)$ where

(1) Ω contains exactly two elements: α and β; that is, $\Omega = \{\alpha, \beta\}$

(2) $\alpha \leqslant \alpha$, $\beta \leqslant \beta$, and $\alpha \leqslant \beta$

(3) $S(\alpha)$ is empty and $S(\beta)$ consists of the single element p; that is, $S(\beta) = \{p\}$

This model is represented by the diagram

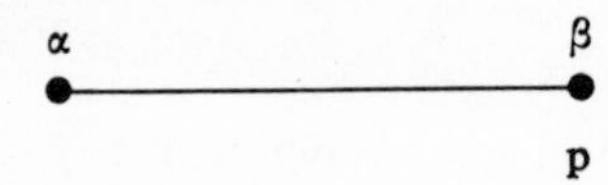

Show that $\mathfrak{M} \not\models_\alpha p \vee \sim p$ and $\mathfrak{M} \not\models_\alpha \sim\sim p \supset p$.

*21. Consider the Kripke model $\mathfrak{M} = (\Omega, \leqslant, S)$ where

(1) $\Omega = \{\alpha, \beta\}$

(2) $\alpha \leqslant \alpha$, $\beta \leqslant \beta$, and $\alpha \leqslant \beta$

(3) $S(\alpha) = \{q\}$ and $S(\beta) = \{p, q\}$

The diagram is

Show that $\mathfrak{M} \not\models_\alpha \sim p \supset \sim q \,.\!\supset\!.\, q \supset p$.

*22. Consider the Kripke model $\mathfrak{M} = (\Omega, \leqslant, S)$ where

(1) $\Omega = \{\alpha, \beta, \gamma\}$

(2) $\alpha \leqslant \alpha$, $\beta \leqslant \beta$, $\gamma \leqslant \gamma$, $\alpha \leqslant \beta$, and $\alpha \leqslant \gamma$

(3) $S(\alpha)$ is empty, $S(\beta) = \{p\}$, and $S(\gamma) = \{q\}$

The diagram is

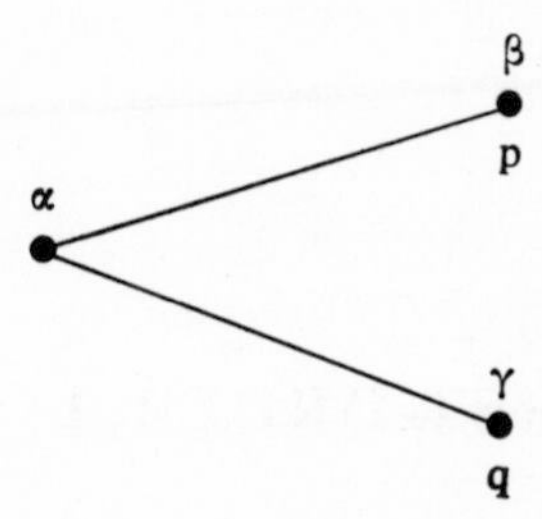

Show that $\mathfrak{M} \nvDash_\alpha [p \supset q] \vee [q \supset p]$. Show that this sentence holds in every Kripke model $\mathfrak{M}$ such that $\leqslant$ is linear. (The relation $\leqslant$ is **linear** iff for all $\alpha, \beta \in \Omega$ either $\alpha \leqslant \beta$ or $\beta \leqslant \alpha$.) Show that $[p \supset q] \vee [q \supset p]$ is a tautology in the system of truth values of Exercise 11.

*23. Find a Kripke model in which $p \supset q \,.\!\supset p \,.\!\supset p$ (Peirce's law) fails. Find a Kripke model in which $[\sim p \supset q] \supset . [p \supset q] \supset q$ fails.

*24. Consider the Kripke model $\mathfrak{M} = (\Omega, \leqslant, S)$ where

(1) Ω is the set of regular sets of wffs (Exercise 18)

(2) $\mathbf{\Gamma} \leqslant \mathbf{\Delta}$ iff $\mathbf{\Gamma} \subseteq \mathbf{\Delta}$ for $\mathbf{\Gamma}, \mathbf{\Delta} \in \Omega$

(3) $S(\mathbf{\Gamma})$ is the set of proposition letters in $\mathbf{\Gamma}$.

Show that for every wff **A** and for every $\mathbf{\Gamma} \in \Omega$, we have $\mathfrak{M} \vDash_{\mathbf{\Gamma}} \mathbf{A}$ if and only if $\mathbf{A} \in \mathbf{\Gamma}$. Conclude that **A** is intuitionistically valid if and only if $\vdash_i \mathbf{A}$.

*25. Given two Kripke models in which **A** and **B** fail respectively, construct a Kripke model in which $\mathbf{A} \vee \mathbf{B}$ fails. Conclude that if $\vdash_i \mathbf{A} \vee \mathbf{B}$, then either $\vdash_i \mathbf{A}$ or $\vdash_i \mathbf{B}$. Is this true in the classical propositional calculus **P**?

*26. Let **A** be a wff containing k occurrences of $\subset$. Show that if $\mathfrak{M} \vDash_\alpha \mathbf{A}$ for every Kripke model $\mathfrak{M} = (\Omega, \leqslant, S)$ such that Ω has at most $k+1$ elements (and every α), then **A** is intuitionistically valid. Since there are only finitely-many such Kripke models, this result, together with Exercise 24, yields a decision procedure for $\mathbf{P}_i$.

Chapter 2 FIRST-ORDER LOGIC

In this chapter we study simultaneously an infinite family of languages known as *first-order languages*. These languages abstract from ordinary language the properties of phrases like "for all" and "there exists." We also study the logical properties of certain linguistic entities called "predicates."

A *predicate* is a group of words like "is a man," "is green," "is less than," "belongs to," or even "is" which can be applied to one or more names of *individuals* to yield meaningful sentences; for example, "Socrates is a man," "two is less than four," "that hat belongs to me," and "he is John." The names of the individuals are called *individual constants*. The number of individual constants to which a given predicate is applied is called the *number of places* of the predicate. For instance, "is a man" is a one-place predicate, and "is less than" is a two-place predicate. In the formal languages of this chapter we denote predicates by letters like P and Q; the sentence "x satisfies P" is written P(x).

A one-place predicate determines a set of things; namely those things for which it is true. Similarly, a two-place predicate determines a set of pairs of things; that is, a *two-place relation*, and, in general, an n-place predicate determines an *n-place relation*. We may think of the predicate as denoting the relation and in this sense the relation constitutes at least part of the meaning of the predicate. For example, the predicate "is a man" determines the set of men and the predicate "is west of" (when applied to American cities) determines the set of pairs (a, b) of American cities such that a is west of b. (For example, the relation holds between Chicago and New York, but not between Chicago and San Francisco.) Different predicates may determine the same relation (for example, "x is west of y" and "y is east of x").

The phrase "for all" is called the *universal quantifier* and is denoted symbolically by $\forall$. The phrases "there exists," "there is a," and "for some" all have the same meaning; "there exists" is called the *existential quantifier* and is denoted symbolically by $\exists$.

The universal quantifier is kind of an iterated conjunction. Suppose there are only finitely-many individuals; that is, the variable x takes on only the values $a_1, a_2, \ldots, a_n$. Then the sentence $\forall x P(x)$ has the same meaning as the conjunction $P(a_1) \wedge P(a_2) \wedge \ldots \wedge P(a_n)$.

The existential quantifier is a kind of iterated disjunction: if there are only finitely-many individuals $a_1, a_2, \ldots, a_n$, then the sentence $\exists x P(x)$ has the same meaning as the disjunction $P(a_1) \vee P(a_2) \vee \ldots \vee P(a_n)$.

Of course, if the number of individuals is infinite, such an interpretation of the quantifiers is not possible, since infinitely long sentences are not allowed.

Now according to De Morgan's laws, the sentence $P(a_1) \vee P(a_2) \vee \ldots \vee P(a_n)$ is (materially) equivalent to $\sim [\sim P(a_1) \wedge \sim P(a_2) \wedge \ldots \wedge \sim P(a_n)]$. This suggests the possibility of defining the existential quantifier from the universal quantifier. In the formal languages we shall do this: $\exists x P(x)$ will be an abbreviation for $\sim \forall x \sim P(x)$. Of course we could also define the universal quantifier from the existential quantifier: $\forall x P(x)$ has the same meaning as $\sim \exists x \sim P(x)$. However, we shall adopt the former course.

In phrases of the form "for all x, P(x)" or "there exists an x such that P(x)" the variable x is a *dummy variable* or a *bound variable*. This means that the meaning of the phrase is not changed if x is replaced everywhere by y. For example, the sentence "there exists an x such that $x + 7 = 5$" has exactly the same meaning as the sentence "there exists a y such that $y + 7 = 5$."

In mathematics, in an equation without quantifiers, universal quantifiers are usually understood. Thus the equation

$$x + y = y + x$$

is understood to assert

"for all x and y: $\quad x + y = y + x$".

We shall follow this convention in our formal languages. In a formal language the second sentence would be called the *universal closure* of the first.

Each of the formal languages which we study will have a set of symbols $\mathfrak{S}$ of predicates and a set of symbols X of individual constants. The first-order language $L(\mathfrak{S}, X)$ is completely determined once we specify $\mathfrak{S}$ and X.

EXERCISES

1. In the following, **N** denotes the set of natural numbers 0, 1, 2, ... The expression $\forall x \in \mathbf{N}$ means "for all natural numbers x" and $\exists x \in \mathbf{N}$ means "there exists a natural number x such that." The notations $x + y$, $=$, $\leqslant$, and $<$ all have their usual meanings. Which of the following are true?

   (1) $\forall x \in \mathbf{N}\, \forall y \in \mathbf{N}\, \forall z \in \mathbf{N}$, if $x + y = z$, then $y + x = z$.

   (2) $\forall x \in \mathbf{N}\, \exists y \in \mathbf{N}\; x + y = x$.

(3) $\exists y \in \mathbf{N}\, \forall x \in \mathbf{N},\ x + y = x.$

(4) $\forall x \in \mathbf{N}\, \exists y \in \mathbf{N}\ x \leqslant y.$

(5) $\exists y \in \mathbf{N}\, \forall x \in \mathbf{N}\ x \leqslant y.$

(6) $\forall x \in \mathbf{N}$, if $\forall y \in \mathbf{N}\ x \leqslant y$, then $x = 0$.

(7) $\forall x \in \mathbf{N}\, \forall y \in \mathbf{N}$, if $x \leqslant y$ and $y \leqslant x$, then $x = y$.

(8) $\forall x \in \mathbf{N}\, \forall y \in \mathbf{N}$, if $x < y$ and $y < x$, then $x \neq x$.

(9) If $\forall x \in \mathbf{N}\, \exists y \in \mathbf{N}\ x < y$, then $\exists y \in \mathbf{N}\ 8 < y$.

(10) If $\forall x \in \mathbf{N}\, \exists y \in \mathbf{N}\ x < y$, then $\exists y \in \mathbf{N}\ y < y$.

(11) $\exists x \in \mathbf{N}\, \forall y \in \mathbf{N}\ x \leqslant y.$

2. Let **Z** denote the set of integers $\ldots, -2, -1, 0, 1, 2, \ldots$ The expression $\forall x \in \mathbf{Z}$ means "for all integers x" and $\exists x \in \mathbf{Z}$ means "there is an integer x such that". Which of the sentences of Exercise 1 remain true where **N** is replaced by **Z** throughout?

§7 Formation Rules for $L(\mathfrak{S}, X)$

In this section we begin our study of first-order logic. We study several languages simultaneously. Each first-order language depends on a set of predicate letters $\mathfrak{S}$ and a set of individual constants X as explained below; the language determined by $\mathfrak{S}$ and X is denoted by $L(\mathfrak{S}, X)$.

A **system of predicate letters for a first-order logic** is a double sequence of symbols

$$
\begin{array}{l}
P_1^1, P_2^1, P_3^1, \ldots \\
P_1^2, P_2^2, P_3^2, \ldots \\
\quad\vdots \\
P_1^k, P_2^k, P_3^k, \ldots \\
P_1^{k+1}, P_2^{k+1}, P_3^{k+1}, \ldots \\
\quad\vdots
\end{array}
$$

Each row of the sequence may be empty, finite, or infinite. We denote a system of predicate letters by the letter $\mathfrak{S}$ and call elements of the sequence **predicate letters** of $\mathfrak{S}$. More precisely, a predicate letter P_i^k is called a k-**place predicate letter**. The subscripts serve merely to distinguish various predicate letters.

Any set X, whether empty, finite, or infinite, may serve as a **set of individual constants for a first-order logic**.

Let $\mathfrak{S}$ be a system of predicate letters and X a set of constants. We shall define $L(\mathfrak{S}, X)$, the **first-order language determined** by $\mathfrak{S}$ and X:

The primitive symbols of $L(\mathfrak{S}, X)$ are the elements of $\mathfrak{S}$ and X and in addition:

1. the infinite list of symbols $x_0\ x_1\ x_2\ x_3 \ldots$ called **individual variables**;
2. the symbol $\supset$ called the **implication sign**;
3. the symbol $\mathfrak{f}$ called the **falsity sign**;
4. the symbol $\forall$ called the **universal quantifier**;
5. the symbols [ ] ( ) and , called respectively the **left bracket**, the **right bracket**, the **left parenthesis**, the **right parenthesis**, and the **comma**.

Any finite sequence of primitive symbols of $L(\mathfrak{S}, X)$ is called a **formula**. The set of **well-formed formulas** or **wffs** of $L(\mathfrak{S}, X)$ is defined inductively by the following rules:

(Wf1) If $\mathbf{P}$ is a k-place predicate letter of $\mathfrak{S}$ and if $\mathbf{a}_1, \mathbf{a}_2, \ldots, \mathbf{a}_k$ is a sequence of (not necessarily distinct) symbols such that each $\mathbf{a}_i$ is either an individual variable or an individual constant from X, then $\mathbf{P}(\mathbf{a}_1, \mathbf{a}_2, \ldots, \mathbf{a}_k)$ is a wff of $L(\mathfrak{S}, X)$;

(Wf2) the symbol $\mathfrak{f}$ is a wff of $L(\mathfrak{S}, X)$;

(Wf3) if **A** and **B** are wffs of $L(\mathfrak{S}, X)$, then so is $[\mathbf{A} \supset \mathbf{B}]$;

(Wf4) if **A** is a wff of $L(\mathfrak{S}, X)$ and **x** is an individual variable, then $\forall\mathbf{x}\mathbf{A}$ is a wff of $L(\mathfrak{S}, X)$;

(Wf5) a formula is a wff of $L(\mathfrak{S}, X)$ only if that is required by rules (Wf1)–(Wf4).

We use all the abbreviations introduced in §1 including the conventions about the omission of brackets and the definition schemas (D1)–(D4) for the negation sign $\sim$, the disjunction sign $\vee$, the conjunction sign $\wedge$, and the equivalence sign $\equiv$. In addition a dot to the right of a universal quantifier indicates the omission of a left bracket at the dot and a right bracket at the end of the formula. Thus we write

$$\forall x_1 \,.\, P_1{}^1(x_1) \supset P_1{}^2(x_1, x_3)$$

instead of

$$\forall x_1[P_1{}^1(x_1) \supset P_1{}^2(x_1, x_3)].$$

We shall make the further abbreviation,
If **A** is a wff, and **x** is an individual variable, then

(D5) $$\exists\mathbf{x}\mathbf{A} \rightsquigarrow \sim \forall\mathbf{x} \sim \mathbf{A}.$$

The symbol $\exists$ is called the existential quantifier.

Finally, we shall omit the superscripts on the predicate letters since they can always be recognized from the context. Thus we write

$$P_1(x_1, x_3, x_4)$$

instead of

$$P_1^3(x_1, x_3, x_4).$$

To further simplify the notation, we shall write P instead of P_1, Q instead of P_2, R instead of P_3, and S instead of P_4. We also shall write x instead of x_1, y instead of x_2, and z instead of x_3.

A formula **A** which is part of a formula **B** and is itself a wff is called a **well-formed part of B**. For example,

$$\forall x \centerdot P(x) \supset Q(x)$$

is a well-formed part of the formula

$$\forall y \centerdot Q(y) \supset \forall x \centerdot P(x) \supset Q(x).$$

EXERCISES

1. Which of the following are wffs or abbreviations for wffs?

(1) $\forall x P$

(2) $\forall x P x$

(3) $\forall x P(x)$

(4) $\forall x \centerdot P(x)$

(5) $\forall x[P(x)]$

(6) $[\forall x P(x)]$

(7) $\forall P(x) \supset Q(x)$

(8) $P(x) \supset \forall x$

(9) $\forall x \centerdot P(x) \supset Q(x)$

(10) $\forall x P(y)$

(11) $\forall x P(x) \supset \forall y P(x)$

2. What are the well formed parts of the following wffs?

(1) $\forall x P(x) \supset Q(x)$

(2) $\forall x[P(x) \supset Q(x)]$

(3) $\forall x \centerdot P(x) \supset \forall y Q(x)$

(4) $\forall x P(x) \supset \forall y \centerdot P(x) \supset Q(x)$

(5) $\forall y \sim P(y) \supset \sim \forall y Q(y)$

(6) $\mathfrak{f} \supset \centerdot \forall y Q(y) \supset Q(x)$

(7) $\forall x \exists y \centerdot P(x, y) \supset \exists z Q(x, y, z)$

§8 Free and Bound Variables

Let $\mathbf{x}$ be an individual variable and suppose the wff $\forall\mathbf{x}\mathbf{B}$ is a well-formed part of the wff $\mathbf{A}$. The well-formed part $\mathbf{B}$ is called the **scope** of the particular occurrence of the universal quantifier $\forall\mathbf{x}$ in $\mathbf{A}$. Every occurrence of the variable $\mathbf{x}$ in $\forall\mathbf{x}\mathbf{B}$ is called a **bound occurrence of x** (in $\mathbf{A}$). Any occurrence of $\mathbf{x}$ in $\mathbf{A}$ which is not a bound occurrence is called a **free occurrence of x** (in $\mathbf{A}$). For example, in the formula

$$P(x, y) \supset \forall x \,.\, \forall y R(x, y) \supset Q(x, y)$$

the first occurrence of x is free, the three remaining occurrences of x are bound, the first and last occurrences of y are free, the second and third occurrences of y are bound, the well-formed part $\forall y R(x, y) \supset Q(x, y)$ is the scope of the quantifier $\forall x$, and the well-formed part $R(x, y)$ is the scope of the universal quantifier $\forall y$.

Now let $\mathbf{x}$ be an individual variable and $\mathbf{a}$ be either an individual variable or an individual constant. If $\mathbf{A}$ is any wff, then

$$\mathbf{S}_{\mathbf{a}}^{\mathbf{x}}\mathbf{A}|$$

denotes the result of replacing each free occurrence of $\mathbf{x}$ in $\mathbf{A}$ by $\mathbf{a}$. Of course, this is again a wff. For example

$$S_z^x P(x, y) \supset \forall x \,.\, \forall y R(x, y) \supset Q(x, y)|$$

is the formula

$$P(z, y) \supset \forall x \,.\, \forall y R(x, y) \supset Q(x, y)$$

while

$$S_z^y P(x, y) \supset \forall x \,.\, \forall y R(x, y) \supset Q(x, y)|$$

is the formula

$$P(x, z) \supset \forall x \,.\, \forall y R(x, y) \supset Q(x, z).$$

Now suppose $\mathbf{x}$ is an individual variable, $\mathbf{a}$ is an individual variable or an individual constant, and $\mathbf{A}$ is a wff. We say **a is free for x in A** iff either

(1) $\mathbf{a}$ is an individual constant; *or*

(2) $\mathbf{a}$ is an individual variable and no free occurrence of $\mathbf{x}$ in $\mathbf{A}$ is in a well-formed part of $\mathbf{A}$ of the form $\forall\mathbf{a}\mathbf{B}$.

[Notice that condition (2) is always satisfied if $\mathbf{a}$ is $\mathbf{x}$ or if $\mathbf{a}$ does not appear in $\mathbf{A}$.] The idea of this definition is this: if $\mathbf{a}$ is free for $\mathbf{x}$ in $\mathbf{A}$ (and $\mathbf{a}$ is an individual variable), then each free occurrence of $\mathbf{x}$ in $\mathbf{A}$ becomes a free occurrence of $\mathbf{a}$ in $\mathbf{S}_{\mathbf{a}}^{\mathbf{x}}\mathbf{A}|$. For example, z is free for x in the formula $\forall y P(x, y)$, however, y is not free for x in this formula. Thus the formula $S_z^x \forall y P(x, y)|$ is $\forall y P(z, y)$ and has no new bound variables, while the formula

$S_y^x \forall y P(x, y)|$ is $\forall y P(y, y)$ which has a bound variable where formerly there was a free variable. The variable z is not free for x in the formula

$$\forall z \centerdot P(x, y) \supset \forall y P(y, z)$$

but y is free for x in that formula.

EXERCISES

1. For each of the wffs of §7 Exercise 2, specify which variables are free, which are bound, and the scope of each quantifier.

2. Is **x** necessarily free for **x** in **A**? Is **y** necessarily free for **x** if **y** has no bound occurrence in **A**? . . . no free occurrence in **A**?

3. In which of the following wffs is y free for x?

   (1) $\forall y P(x, y)$
   (2) $\forall x \forall y \centerdot (Px, y) \supset Q(x)$
   (3) $\forall x \forall y P(x, y) \supset Q(x)$
   (4) $\forall y P(x, y) \supset Q(x)$
   (5) $\forall y \exists x P(x, y) \supset Q(x)$
   (6) $P(x) \supset \exists x Q(x, y)$
   (7) $\exists z Q(x, y, z)$

4. Compute the following wffs:

   $S_y^x P(x) \supset \forall x Q(x, y)|$
   $S_x^y P(x) \supset \forall x Q(x, y)|$
   $S_z^x P(x) \supset \forall x Q(x, y)|$
   $S_z^y P(x) \supset \forall x Q(x, y)|$
   $S_x^z P(x) \supset \forall x Q(x, y)|$
   $S_y^y P(x) \supset \forall x Q(x, y)|$

5. Compute $S_y^x \mathbf{A}|$, $S_x^y \mathbf{A}|$, and $S_z^x \mathbf{A}|$ for each of the wffs **A** of Exercise 3.

§9 Models

Let X be a set and k a positive integer ($k = 1, 2, \ldots$). A **k-tuple of elements of X** is an ordered sequence of k elements of X. The elements need not be distinct and the order is important. Thus (1, 2, 4), (4, 1, 2), and (1, 1, 5) are all distinct 3-tuples of integers. The set of all k-tuples of elements of X is denoted by X^k.

A k-**place relation** on X is a set of k-tuples of elements of X; that is, a subset of X^k. The elements of the relation are said to **satisfy** the relation.

For example, let X be the set of natural numbers 0, 1, 2, ... The set of all pairs (x, y) of elements of X such that $x < y$ is a 2-place relation on X. This set is more simply denoted by

$$\{(x, y) \in X^2 | x < y\}.$$

This 2-place relation is satisfied by the 2-tuple (3, 4). It is not satisfied by the 2-tuple (4, 3). The set

$$\{(x, y, z) \in X^3 | x + y = z\}$$

is a 3-place relation on x. It is satisfied by (3, 5, 8) and (4, 4, 8) but not by (3, 8, 5) or (8, 4, 4).

Let $\mathfrak{S}$ be a system of predicates. A **model of type** $\mathfrak{S}$ is a pair

$$\mathfrak{M} = (X, V)$$

where X is a nonempty set and V is a function which assigns to each k-place predicate letter $\mathbf{P}$ of $\mathfrak{S}$ a k-place relation $V(\mathbf{P})$ on X.

A **sentence** is a wff having no free variables. If $\mathfrak{M} = (X, V)$ is a model of type $\mathfrak{S}$ and $\mathbf{A}$ is a sentence of $L(\mathfrak{S}, X)$ we shall define what it means for $\mathbf{A}$ to **hold** in $\mathfrak{M}$. If $\mathbf{A}$ holds in $\mathfrak{M}$ we write

$$\mathfrak{M} \models \mathbf{A}.$$

If $\mathbf{A}$ does not hold in $\mathfrak{M}$, we write

$$\mathfrak{M} \not\models \mathbf{A}.$$

This relation is defined inductively as follows:

(M1) If $\mathbf{P}$ is a k-place predicate letter and $a_1, a_2, \ldots, a_k$ are constants from X, then

$$\mathfrak{M} \models \mathbf{P}(a_1, a_2, \ldots, a_k) \quad \text{if } (a_1, a_2, \ldots, a_k) \text{ satisfies } V(\mathbf{P})$$

$$\mathfrak{M} \not\models \mathbf{P}(a_1, a_2, \ldots, a_k) \quad \text{otherwise.}$$

(M2) $\mathfrak{M} \not\models \mathfrak{f}$

(M3) $\mathfrak{M} \not\models \mathbf{A} \supset \mathbf{B}$ if $\mathfrak{M} \models \mathbf{A}$ and $\mathfrak{M} \not\models \mathbf{B}$

$\mathfrak{M} \models \mathbf{A} \supset \mathbf{B}$ otherwise

(M4) $\mathfrak{M} \models \forall \mathbf{x} \mathbf{A}$ if for every $a \in X$, $\mathfrak{M} \models \mathbf{S}_a{}^{\mathbf{x}} \mathbf{A}|$

$\mathfrak{M} \not\models \forall \mathbf{x} \mathbf{A}$ otherwise.

For example, let $\mathfrak{S}$ consist of the single 2-place predicate P. Let $\mathfrak{M} = (X, V)$ be the model obtained by taking for X the set of natural numbers 0, 1, 2, 3, . . ., and for $V(\mathrm{P})$ the 2-place relation $<$. Then

$$\mathfrak{M} \models \forall x \,.\, \mathrm{P}(4, x) \supset \mathrm{P}(2, x) \qquad \text{and} \qquad \mathfrak{M} \not\models \forall x \,.\, \mathrm{P}(2, x) \supset \mathrm{P}(4, x).$$

The following proposition is analogous to the truth tables (TT1)–(TT5) of §2.

9.1 Proposition. Let $\mathfrak{M} = (X, V)$ be a model of type $\mathfrak{S}$, **A** and **B** sentences of $\mathrm{L}(\mathfrak{S}, X)$, and **C** a wff of $\mathrm{L}(\mathfrak{S}, X)$ with a single free variable **x**. Then

(I) $\mathfrak{M} \models \mathbf{A} \supset \mathbf{B}$ if and only if $\mathfrak{M} \models \mathbf{A}$ (materially) implies $\mathfrak{M} \models \mathbf{B}$;

(II) $\mathfrak{M} \models \sim \mathbf{A}$ if and only if $\mathfrak{M} \not\models \mathbf{A}$;

(III) $\mathfrak{M} \models \mathbf{A} \vee \mathbf{B}$ if and only if $\mathfrak{M} \models \mathbf{A}$ or $\mathfrak{M} \models \mathbf{B}$;

(IV) $\mathfrak{M} \models \mathbf{A} \wedge \mathbf{B}$ if and only if $\mathfrak{M} \models \mathbf{A}$ and $\mathfrak{M} \models \mathbf{B}$;

(V) $\mathfrak{M} \models \mathbf{A} \equiv \mathbf{B}$ if and only if $\mathfrak{M} \models \mathbf{A}$ is (materially) equivalent to $\mathfrak{M} \models \mathbf{B}$;

(VI) $\mathfrak{M} \models \forall \mathbf{x}\mathbf{C}$ if and only if for every $a \in X$, $\mathfrak{M} \models \mathbf{S}_a{}^{\mathbf{x}}\mathbf{C}|$;

(VII) $\mathfrak{M} \models \exists \mathbf{x}\mathbf{C}$ if and only if there exists $a \in X$ such that $\mathfrak{M} \models \mathbf{S}_a{}^{\mathbf{x}}\mathbf{C}|$.

These statements follow from the clauses (M1)–(M4) in the definition of $\models$ and from the definition schemas (D1)–(D4) of §1 and (D5) of §7.

EXERCISES

1. Let $\mathfrak{S}$ be the system of predicates consisting of a two-place predicate P and a three-place predicate Q. Let $\mathfrak{M} = (X, V)$ be the model of type $\mathfrak{S}$ defined as follows:

   (i) X is the set of natural numbers 0, 1, 2, . . .

   (ii) For natural numbers $a, b \in X$, $V(\mathrm{P})$ holds for (a, b) iff $a \leqslant b$.

   (iii) For natural numbers $a, b, c \in X$, $V(\mathrm{Q})$ holds for (a, b, c) iff $a + b = c$.

   Which of the following sentences hold in $\mathfrak{M}$?

   (1) $\forall x \forall y \forall z \,.\, \mathrm{Q}(x, y, z) \supset \mathrm{Q}(y, x, z)$

   (2) $\forall x \forall y \,.\, \mathrm{Q}(x, x, y) \supset \mathrm{P}(x, y)$

   (3) $\forall x \forall y \,.\, \mathrm{P}(x, y) \supset \mathrm{Q}(x, x, y)$

   (4) $\exists x \forall y \mathrm{Q}(x, y, y)$

   (5) $\exists x \forall y \mathrm{P}(x, y)$

   (6) $\forall y \exists x \mathrm{P}(x, y)$

   (7) $\exists y \forall x \mathrm{P}(x, y)$

   (8) $\forall x \exists y \mathrm{P}(x, y)$

(9) $\forall x\,\exists y P(x, y) \supset \exists y\,\forall x P(x, y)$

(10) $\forall x\,\exists y P(y, x) \supset \exists y\,\forall x P(y, x)$

(11) $\forall x\,\forall y\,\forall z \,.\, Q(x, y, z) \supset P(x, z)$

(12) $\forall x\,\forall z \,.\, \exists y Q(x, y, z) \supset P(x, z)$

(13) $\forall x\,\forall z \,.\, \forall y Q(x, y, z) \supset P(x, z)$

(14) $\forall x\,\forall y \,.\, P(x, y) \vee P(y, x)$

(15) $\forall x \,.\, \forall y P(x, y) \equiv \forall y Q(x, y, y)$

(16) $\forall x \,.\, \sim \forall y P(x, y) \supset \exists y P(x, y)$

(17) $\forall z \,.\, \forall x\,\exists y \sim P(x, y) \supset \exists y \sim P(z, y)$

(18) $\forall x\,\exists y \sim P(x, y) \supset \exists y \sim P(y, y)$

2. Let $\mathfrak{S}$ and $\mathfrak{M} = (X, V)$ be as in Exercise 1, except now let X be the set of integers $\ldots, -2, -1, 0, 1, 2, \ldots$. Which of the sentences (1)–(18) of Exercise 1 hold in this model $\mathfrak{M}$?

3. Let **P** be a 2-place predicate letter. We shall write $\mathbf{x} < \mathbf{y}$ as an abbreviation for $\mathbf{P}(\mathbf{x}, \mathbf{y})$. Let $\mathbf{A}_1$ be the sentence $\forall x \,.\, \sim x < x$, $\mathbf{A}_2$ the sentence $\forall x\,\forall y\,\forall z \,.\, [x < y \wedge y < z] \supset x < z$, and $\mathbf{A}_3$ the sentence $\forall x\,\forall y\,\exists z \,.\, x < z \wedge y < z$. Let **A** be the sentence $\mathbf{A}_1 \wedge \mathbf{A}_2 \wedge \mathbf{A}_3$. Show that **A** has infinite models but no finite models.

*4. Let $\mathfrak{M} = (X, V)$ be a model of type $\mathfrak{S}$ such that X is finite. Give an algorithm for determining if a sentence **A** of $L(\mathfrak{S}, X)$ holds in $\mathfrak{M}$. *Hint:* Replace each wff part $\forall \mathbf{x}\mathbf{B}$ of **A** by

$$\mathbf{S}^{\mathbf{x}}_{a_1}\mathbf{B}| \wedge \mathbf{S}^{\mathbf{x}}_{a_2}\mathbf{B}| \wedge \ldots \wedge \mathbf{S}^{\mathbf{x}}_{a_n}\mathbf{B}|$$

where $a_1, a_2, \ldots, a_n$ are the elements of X. If $\mathbf{A}^*$ denotes the result of making these replacements, then $\mathfrak{M} \models \mathbf{A}$ if and only if $\mathfrak{M} \models \mathbf{A}^*$. But $\mathbf{A}^*$ contains no quantifiers and is thus essentially a formula of the propositional calculus. (We are, of course, assuming that the model $\mathfrak{M}$ is presented in such a way that it is known exactly when

$$\mathfrak{M} \models \mathbf{P}(b_1, b_2, \ldots, b_k)$$

for each k-place predicate **P** of $\mathfrak{S}$ and each k-tuple $(b_1, b_2, \ldots, b_k)$ of elements of X).

§10 Validity

Roughly speaking, a sentence is valid iff it is true in every model. More precisely, a sentence **A** is **valid** iff $\mathfrak{M} \models \mathbf{A}$ for every model $\mathfrak{M} = (X, V)$ of type $\mathfrak{S}$ such that **A** is a sentence of $L(\mathfrak{S}, X)$.

Let **A** be a wff. The **universal closure** of **A** is the wff formed by universally quantifying over all the free variables of **A**; that is, if $\mathbf{x}_1, \mathbf{x}_2, \ldots, \mathbf{x}_n$ are the free variables of **A**, then the universal closure of **A** is the wff

$$\forall \mathbf{x}_1 \, \forall \mathbf{x}_2 \ldots \forall \mathbf{x}_n \, \mathbf{A}.$$

It has no free variables and is therefore a sentence. A wff **A** is **valid** iff its universal closure is valid.

If **A** is a sentence which is not valid, then there is a model $\mathfrak{M}$ such that $\mathfrak{M} \nvDash \mathbf{A}$. Such a model is called a **countermodel** for **A**.

Examples. The sentences

$$\forall x \,\blacksquare\, P(x) \supset P(x)$$

and

$$\exists y \, \forall x Q(x, y) \supset \forall x \, \exists y Q(x, y)$$

both are valid. The wff

$$\forall x \,\blacksquare\, Q(x, y) \supset Q(x, y)$$

also is valid. The sentences

$$\forall x \,\blacksquare\, P(x) \supset Q(x)$$

and

$$\forall x \, \exists y Q(x, y) \supset \exists y \, \forall x Q(x, y)$$

are not valid. Also the wff

$$\forall x \,\blacksquare\, P(x, y) \supset P(y, x)$$

is not valid.

EXERCISES

1. Which of the following wffs are valid? Construct countermodels for those which are not valid.

(1) $\forall x \, \forall y P(x, y) \supset \forall y \, \forall x P(x, y)$

(2) $\forall x \, \forall y P(x, y) \supset \forall x \, \forall y P(y, x)$

(3) $\forall x \, \forall y P(x, y) \supset \forall y \, \forall x P(y, x)$

(4) $\exists y \, \forall x P(x, y) \supset \forall x \, \exists y P(x, y)$

(5) $\forall x \, \exists y P(x, y) \supset \exists y \, \forall x P(x, y)$

(6) $\sim \blacksquare\, \forall x \, \exists y P(x, y) \supset \exists y \, \forall x P(x, y)$

(7) $\forall x[P(y) \supset Q(x)] \supset \blacksquare\, P(y) \supset \forall x \, Q(x)$

(8) $\forall x[P(x) \supset Q(x)] \supset . P(x) \supset \forall xQ(x)$

(9) $\forall xP(x) \supset P(y)$

(10) $\forall x . P(x) \supset P(y)$

(11) $\forall xP(x) \supset P(x)$

(12) $\forall x . P(x) \supset P(x)$

(13) $\forall x \exists yP(x, y) \supset \exists yP(z, y)$

(14) $\forall x \exists yP(x, y) \supset \exists P(y, y)$

(15) $\sim . \forall x \exists yP(x, y) \supset \exists yP(y, y)$

(16) $\forall x \forall yP(x, y) \supset \forall yP(y, y)$

2. Let **A** be a wff and **x** and **y** variables. Is $\forall \mathbf{xA} \supset \mathbf{S_y}^{\mathbf{x}}\mathbf{A}|$ always valid if **y** is free for **x** in **A**? Give an example of a wff **A** such that $\forall \mathbf{xA} \supset \mathbf{S_y}^{\mathbf{x}}\mathbf{A}|$ is valid and **y** is not free for **x**. Give an example of a wff **A** such that $\forall \mathbf{xA} \supset \mathbf{S_y}^{\mathbf{x}}\mathbf{A}|$ is not valid.

§11 Axiomatization of $L(\mathfrak{S}, X)$

Let $\mathfrak{S}$ be a system of predicates and X a set of constants. Any wff of $L(\mathfrak{S}, X)$ which is one of the following five forms is an axiom of $L(\mathfrak{S}, X)$:

11.1 $\mathbf{A} \supset . \mathbf{B} \supset \mathbf{A}$

11.2 $\mathbf{A} \supset [\mathbf{B} \supset \mathbf{C}] \supset . [\mathbf{A} \supset \mathbf{B}] \supset [\mathbf{A} \supset \mathbf{C}]$

11.3 $\sim\sim \mathbf{A} \supset \mathbf{A}$

11.4 $\forall \mathbf{xA} \supset \mathbf{S_a}^{\mathbf{x}}\mathbf{A}|$

where **x** is an individual variable and **a** is an individual variable or an individual constant which is free for **x** in **A**.

11.5 $\forall \mathbf{x}[\mathbf{A} \supset \mathbf{B}] \supset . \mathbf{A} \supset \forall \mathbf{xB}$

where **x** is an individual variable which is not free in **A**.

The **rules of inference** of $L(\mathfrak{S}, X)$ are:

11.6 (*modus ponens*) from **A** and $\mathbf{A} \supset \mathbf{B}$ to infer **B**.

11.7 (*generalization*) from **A**, if **x** is an individual variable, to infer $\forall \mathbf{xA}$.

A sequence $\mathbf{B}_1, \mathbf{B}_2, \ldots, \mathbf{B}_m$ of wffs of $L(\mathfrak{S}, X)$ is called a **deduction** (of $\mathbf{B}_m$) in $L(\mathfrak{S}, X)$ iff for each $k = 1, 2, \ldots, m$, *either*

(DDL1) the wff $\mathbf{B}_k$ is an axiom (that is, $\mathbf{B}_k$ has one of the forms 5.1–5.5); *or*

(DDL2) for some $i, j < k$, $\mathbf{B}_k$ results from $\mathbf{B}_i$ and $\mathbf{B}_j$ by the rule 5.6 (that is, $\mathbf{B}_j$ is $\mathbf{B}_i \supset \mathbf{B}_k$); *or*

(DDL3) for some $i < k$, $\mathbf{B}_k$ results from $\mathbf{B}_i$ by rule 5.7 (that is, $\mathbf{B}_k$ is $\forall \mathbf{xB}_i$).

We say $\mathbf{B}$ is a **theorem** of L($\mathfrak{S}$, X) iff there is a deduction $\mathbf{B}_1, \mathbf{B}_2, \ldots, \mathbf{B}_m$ such that $\mathbf{B}_m$ is $\mathbf{B}$. The notation

$$\vdash \mathbf{B}$$

means $\mathbf{B}$ is a theorem of L($\mathfrak{S}$, X).[1]

The following sequence of four wffs is a deduction:

$$\forall x P(x) \supset P(y)$$
$$\forall y \,.\, \forall x P(x) \supset P(y)$$
$$\forall y[\forall x P(x) \supset P(y)] \supset . \forall x P(x) \supset \forall y P(y)$$
$$\forall x P(x) \supset \forall y P(y).$$

The first wff is an instance of 11.4; the second is obtained from the first by 11.7; the third is an instance of 11.5; and the fourth is obtained from the second and third by 11.6.

EXERCISES

1. Let $\mathfrak{S}_1$ and $\mathfrak{S}_2$ be systems of predicates and X_1 and X_2 sets of constants. Let $\mathbf{A}$ be a wff of L($\mathfrak{S}_1$, X_1) that also is a wff of L($\mathfrak{S}_2$, X_2). Show that if $\mathbf{A}$ is a theorem of L($\mathfrak{S}_1$, X_1), then $\mathbf{A}$ is a theorem of L($\mathfrak{S}_2$, X_2).

2. Prove the following substitution rule for L($\mathfrak{S}$, X): Let $\mathbf{A}$ be a wff of L($\mathfrak{S}$, X), $\mathbf{x}$ an individual variable, and $\mathbf{a}$ an individual variable or constant which is free for $\mathbf{x}$ in $\mathbf{A}$. Then, if $\vdash \mathbf{A}$, then $\vdash \mathbf{S_a}^{\mathbf{x}}\mathbf{A}|$.

§12 Propositional Calculus

Because of the correspondence between the schemas 11.1, 11.2, 11.3, and the rule 11.6 and the schemas and rule for the propositional calculus 3.1–3.4, it is clear that anything we can prove in the propositional calculus also can be proved in first-order logic. We formulate this precisely.

12.1 Proposition. Let $\mathbf{C}$ be any wff of the propositional calculus and let $\mathbf{p}_1, \mathbf{p}_2, \ldots, \mathbf{p}_n$ be the proposition letters appearing in $\mathbf{C}$. Let $\mathbf{B}_1, \mathbf{B}_2, \ldots, \mathbf{B}_n$ be any wffs of a first order language L($\mathfrak{S}$, X). Form the wff $\mathbf{A}$ of L($\mathfrak{S}$, X) by replacing each occurrence of $\mathbf{p}_i$ ($i = 1, 2, \ldots, n$) in $\mathbf{C}$ by $\mathbf{B}_i$. If $\mathbf{C}$ is a tautology, then $\vdash \mathbf{A}$.

---

[1] The notation $\vdash \mathbf{B}$ does not mention the language L($\mathfrak{S}$, X) because it is independent of L($\mathfrak{S}$, X). See Exercise 1 at the end of this section.

PROOF. If **C** is a tautology, then by the completeness of the propositional calculus 6.3, there is a deduction of **C** in the propositional calculus. In this deduction replace each occurrence of $\mathbf{p}_i$ by $\mathbf{B}_i$ and replace any other proposition letters which occur by some fixed wff of L($\mathfrak{S}$, X), say ∀xP(x). The resulting sequence of wffs of the predicate calculus is a deduction of **A** [in L($\mathfrak{S}$, X)]. ∎

§13 The Deduction Theorem

The axiom system 11.1–11.7 is, like the axiomatization of the propositional calculus given in §3, designed so that the deduction theorem is especially easy to prove. The deduction theorem, in turn, greatly facilitates formal theorem proving in the language.

Let $\mathfrak{S}$ be a system of predicates, X a set of constants, and $\mathbf{A}_1, \mathbf{A}_2, \ldots, \mathbf{A}_n$ a finite sequence of wffs of L($\mathfrak{S}$, X). A finite sequence $\mathbf{B}_1, \mathbf{B}_2, \ldots, \mathbf{B}_m$ of wffs of L($\mathfrak{S}$, X) is called a **deduction (of $\mathbf{B}_m$) from the hypotheses $\mathbf{A}_1, \mathbf{A}_2, \ldots, \mathbf{A}_n$** iff for each $k = 1, 2, \ldots, m$, *either*

(DHL1) $\mathbf{B}_k$ is one of the formulas $\mathbf{A}_j$ $(j = 1, 2, \ldots, n)$; *or*

(DHL2) $\mathbf{B}_k$ is an axiom (that is, $\mathbf{B}_k$ has one of the forms 11.1 to 11.5); *or*

(DHL3) for some $i, j < k$, $\mathbf{B}_k$ results from $\mathbf{B}_i$ and $\mathbf{B}_j$ by *modus ponens* (11.6) (that is, $\mathbf{B}_j$ is $\mathbf{B}_i \supset \mathbf{B}_k$); *or*

(DHL4) for some $i < k$, $\mathbf{B}_k$ results from $\mathbf{B}_i$ by generalization (11.7) on an individual variable which does not occur free in $\mathbf{A}_1, \mathbf{A}_2, \ldots, \mathbf{A}_n$ (that is, $\mathbf{B}_k$ is $\forall \mathbf{x} \mathbf{B}_i$ where **x** has no free occurrence in any of the formulas $\mathbf{A}_1, \mathbf{A}_2, \ldots, \mathbf{A}_n$).

The notation

$$\mathbf{A}_1, \mathbf{A}_2, \ldots, \mathbf{A}_n \vdash \mathbf{B}$$

means there is a deduction $\mathbf{B}_1, \mathbf{B}_2, \ldots, \mathbf{B}_m$ from the hypotheses $\mathbf{A}_1, \mathbf{A}_2, \ldots,$ $\mathbf{A}_n$ such that $\mathbf{B}_m$ is **B**. The use of the sign ⊢ in §11 is a special case of the above, namely the case $n = 0$. Indeed, a deduction of **B** from the empty set of hypotheses is precisely the same thing as a deduction of **B**.

The intuitive meaning of $\mathbf{A}_1, \mathbf{A}_2, \ldots, \mathbf{A}_n \vdash \mathbf{B}$ is that **B** can be proved on the assumption that $\mathbf{A}_1, \mathbf{A}_2, \ldots, \mathbf{A}_n$ are true. This explains the restriction on generalization in (DHL4). Without that restriction we could prove P(x) ⊢ ∀xP(x) [as follows: P(x) ⊢ P(x) by (DHL1) and then P(x) ⊢ ∀xP(x) by (DHL4) without the restriction]. This clearly should not be allowed; it amounts to saying that if P is true for one x, it is true for every x.

On the other hand, it can be argued that the definition of deduction from hypothesis is still incorrect. Consider, for example, the following (correct) deduction from hypothesis:

$$\forall x P(x) \vdash \forall x P(x)$$
$$\forall x P(x) \vdash \forall x P(x) \supset P(y)$$
$$\forall x P(x) \vdash P(y)$$
$$\forall x P(x) \vdash \forall y P(y)$$

The first step is by (DHL1), the second by (DHL2) and 5.4, the third by (DHL3), and the fourth by (DHL4). If, however, we add the additional hypothesis Q(y), then the deduction is no longer correct: according to (DHL4) we may not generalize on y if y is free in one of the hypotheses. We are put in the paradoxical position of asserting that something which can be proved from given hypotheses can no longer be proved if we add additional hypotheses. We could have avoided this by slightly modifying the definition of deduction from hypotheses; however, it doesn't seem worth the complication.[2]

The following proposition shows that the above difficulty isn't very serious:

13.1 Proposition. Suppose $\mathbf{A}_1, \mathbf{A}_2, \ldots, \mathbf{A}_n \vdash \mathbf{B}$. Then if $\mathbf{C}_1, \mathbf{C}_2, \ldots, \mathbf{C}_r$ are sentences, then

$$\mathbf{A}_1, \mathbf{A}_2, \ldots, \mathbf{A}_n, \mathbf{C}_1, \mathbf{C}_2, \ldots, \mathbf{C}_r \vdash \mathbf{B}.$$

PROOF. Since $\mathbf{C}_1, \mathbf{C}_2, \ldots, \mathbf{C}_r$ have no free variables, adding them as additional hypotheses could not possibly invalidate an application of (DHL4). A deduction from hypotheses $\mathbf{A}_1, \mathbf{A}_2, \ldots, \mathbf{A}_n$ is therefore also a deduction from the hypotheses $\mathbf{A}_1, \mathbf{A}_2, \ldots, \mathbf{A}_n, \mathbf{C}_1, \mathbf{C}_2, \ldots, \mathbf{C}_r$. ▌

13.2 The Deduction Theorem for First-Order Logic. If $\mathbf{A}_1, \mathbf{A}_2, \ldots, \mathbf{A}_n \vdash \mathbf{B}$, then $\mathbf{A}_1, \mathbf{A}_2, \ldots, \mathbf{A}_{n-1} \vdash \mathbf{A}_n \supset \mathbf{B}$.

PROOF. Assume $\mathbf{A}_1, \mathbf{A}_2, \ldots, \mathbf{A}_n \vdash \mathbf{B}$. Then there is a deduction $\mathbf{B}_1, \mathbf{B}_2, \ldots, \mathbf{B}_m$ of $\mathbf{B}$ from $\mathbf{A}_1, \mathbf{A}_2, \ldots, \mathbf{A}_n$ ($\mathbf{B}$ is $\mathbf{B}_m$). We shall prove

(†) $\quad \mathbf{A}_1, \mathbf{A}_2, \ldots, \mathbf{A}_{n-1} \vdash \mathbf{A}_n \supset \mathbf{B}_k$

for $k = 1, 2, \ldots, m$. Then taking $k = m$ in (†) we have 13.2.

We prove (†) by induction. Accordingly, we assume as hypothesis of induction that (†) holds for all values of k up to some fixed value of k and prove (†) for that fixed value of k.

---

[2] See §45; in particular 45.10.

CASE 1. Assume $\mathbf{B}_k$ satisfies (DHL1) in the definition of deduction from hypotheses. Then $\mathbf{B}_k$ is $\mathbf{A}_j$ for some $j = 1, 2, \ldots, n$.

Subcase 1*a*. Assume $j = 1, 2, \ldots, n-1$. Proceed as in Subcase 1a of the proof of the deduction theorem for the propositional calculus 4.1.

Subcase 1*b*. Assume $j = n$. Proceed as in Subcase 1b of 4.1.

CASE 2. Assume $\mathbf{B}_k$ satisfies (DHL2) in the definition. Then $\mathbf{B}_k$ is an axiom. Proceed as in Case 2 of 4.1.

CASE 3. Assume $\mathbf{B}_k$ satisfies (DHL3) in the definition. Then $\mathbf{B}_k$ is obtained from $\mathbf{B}_i$ and $\mathbf{B}_j$ $(i, j < k)$ by *modus ponens*. By the induction hypothesis, (†) holds for $\mathbf{B}_i$ and $\mathbf{B}_j$. Proceed as in Case 3 of 4.1.

CASE 4. Assume $\mathbf{B}_k$ satisfies (DHL4) in the definition. Then $\mathbf{B}_k$ results from some $\mathbf{B}_i$ $(i < k)$ by generalization (11.7); that is, $\mathbf{B}_k$ is $\forall \mathbf{x} \mathbf{B}_i$. Furthermore $\mathbf{x}$ does not occur free in $\mathbf{A}_1, \mathbf{A}_2, \ldots, \mathbf{A}_n$. By the hypothesis of induction,

$$\mathbf{A}_1, \mathbf{A}_2, \ldots, \mathbf{A}_{n-1} \vdash \mathbf{A}_n \supset \mathbf{B}_i.$$

Hence by generalization (DHL4),

$$\mathbf{A}_1, \mathbf{A}_2, \ldots, \mathbf{A}_{n-1} \vdash \forall \mathbf{x} \,\blacksquare\, \mathbf{A}_n \supset \mathbf{B}_i.$$

By (DHL2) and 11.5,

$$\mathbf{A}_1, \mathbf{A}_2, \ldots, \mathbf{A}_{n-1} \vdash \forall \mathbf{x}[\mathbf{A}_n \supset \mathbf{B}_i] \supset \blacksquare\, \mathbf{A}_n \supset \forall \mathbf{x} \mathbf{B}_i.$$

Hence by *modus ponens* (DHL3),

$$\mathbf{A}_1, \mathbf{A}_2, \ldots, \mathbf{A}_{n-1} \vdash \mathbf{A}_n \supset \forall \mathbf{x} \mathbf{B}_i$$

that is,

$$\mathbf{A}_1, \mathbf{A}_2, \ldots, \mathbf{A}_{n-1} \vdash \mathbf{A}_n \supset \mathbf{B}_k.$$

This completes the proof of the deduction theorem. ▌

Notice that axiom 11.5 is precisely what is needed to carry out Case 4 in the proof. This is what we mean when we say that the axiom system 11.1–11.7 is designed to make the deduction theorem easy to prove.

The main tools used to prove theorem schemas in $L(\mathfrak{S}, X)$ are the deduction theorem (13.2) and the propositional calculus (see 12.1). To obtain the full strength of 12.1 note that if $\mathbf{C}$ is a tautology of the propositional calculus, $\mathbf{p}_1, \mathbf{p}_2, \ldots, \mathbf{p}_n$ are the proposition letters appearing in $\mathbf{C}$, and the $\mathbf{B}$ of $L(\mathfrak{S}, X)$ results by replacing of each occurrence of each $\mathbf{p}_i$ $(i = 1, \ldots, n)$ in $\mathbf{C}$ by a wff $\mathbf{B}_i$ of $L(\mathfrak{S}, X)$, then $\mathbf{A}_1, \mathbf{A}_2, \ldots, \mathbf{A}_m \vdash \mathbf{B}$ where $\mathbf{A}_1, \mathbf{A}_2, \ldots, \mathbf{A}_m$ are any wffs of $L(\mathfrak{S}, \mathcal{X})$. This is because the deduction of **B** constructed in the proof of 12.1 never uses generalization (11.7) and is hence also a deduction from the hypotheses $\mathbf{A}_1, \mathbf{A}_2, \ldots, \mathbf{A}_m$. Thus when trying to prove theorem schemas in $L(\mathfrak{S}, \mathcal{X})$ you may always use any "substitution instance" of a tautology. For example, if $\mathbf{A}_1, \mathbf{A}_2, \ldots, \mathbf{A}_m$, **A**, and **B** are wffs of $L(\mathfrak{S}, \mathcal{X})$, then

$$\mathbf{A}_1, \mathbf{A}_2, \ldots, \mathbf{A}_m \vdash \mathbf{A} \supset \mathbf{B} \,.\!\supset \mathbf{A} \,.\!\supset \mathbf{A}$$

inasmuch as $\mathbf{A} \supset \mathbf{B} \,.\!\supset \mathbf{A} \,.\!\supset \mathbf{A}$ results from the tautology $p \supset q \,.\!\supset p \,.\!\supset p$ by replacing p by **A** and q by **B**.

§14 Some Theorems of First-Order Logic

In this section **A** and **B** denote arbitrary wffs of some first-order language $L(\mathfrak{S}, \mathcal{X})$ and **x** and **y** are individual variables. The proofs of all the theorems of this section are left as exercises although many appear in the section at the back of the book entitled "Answers to Selected Exercises." Only 14.1 will be needed for the proof of the completeness theorem 17.2.

14.1 $\vdash \forall \mathbf{x}\mathbf{A} \supset \forall \mathbf{y} S_{\mathbf{y}}^{\mathbf{x}}\mathbf{A}|$ if **y** does not occur free in **A** and if **y** is free for **x** in **A**.

Hint: By 11.4 $\forall \mathbf{x}\mathbf{A} \vdash S_{\mathbf{y}}^{\mathbf{x}}\mathbf{A}|$. Generalize on **y** and use 13.2.

14.2 $\vdash \forall \mathbf{x}\mathbf{A} \equiv \forall \mathbf{y} S_{\mathbf{y}}^{\mathbf{x}}\mathbf{A}|$ if **y** does not occur in **A**.

Hint: Use 14.1 to prove $\vdash \forall \mathbf{x}\mathbf{A} \supset \forall \mathbf{y} S_{\mathbf{y}}^{\mathbf{x}}\mathbf{A}|$ and $\vdash \forall \mathbf{y} S_{\mathbf{y}}^{\mathbf{x}}\mathbf{A}| \supset \forall \mathbf{x}\mathbf{A}$. Then use the propositional calculus.

The scheme 14.2 sometimes is called the *schema of alphabetic change of a bound variable*.

14.3 $\vdash \forall \mathbf{x}\, \forall \mathbf{y}\mathbf{A} \equiv \forall \mathbf{y}\, \forall \mathbf{x}\mathbf{A}$.

14.4 $\vdash \exists \mathbf{x}\, \exists \mathbf{y}\mathbf{A} \equiv \exists \mathbf{y}\, \exists \mathbf{x}\mathbf{A}$.

14.5 $\vdash \mathbf{A} \supset \forall \mathbf{x}\mathbf{B} \,.\!\supset \forall \mathbf{x}[\mathbf{A} \supset \mathbf{B}]$ if **x** is not free in **A**.

Hint: Prove $\mathbf{A} \supset \forall \mathbf{x}\mathbf{B} \vdash \mathbf{A} \supset \mathbf{B}$.

14.6 $\vdash \forall \mathbf{x}[\mathbf{A} \supset \mathbf{B}] \supset .\, \forall \mathbf{x}\mathbf{A} \supset \forall \mathbf{x}\mathbf{B}$.

14.7 $\vdash \forall \mathbf{x}[\mathbf{A} \equiv \mathbf{B}] \supset .\, \forall \mathbf{x}\mathbf{A} \equiv \forall \mathbf{x}\mathbf{B}$.

***14.8** (Substitutivity of Equivalence) Let **M** and **N** be wffs and suppose **B** results from **A** by replacing zero or more occurrences of **M** in **A** by **N**. Let $[\mathbf{M} \equiv \mathbf{N}]'$ be the universal closure of $\mathbf{M} \equiv \mathbf{N}$. Show that $\vdash [\mathbf{M} \equiv \mathbf{N}]' \supset .\, \mathbf{A} \equiv \mathbf{B}$. Hence, if $\vdash \mathbf{M} \equiv \mathbf{N}$, then $\vdash \mathbf{A} \equiv \mathbf{B}$.

Hint: Use induction on the length of **A**. There are three cases: (1) **A** is **M** itself; (2) **A** is $\mathbf{A}_1 \supset \mathbf{A}_2$; (3) **A** is $\forall\mathbf{x}\mathbf{A}_1$. In Case (3) use 14.7.

14.9 $\vdash \mathbf{S}_\mathbf{y}^\mathbf{x}\mathbf{A}| \supset \exists\mathbf{x}\mathbf{A}$ if **y** is free for **x** in **A**.

Hint: $\exists\mathbf{x}\mathbf{A}$ is $\sim\forall\mathbf{x}\sim\mathbf{A}$. By 11.4 $\forall\mathbf{x}\sim\mathbf{A}\supset\sim\mathbf{S}_\mathbf{y}^\mathbf{x}\mathbf{A}|$. Use the propositional calculus.

14.10 $\vdash \forall\mathbf{x}[\mathbf{A}\supset\mathbf{B}] \equiv . \mathbf{A}\supset\forall\mathbf{x}\mathbf{B}$ if **x** is not free in **A**.

Hint: Use 11.5 and 14.5.

14.11 $\vdash \exists\mathbf{x}\mathbf{A}[\mathbf{A}\supset\mathbf{B}] \equiv . \mathbf{A}\supset\exists\mathbf{x}\mathbf{B}$ if **x** is not free in **A**.

14.12 $\vdash \forall\mathbf{x}[\mathbf{A}\supset\mathbf{B}] \equiv . \exists\mathbf{x}\mathbf{A}\supset\mathbf{B}$ if **x** is not free in **B**.

14.13 $\vdash \exists\mathbf{x}[\mathbf{A}\supset\mathbf{B}] \equiv . \forall\mathbf{x}\mathbf{A}\supset\mathbf{B}$ if **x** is not free in **B**.

A wff is in *prenex normal form* iff it has the form $\mathbf{Q}_1\,\mathbf{Q}_2\ldots\mathbf{Q}_n\,\mathbf{M}$ where each $\mathbf{Q}_i$ ($i = 1, 2, \ldots, n$) is either $\forall\mathbf{x}_i$ or $\exists\mathbf{x}_i$ and where **M** contains no quantifiers. The sequence $\mathbf{Q}_1, \mathbf{Q}_2 \ldots \mathbf{Q}_n$ is called the *prefix* and **M** is called the *matrix* of the wff.

***14.14 Prenex Normal-Form Theorem.** For every wff **A** there is a formula **B** in prenex normal form such that $\vdash \mathbf{A}\equiv\mathbf{B}$.

Hint: Use 14.2 (and 14.8) to change all the quantifiers in **A** so that they all have different variables and so that no bound variable of **A** occurs free in **A**. Then use 14.10–14.13 (and 14.8) to move the quantifiers to the front.

14.15 $\vdash \exists\mathbf{x}[\mathbf{A}\vee\mathbf{B}] \equiv . \exists\mathbf{x}\mathbf{A}\vee\exists\mathbf{x}\mathbf{B}$.

14.16 $\vdash \forall\mathbf{x}[\mathbf{A}\wedge\mathbf{B}] \equiv . \forall\mathbf{x}\mathbf{A}\wedge\forall\mathbf{x}\mathbf{B}$.

14.17 $\vdash \exists\mathbf{x}[\mathbf{A}\wedge\mathbf{B}] \supset . \exists\mathbf{x}\mathbf{A}\wedge\exists\mathbf{x}\mathbf{B}$.

Question: Is $\exists\mathbf{x}\mathbf{A}\wedge\exists\mathbf{x}\mathbf{B} . \supset \exists\mathbf{x} . \mathbf{A}\wedge\mathbf{B}$ (the "converse" of 14.17) a theorem schema?

14.18 $\vdash \forall\mathbf{x}\mathbf{A}\vee\forall\mathbf{x}\mathbf{B} . \supset \forall\mathbf{x} . \mathbf{A}\vee\mathbf{B}$. ✓

Question: Is the converse of 14.18 a theorem schema?

14.19 $\vdash \exists\mathbf{y}\,\forall\mathbf{x}\mathbf{A}\supset\forall\mathbf{x}\,\exists\mathbf{y}\mathbf{A}$. ✓

Question: Is the converse of 14.19 a theorem schema?

14.20 $\vdash \mathbf{A}\equiv\forall\mathbf{x}\mathbf{A}$ if **x** is not free in **A**. ✓

14.21 $\vdash \mathbf{A}\equiv\exists\mathbf{x}\mathbf{A}$ if **x** is not free in **A**. ✓

14.22 $\vdash \exists\mathbf{x}[\mathbf{A}\wedge\mathbf{B}] \equiv . \exists\mathbf{x}\mathbf{A}\wedge\mathbf{B}$ if **x** is not free in **B**. ✓

14.23 $\vdash \forall \mathbf{x}[\mathbf{A} \vee \mathbf{B}] \equiv . \forall \mathbf{x}\mathbf{A} \vee \mathbf{B}$ if $\mathbf{x}$ is not free in $\mathbf{B}$.

14.24 $\vdash \forall \mathbf{x}[\mathbf{A} \supset \mathbf{B}] \supset . \exists \mathbf{x}\mathbf{A} \supset \exists \mathbf{x}\mathbf{B}$.

14.25 $\vdash \forall \mathbf{x}[\mathbf{A} \equiv \mathbf{B}] \supset . \exists \mathbf{x}\mathbf{A} \equiv \exists \mathbf{x}\mathbf{B}$.

14.26 If $\mathbf{A}_1, \mathbf{A}_2, \ldots, \mathbf{A}_n, \mathbf{A} \vdash \mathbf{B}$ and $\mathbf{x}$ is not free in $\mathbf{A}_1, \mathbf{A}_2, \ldots, \mathbf{A}_n$ or $\mathbf{B}$, then $\mathbf{A}_1, \mathbf{A}_2, \ldots, \mathbf{A}_n, \exists \mathbf{x}\mathbf{A} \vdash \mathbf{B}$.

14.27 If $\mathbf{A}_1, \mathbf{A}_2, \ldots, \mathbf{A}_n, \mathbf{A} \vdash \mathbf{B}$ and $\mathbf{x}$ is not free in $\mathbf{A}_1, \mathbf{A}_2, \ldots, \mathbf{A}_n$, then $\mathbf{A}_1, \mathbf{A}_2, \ldots, \mathbf{A}_n, \exists \mathbf{x}\mathbf{A} \vdash \exists \mathbf{x}\mathbf{B}$.

§15 The Soundness Theorem

Let $\mathfrak{S}$ be a system of predicates and $\mathfrak{M} = (X, V)$ a model of type $\mathfrak{S}$. Let $\mathbf{\Gamma}$ be a set of sentences of $L(\mathfrak{S}, X)$. Then the notation

$$\mathfrak{M} \models \mathbf{\Gamma}$$

means that $\mathfrak{M} \models \mathbf{A}$ for every $\mathbf{A} \in \mathbf{\Gamma}$. If $\mathbf{B}$ is a wff of $L(\mathfrak{S}, X)$, then the notation

$$\mathbf{\Gamma} \vdash \mathbf{B}$$

means there is a finite sequence $\mathbf{A}_1, \mathbf{A}_2, \ldots, \mathbf{A}_n$ of sentences of $\mathbf{\Gamma}$ such that $\mathbf{A}_1, \mathbf{A}_2, \ldots, \mathbf{A}_n \vdash \mathbf{B}$. Then, where $\mathbf{A}$ is a sentence of $L(\mathfrak{S}, x)$, we have

15.1 The Soundness Theorem. If $\mathfrak{M} \models \mathbf{\Gamma}$ and $\mathbf{\Gamma} \vdash \mathbf{A}$, then $\mathfrak{M} \models \mathbf{A}$.

PROOF. Suppose $\mathfrak{M} \models \mathbf{\Gamma}$. We shall prove a more general statement: If $\mathbf{A}$ is any wff of $L(\mathfrak{S}, X)$ and if $\mathbf{\Gamma} \vdash \mathbf{A}$, then $\mathfrak{M} \models \mathbf{A}'$ where $\mathbf{A}'$ is the universal closure of $\mathbf{A}$. This statement implies 15.1 since the universal closure of a sentence is simply the sentence itself.

Before proceeding we prove some facts about validity.

(1) Let $\mathbf{A}$ be a wff of $L(\mathfrak{S}, X)$ with free variables $\mathbf{x}_1, \mathbf{x}_2, \ldots, \mathbf{x}_n$ and let $\mathbf{A}'$ denote the universal closure of $\mathbf{A}$. Then $\mathfrak{M} \models \mathbf{A}'$ if and only if for all $a_1, a_2, \ldots, a_n \in X \mathfrak{M} \models \mathrm{S}^{\mathbf{x}_1}_{a_1} \mathrm{S}^{\mathbf{x}_2}_{a_2} \ldots \mathrm{S}^{\mathbf{x}_n}_{a_n} \mathbf{A}| |\ldots|$.

PROOF. (1) is obvious as $\mathbf{A}'$ is the wff $\forall \mathbf{x}_1 \forall \mathbf{x}_2 \ldots \forall \mathbf{x}_n \mathbf{A}$. ▌

(2) Any axiom of one of the forms 11.1–11.3 is valid; that is, its universal closure holds in $\mathfrak{M}$.

PROOF. We consider only 11.1; the other two cases are similar. An axiom of form 11.1 has the form $\mathbf{A} \supset . \mathbf{B} \supset \mathbf{A}$. By (1) above we may assume $\mathbf{A}$ and

$\mathbf{B}$ are sentences. If $\mathfrak{M} \nvDash \mathbf{A}$ then $\mathfrak{M} \vDash \mathbf{A} \supset . \mathbf{B} \supset \mathbf{A}$ and if $\mathfrak{M} \vDash \mathbf{A}$, then $\mathfrak{M} \vDash \mathbf{B} \supset \mathbf{A}$, so $\mathfrak{M} \vDash \mathbf{A} \supset . \mathbf{B} \supset \mathbf{A}$. ▮

(3) Any axiom of form 11.4 is valid; that is its universal closure holds in $\mathfrak{M}$.

PROOF. An axiom of form 11.4 has the form

$$\forall \mathbf{x}\mathbf{A} \supset \mathbf{S}_{\mathbf{a}}^{\mathbf{x}}\mathbf{A}|$$

where $\mathbf{a}$ is free for $\mathbf{x}$ in $\mathbf{A}$. Suppose $\mathbf{a}$ is an individual variable (rather than an individual constant). By (1) above we may suppose this axiom contains no free variable other than $\mathbf{a}$ and we must show

$$\mathfrak{M} \vDash \forall \mathbf{a} . \forall \mathbf{x}\mathbf{A} \supset \mathbf{S}_{\mathbf{a}}^{\mathbf{x}}\mathbf{A}|$$

namely, that

$$\mathfrak{M} \vDash \mathbf{S}_{b}^{\mathbf{a}} . \forall \mathbf{x}\mathbf{A} \supset \mathbf{S}_{\mathbf{a}}^{\mathbf{x}}\mathbf{A}||$$

for every $b \in X$. As $\mathbf{a}$ is free for $\mathbf{x}$ in $\mathbf{A}$, it follows that $\mathbf{S}_{b}^{\mathbf{a}}\mathbf{S}_{\mathbf{a}}^{\mathbf{x}}\mathbf{A}||$ is $\mathbf{S}_{b}^{\mathbf{x}}\mathbf{B}|$ where $\mathbf{B}$ is $\mathbf{S}_{b}^{\mathbf{a}}\mathbf{A}|$. Thus we must show

$$\mathfrak{M} \vDash \forall \mathbf{x}\mathbf{B} \supset \mathbf{S}_{b}^{\mathbf{x}}\mathbf{B}|$$

for each $b \in X$. If $\mathfrak{M} \nvDash \forall \mathbf{x}\mathbf{B}$ then $\mathfrak{M} \vDash \forall \mathbf{x}\mathbf{B} \supset \mathbf{S}_{b}^{\mathbf{x}}\mathbf{B}|$ and if $\mathfrak{M} \vDash \forall \mathbf{x}\mathbf{B}$, then by definition $\mathfrak{M} \vDash \mathbf{S}_{b}^{\mathbf{x}}\mathbf{B}|$ for each b and so $\mathfrak{M} \vDash \forall \mathbf{x}\mathbf{B} \supset \mathbf{S}_{b}^{\mathbf{x}}\mathbf{B}|$. The case when $\mathbf{a}$ is a constant (namely, $\mathbf{a} \in X$) is even simpler. ▮

(4) Any axiom of the form 11.5 is valid; that is, its universal closure holds in $\mathfrak{M}$.

PROOF. An axiom of form 11.5 has the form

$$\forall \mathbf{x}[\mathbf{A} \supset \mathbf{B}] \supset . \mathbf{A} \supset \forall \mathbf{x}\mathbf{B}$$

where $\mathbf{x}$ is not free in $\mathbf{A}$. By (1) we may suppose it is a sentence. If $\mathfrak{M} \nvDash \forall \mathbf{x}[\mathbf{A} \supset \mathbf{B}]$ or $\mathfrak{M} \nvDash \mathbf{A}$, then $\mathfrak{M} \vDash \forall \mathbf{x}[\mathbf{A} \supset \mathbf{B}] \supset . \mathbf{A} \supset \forall \mathbf{x}\mathbf{B}$. Suppose $\mathfrak{M} \vDash \forall \mathbf{x}[\mathbf{A} \supset \mathbf{B}]$ and $\mathfrak{M} \vDash \mathbf{A}$. Then for each $b \in X$, $\mathfrak{M} \vDash \mathbf{S}_{b}^{\mathbf{x}}\mathbf{A} \supset \mathbf{B}|$. But as $\mathbf{x}$ is not free in $\mathbf{A}$, $\mathbf{S}_{b}^{\mathbf{x}}\mathbf{A} \supset \mathbf{B}|$ is the same as $\mathbf{A} \supset \mathbf{S}_{b}^{\mathbf{x}}\mathbf{B}|$ for each $b \in X$. As $\mathfrak{M} \vDash \mathbf{A}$ this implies $\mathfrak{M} \vDash \mathbf{S}_{b}^{\mathbf{x}}\mathbf{B}|$ for each $b \in X$; in other words, $\mathfrak{M} \vDash \forall \mathbf{x}\mathbf{B}$. ▮

(5) If $\mathfrak{M} \vDash [\mathbf{A} \supset \mathbf{B}]'$ and $\mathfrak{M} \vDash \mathbf{A}'$ then $\mathfrak{M} \vDash \mathbf{B}'$.

(6) If $\mathfrak{M} \vDash \mathbf{A}'$, then $\mathfrak{M} \vDash (\forall \mathbf{x}\mathbf{A})'$.

PROOF. Statement (5) follows easily from (1), and (6) follows because $\mathbf{A}'$ and $(\forall \mathbf{x}\mathbf{A})'$ are the same sentence, except possibly for the order of some initially placed universal quantifiers. ▮

Now (2)–(4) say that the universal closure of each axiom holds in $\mathfrak{M}$ and

(5) and (6) say that the rules of inference (*modus ponens* and generalization) preserve the property of modeling the universal closure.

We now return to the proof of 15.1. We shall show that if **A** is any wff of L($\mathfrak{S}$, X) such that $\mathbf{\Gamma} \vdash \mathbf{A}$, then $\mathfrak{M} \models \mathbf{A}'$.

Suppose $\mathbf{\Gamma} \vdash \mathbf{A}$ where **A** is a wff of L($\mathfrak{S}$, X). Then there is a deduction of **A** from sentences in **Γ**. Each wff in this deduction is a sentence of **Γ** (in which case $\mathfrak{M}$ models it by hypothesis), or an axiom (in which case $\mathfrak{M}$ models it since the axioms are all valid), or obtained from earlier members of the sequence by application of a rule of inference. The rules of inference clearly preserve the property of being modeled by $\mathfrak{M}$. Hence, by an induction on the length of the deduction, every wff of the deduction has the property that $\mathfrak{M}$ models its universal closure. ▮

The *soundness theorem* says that any sentence which is deducible from sentences which hold in a model must itself hold in that model. If we take **Γ** to be the empty set of sentences, we obtain a not-unexpected corollary:

15.2 If $\vdash \mathbf{A}$, then **A** is valid.

The completeness theorems of §17 are converses to these theorems.

§16 The Extension Lemma

In this section we prove a lemma which is the key step in the proof of the completeness theorem. The proof of the completeness theorem that we give was discovered by L. Henkin in 1947.[3]

We first make several preliminary definitions. Let $\mathfrak{S}$ be a system of predicates, X a set of constants, and **Γ** a set of sentences of L($\mathfrak{S}$, X). The set **Γ** is **inconsistent** iff $\mathbf{\Gamma} \vdash \mathfrak{f}$. The set **Γ** is **consistent** iff **Γ** is not inconsistent. The set **Γ** is **complete in** L($\mathfrak{S}$, X) iff for every sentence **A** of L($\mathfrak{S}$, X) either $\mathbf{A} \in \mathbf{\Gamma}$ or $\sim\mathbf{A} \in \mathbf{\Gamma}$. The set **Γ** is **universal** in L($\mathfrak{S}$, X) iff $\forall\mathbf{x}\mathbf{B} \in \mathbf{\Gamma}$ whenever **B** is a wff of L($\mathfrak{S}$, X) such that $\mathbf{S}_c^{\mathbf{x}}\mathbf{B}| \in \mathbf{\Gamma}$ for every $c \in \mathbf{X}$.

16.1 The Extension Lemma. Let **Γ** be a consistent set of sentences of L($\mathfrak{S}$, X). Then there is a set of constants Y extending X and a set of sentences **Δ** of L($\mathfrak{S}$, Y) such that $\mathbf{\Gamma} \subseteq \mathbf{\Delta}$ and

(1) **Δ** is consistent;

(2) **Δ** is complete in L($\mathfrak{S}$, Y);

(3) **Δ** is universal in L($\mathfrak{S}$, Y).

---

[3] *Journal of Symbolic Logic* **14**, 159–166 (1949).

PROOF. For simplicity, we shall consider only the case when X is countable. Let Y be obtained from X by adjoining a countably infinite set of constants $b_1, b_2, b_3, \ldots$ which are not members of X. Then Y is countable and hence the sentences of L($\mathfrak{S}$, Y) may be enumerated (say in alphabetical order). Let the infinite list $\mathbf{A}_1, \mathbf{A}_2, \mathbf{A}_3, \ldots$ be all the sentences of L($\mathfrak{S}$, Y). We shall inductively define a sequence $\mathbf{\Gamma}_0, \mathbf{\Gamma}_1, \mathbf{\Gamma}_2, \ldots$ of sets of sentences of L($\mathfrak{S}$, Y) such that each $\mathbf{\Gamma}_n$ is obtained from $\mathbf{\Gamma}$ by adjoining a finite set of sentences of L($\mathfrak{S}$, Y). Then clearly only finitely many of the constants $b_1, b_2, \ldots$ will appear in some sentence of $\mathbf{\Gamma}_n$. The inductive definition of $\mathbf{\Gamma}_n$ is $\mathbf{\Gamma}_0 = \mathbf{\Gamma}$. If $\mathbf{\Gamma}_n$ has been defined, $\mathbf{\Gamma}_{n+1}$ is defined by the appropriate case.

CASE 1. If $\mathbf{\Gamma}_n \cup \{\mathbf{A}_{n+1}\}$ is consistent, then $\mathbf{\Gamma}_{n+1} = \mathbf{\Gamma}_n \cup \{\mathbf{A}_{n+1}\}$.

CASE 2. If $\mathbf{\Gamma}_n \cup \{\mathbf{A}_{n+1}\}$ is inconsistent and if $\mathbf{A}_{n+1}$ is not of the form $\forall\mathbf{xB}$, then $\mathbf{\Gamma}_{n+1} = \mathbf{\Gamma}_n \cup \{\sim \mathbf{A}_{n+1}\}$.

CASE 3. If $\mathbf{\Gamma}_n \cup \{\mathbf{A}_{n+1}\}$ is inconsistent and $\mathbf{A}_{n+1}$ has the form $\forall\mathbf{xB}$, then $\mathbf{\Gamma}_{n+1} = \mathbf{\Gamma}_n \cup \{\sim \mathbf{A}_{n+1}, \sim \mathbf{S}_b{}^{\mathbf{x}}\mathbf{B}|\}$ where b is the first constant in the list $b_1, b_2, \ldots$ which does not appear in $\mathbf{\Gamma}_n$.

Claim: Each $\mathbf{\Gamma}_n$ is consistent.

We prove the claim by induction on n. In case $n = 0$, then $\mathbf{\Gamma}_n = \mathbf{\Gamma}$ and consistency is a hypothesis of the theorem. We assume as hypothesis of induction that $\mathbf{\Gamma}_n$ is consistent. We shall prove that $\mathbf{\Gamma}_{n+1}$ is consistent.

CASE 1. If Case 1 in the definition of $\mathbf{\Gamma}_{n+1}$ obtains, then $\mathbf{\Gamma}_{n+1}$ is consistent by the hypothesis of Case 1.

CASE 2. If Case 2 in the definition of $\mathbf{\Gamma}_{n+1}$ obtains, then by the hypothesis of Case 2, $\mathbf{\Gamma}_n \cup \{\mathbf{A}_{n+1}\}$ is inconsistent. Hence $\mathbf{\Gamma}_n, \mathbf{A}_{n+1} \vdash \mathfrak{f}$ and by the deduction theorem $\mathbf{\Gamma}_n \vdash \sim \mathbf{A}_{n+1}$. Now $\mathbf{\Gamma}_{n+1} = \mathbf{\Gamma}_n \cup \{\sim \mathbf{A}_{n+1}\}$. Suppose $\mathbf{\Gamma}_{n+1}$ is inconsistent. Then $\mathbf{\Gamma}_n, \sim \mathbf{A}_{n+1} \vdash \mathfrak{f}$. Hence by the deduction theorem and *modus ponens* $\mathbf{\Gamma}_n \vdash \mathfrak{f}$. This contradicts the induction hypothesis that $\mathbf{\Gamma}_n$ is consistent. Hence the assumption that $\mathbf{\Gamma}_{n+1}$ is inconsistent is wrong; that is, $\mathbf{\Gamma}_{n+1}$ is consistent.

CASE 3. If Case 3 in the definition of $\mathbf{\Gamma}_{n+1}$ obtains, then, exactly as in Case 2 above, we have $\mathbf{\Gamma}_n \vdash \sim \mathbf{A}_{n+1}$. Now suppose $\mathbf{\Gamma}_{n+1} = \mathbf{\Gamma}_n \cup \{\sim \mathbf{A}_{n+1}, \sim \mathbf{S}_b{}^{\mathbf{x}}\mathbf{B}|\}$ is inconsistent. Then $\mathbf{\Gamma}_n, \sim \mathbf{A}_{n+1} \sim \mathbf{S}_b{}^{\mathbf{x}}\mathbf{B}| \vdash \mathfrak{f}$. By the deduction theorem $\mathbf{\Gamma}_n$, $\sim \mathbf{S}_b{}^{\mathbf{x}}\mathbf{B}| \vdash \sim \mathbf{A}_{n+1} \supset \mathfrak{f}$. Hence by *modus ponens* $\mathbf{\Gamma}_n, \sim \mathbf{S}_b{}^{\mathbf{x}}\mathbf{B} \vdash \mathfrak{f}$. Now by the deduction theorem and the propositional calculus, $\mathbf{\Gamma}_n \vdash \mathbf{S}_b{}^{\mathbf{x}}\mathbf{B}|$. The constant b does not occur in $\mathbf{\Gamma}_n$ by definition (Case 3). Hence we may replace every occurrence of b in the deduction of $\mathbf{S}_b{}^{\mathbf{x}}\mathbf{B}|$ from $\mathbf{\Gamma}_n$ by a variable $\mathbf{y}$ which occurs nowhere in that deduction. The result still is a deduction; therefore, $\mathbf{\Gamma}_n \vdash \mathbf{S}_{\mathbf{y}}{}^{\mathbf{x}}\mathbf{B}|$. Generalizing on $\mathbf{y}$ we get $\mathbf{\Gamma}_n \vdash \forall\mathbf{y}\mathbf{S}_{\mathbf{y}}{}^{\mathbf{x}}\mathbf{B}|$. Hence by 14.1 and *modus ponens*, we have $\mathbf{\Gamma}_n \vdash \forall\mathbf{x}\mathbf{B}$; in other words, $\mathbf{\Gamma}_n \vdash \mathbf{A}_{n+1}$. Since we showed above that $\mathbf{\Gamma}_n \vdash \sim\mathbf{A}_{n+1}$, we obtain by *modus ponens* that $\mathbf{\Gamma}_n \vdash \mathfrak{f}$. This contradicts the induction hypothesis that $\mathbf{\Gamma}_n$ is consistent. Hence the assumption that $\mathbf{\Gamma}_{n+1}$ is inconsistent is wrong; that is, $\mathbf{\Gamma}_{n+1}$ is consistent. This completes the proof of the claim. ▮

Now define the set of sentences $\mathbf{\Delta}$ by

$$\mathbf{\Delta} = \bigcup_{n=0}^{\infty} \mathbf{\Gamma}_n.$$

(1) The set $\mathbf{\Delta}$ is consistent. For if not, some finite subset of $\mathbf{\Delta}$ is inconsistent, and that finite subset must lie in some $\mathbf{\Gamma}_n$ (for n sufficiently large) contradicting the claim proved in the preceding discussion that each $\mathbf{\Gamma}_n$ is consistent.

(2) The set $\mathbf{\Delta}$ is complete in $L(\mathfrak{S}, Y)$. Indeed, let $\mathbf{A}$ be any sentence of $L(\mathfrak{S}, Y)$. Then $\mathbf{A}$ is $\mathbf{A}_{n+1}$ for some n. Thus, according to Cases 1, 2, and 3 in the definition of $\mathbf{\Gamma}_{n+1}$, either $\mathbf{A}_{n+1} \in \mathbf{\Gamma}_{n+1}$ or $\sim\mathbf{A}_{n+1} \in \mathbf{\Gamma}_{n+1}$. Hence either $\mathbf{A} \in \mathbf{\Delta}$ or $\sim\mathbf{A} \in \mathbf{\Delta}$.

(3) The set $\mathbf{\Delta}$ is universal in $L(\mathfrak{S}, Y)$. Suppose $\forall\mathbf{x}\mathbf{B}$ is a sentence of $L(\mathfrak{S}, Y)$ such that $\mathbf{S}_c{}^{\mathbf{x}}\mathbf{B}| \in \mathbf{\Delta}$ for every $c \in Y$. Suppose $\forall\mathbf{x}\mathbf{B} \notin \mathbf{\Delta}$. Then since $\mathbf{\Delta}$ is complete, then $\sim\forall\mathbf{x}\mathbf{B} \in \mathbf{\Delta}$. Let $\forall\mathbf{x}\mathbf{B}$ be $\mathbf{A}_{n+1}$. According to Case 3 in the definition of $\mathbf{\Gamma}_{n+1}$, the $\mathbf{\Gamma}_{n+1} = \mathbf{\Gamma}_n \cup \{\sim\mathbf{A}_{n+1}, \sim\mathbf{S}_b{}^{\mathbf{x}}\mathbf{B}|\}$. Therefore $\sim\mathbf{S}_b{}^{\mathbf{x}}\mathbf{B}| \in \mathbf{\Delta}$. But we have assumed $\mathbf{S}_c{}^{\mathbf{x}}\mathbf{B}| \in \mathbf{\Delta}$ for every $c \in Y$; therefore, $\mathbf{S}_b{}^{\mathbf{x}}\mathbf{B}| \in \mathbf{\Delta}$. Hence $\mathbf{\Delta}$ is inconsistent, a contradiction. Thus the assumption that $\forall\mathbf{x}\mathbf{B} \notin \mathbf{\Delta}$ is wrong; in other words, $\forall\mathbf{x}\mathbf{B} \in \mathbf{\Delta}$. This completes the proof. ▮

§17 The Completeness Theorem

Let $\mathfrak{S}$ be a system of predicates, Y a nonempty set of constants, and $\mathbf{\Delta}$ a set of sentences of $L(\mathfrak{S}, Y)$. We define the model

$$\mathfrak{M}_{\mathbf{\Delta}} = (Y, V)$$

by stipulating that for each k-place predicate letter $\mathbf{P}$ in $\mathfrak{S}$ a k-tuple $(c_1, c_2, \ldots, c_k)$ of elements of Y satisfies $V(\mathbf{P})$ if and only if the sentence $\mathbf{P}(c_1, c_2, \ldots, c_k) \in \mathbf{\Delta}$.

17.1 Lemma. Suppose $\mathbf{\Delta}$ is consistent, complete in $L(\mathfrak{S}, Y)$, and universal in $L(\mathfrak{S}, Y)$. Let $\mathbf{A}$ be any sentence of $L(\mathfrak{S}, Y)$. Then $\mathfrak{M}_{\mathbf{\Delta}} \models \mathbf{A}$ if and only if $\mathbf{A} \in \mathbf{\Delta}$.

PROOF. We prove this by induction on the length of **A**.

CASE 1. The sentence **A** is $\mathbf{P}(c_1, c_2, \ldots, c_k)$. Then the lemma follows immediately from the definition of $\mathfrak{M}_\Delta$.

CASE 2. The sentence **A** is $\mathfrak{f}$. Since $\mathbf{\Gamma}$ is consistent, $\mathfrak{f} \notin \mathbf{\Delta}$. By definition $\mathfrak{M}_\Delta \nvDash \mathfrak{f}$.

CASE 3. The sentence **A** is $\mathbf{B} \supset \mathbf{C}$. By hypothesis of induction we may assume the lemma for **B** and **C**. Suppose $\mathbf{A} \notin \mathbf{\Delta}$. Then $\sim\mathbf{A} \in \mathbf{\Delta}$ since $\mathbf{\Delta}$ is complete. But $\sim[\mathbf{B} \supset \mathbf{C}] \vdash \mathbf{B}$ and $\sim[\mathbf{B} \supset \mathbf{C}] \vdash \sim\mathbf{C}$. Hence $\mathbf{\Delta} \vdash \mathbf{B}$ and $\mathbf{\Delta} \vdash \sim\mathbf{C}$. Since $\mathbf{\Delta}$ is complete and consistent, then $\mathbf{B} \in \mathbf{\Delta}$ and $\mathbf{C} \notin \mathbf{\Delta}$. By the hypothesis of induction, $\mathfrak{M}_\Delta \vDash \mathbf{B}$ and $\mathfrak{M}_\Delta \nvDash \mathbf{C}$; hence $\mathfrak{M}_\Delta \nvDash \mathbf{A}$. Suppose, conversely, $\mathfrak{M}_\Delta \nvDash \mathbf{A}$. Then $\mathfrak{M}_\Delta \vDash \mathbf{B}$ and $\mathfrak{M}_\Delta \nvDash \mathbf{C}$. By the induction hypothesis, $\mathbf{B} \in \mathbf{\Delta}$ and $\mathbf{C} \notin \mathbf{\Delta}$. By completeness, $\sim\mathbf{C} \in \mathbf{\Delta}$. Since $\mathbf{B}, \sim\mathbf{C} \vdash \sim . \mathbf{B} \supset \mathbf{C}$, then we have $\mathbf{\Delta} \vdash \sim . \mathbf{B} \supset \mathbf{C}$. Therefore, by completeness and consistency, $\sim . \mathbf{B} \supset \mathbf{C} \in \mathbf{\Delta}$; that is, $\sim\mathbf{A} \in \mathbf{\Delta}$. Hence by consistency $\mathbf{A} \notin \mathbf{\Delta}$.

CASE 4. The sentence **A** is $\forall \mathbf{x}\mathbf{B}$. Suppose $\mathfrak{M}_\Delta \vDash \mathbf{A}$. Then for each $c \in Y$, $\mathfrak{M}_\Delta \vDash \mathbf{S}_c^{\mathbf{x}}\mathbf{B}|$. By the induction hypothesis, $\mathbf{S}_c^{\mathbf{x}}\mathbf{B}| \in \mathbf{\Delta}$ for each $c \in Y$. Since $\mathbf{\Delta}$ is universal, $\forall \mathbf{x}\mathbf{B} \in \mathbf{\Delta}$; namely $\mathbf{A} \in \mathbf{\Delta}$. Suppose conversely that $\mathbf{A} \in \mathbf{\Delta}$. Since $\mathbf{A} \vdash \mathbf{S}_c^{\mathbf{x}}\mathbf{B}|$ we have $\mathbf{\Delta} \vdash \mathbf{S}_c^{\mathbf{x}}\mathbf{B}|$ and hence (by completeness and consistency) $\mathbf{S}_c^{\mathbf{x}}\mathbf{B}| \in \mathbf{\Delta}$ for every c in Y. Thus by the induction hypothesis $\mathfrak{M}_\Delta \vDash \mathbf{S}_c^{\mathbf{x}}\mathbf{B}|$ for every $c \in Y$; that is, $\mathfrak{M}_\Delta \vDash \forall \mathbf{x}\mathbf{B}$; and so $\mathfrak{M}_\Delta \vDash \mathbf{A}$. This completes the proof. ▌

Now let $\mathfrak{S}$ be a system of predicates, X a set of constants, and $\mathbf{\Gamma}$ a set of sentences of $L(\mathfrak{S}, X)$.

17.2 The Completeness Theorem. The set $\mathbf{\Gamma}$ is consistent if and only if $\mathbf{\Gamma}$ has a model.

PROOF. The "if" statement is simply the soundness theorem (15.1), for if $\mathbf{\Gamma} \vdash \mathfrak{f}$ and $\mathfrak{M} \vDash \mathbf{\Gamma}$, then $\mathfrak{M} \vDash \mathfrak{f}$ which is absurd. To prove "only if" suppose $\mathbf{\Gamma}$ is consistent. By the extension lemma (16.1) we may extend X to Y and $\mathbf{\Gamma}$ to $\mathbf{\Delta}$ where $\mathbf{\Delta}$ is consistent, complete in $L(\mathfrak{S}, Y)$, and universal in $L(\mathfrak{S}, Y)$. Then by Lemma 17.1, we have $\mathfrak{M}_\Delta \vDash \Delta$ and hence certainly $\mathfrak{M}_\Delta \vDash \mathbf{\Gamma}$. ▌

17.3 Corollary (Gödel 1931). A wff **A** is valid if and only if $\vdash \mathbf{A}$.

PROOF. The "if" statement is 15.2. For "only if" suppose $\nvdash \mathbf{A}$. Then the set $\mathbf{\Gamma} = \{\sim\mathbf{A}'\}$ (where $\mathbf{A}'$ is the universal closure of **A**) is consistent. Therefore, by 17.2 there is a model $\mathfrak{M}$ of $\mathbf{\Gamma}$, namely $\mathfrak{M} \vDash \sim\mathbf{A}'$; that is $\mathfrak{M} \nvDash \mathbf{A}'$. Hence **A** is not valid. ▌

Notice that the proof of 17.3 which we have given is not effective; it does not tell us how to construct a deduction of a valid wff **A**. This should be contrasted with the proof of the completeness theorem for propositional calculus (6.2); that proof showed not only that every tautology is a theorem of **P** but it also gave a procedure or algorithm for constructing a deduction of an arbitrary tautology.

EXERCISES

1. Let $\mathbf{\Gamma}$ be a set of sentences which is consistent and complete in $L(\mathfrak{S}, X)$ and let **A** and **B** be sentences of $L(\mathfrak{S}, X)$. Show that

   (1) $\mathbf{A} \in \mathbf{\Gamma}$ if and only if $\mathbf{\Gamma} \vdash \mathbf{A}$

   (2) $\sim\mathbf{A} \in \mathbf{\Gamma}$ if and only if $\mathbf{A} \notin \mathbf{\Gamma}$

   (3) $\mathbf{A} \supset \mathbf{B} \in \mathbf{\Gamma}$ if and only if $\mathbf{A} \in \mathbf{\Gamma}$ materially implies $\mathbf{B} \in \mathbf{\Gamma}$

   (4) $\mathbf{A} \vee \mathbf{B} \in \mathbf{\Gamma}$ if and only if $\mathbf{A} \in \mathbf{\Gamma}$ or $\mathbf{B} \in \mathbf{\Gamma}$

   (5) $\mathbf{A} \wedge \mathbf{B} \in \mathbf{\Gamma}$ if and only if $\mathbf{A} \in \mathbf{\Gamma}$ and $\mathbf{B} \in \mathbf{\Gamma}$

2. A set of sentences $\mathbf{\Gamma}$ is **existential in** $L(\mathfrak{S}, X)$ iff for each wff $\exists \mathbf{x} \mathbf{B} \in \mathbf{\Gamma}$ there is a constant $c \in X$ such that $\mathbf{S}_c^{\mathbf{x}}\mathbf{B}| \in \mathbf{\Gamma}$. Let $\mathbf{\Gamma}$ be consistent and complete in $L(\mathfrak{S}, X)$. Show that $\mathbf{\Gamma}$ is existential in $L(\mathfrak{S}, X)$ if and only if $\mathbf{\Gamma}$ is universal in $L(\mathfrak{S}, X)$.

3. Let $\mathbf{\Gamma}$ be a consistent set of sentences of $L(\mathfrak{S}, X)$. Show that $\mathbf{\Gamma}$ is complete in $L(\mathfrak{S}, X)$ if and only if for every sentence **A** of $L(\mathfrak{S}, X)$ that if $\mathbf{A} \notin \mathbf{\Gamma}$, then $\mathbf{\Gamma} \cup \{\mathbf{A}\}$ is inconsistent. (Because of this many authors call complete sets of sentences *maximal*.)

§18 First-Order Logic with Equality

Suppose $L(\mathfrak{S}, X)$ is a first-order language and that the system of predicates $\mathfrak{S}$ has a distinguished two-place predicate $\mathbf{I}^2$. We immediately introduce abbreviations

$$\mathbf{a} = \mathbf{b} \rightsquigarrow \mathbf{I}^2(\mathbf{a}, \mathbf{b})$$

$$\mathbf{a} \neq \mathbf{b} \rightsquigarrow \sim \mathbf{a} = \mathbf{b}$$

The language $L^{=}(\mathfrak{S}, X)$ is obtained from $L(\mathfrak{S}, X)$ by adding the axioms

18.1 $\mathrm{x} = \mathrm{x}$

18.2 $\mathbf{a} = \mathbf{b} \supset . \mathbf{A} \equiv \mathbf{B}$

where **a** is an individual variable or an individual constant, **b** is an individual variable or an individual constant, and **B** is obtained from **A** by replacing of one particular occurrence of **a** by **b** such that this occurrence of **a** is not in a well-formed part of **A** of form $\forall\mathbf{aC}$ or $\forall\mathbf{bC}$.

Axiom 18.1 is a single axiom, while 18.2 is an axiom schema. Axiom schema 18.2 is called the *law of substitutivity of equality*.

We shall use the notation

$$L^{=}(\mathfrak{S}, X) \vdash \mathbf{B}$$

to mean **B** is a *theorem* of $L^{=}(\mathfrak{S}, X)$; that is, there is a sequence $\mathbf{B}_1, \mathbf{B}_2, \ldots, \mathbf{B}_m$ of wffs of $L(\mathfrak{S}, X)$ each of which either is an instance of 11.1–11.5 or of 18.1 or 18.2, or is obtained from earlier wffs in the sequence by *modus ponens* (11.6) or by generalization (11.7).

Now let us suppose for simplicity that $X = \emptyset$ the empty set of constants (that is, $L(\mathfrak{S}, X)$ has no individual constants). A model $\mathfrak{M} = (Y, V)$ of type $\mathfrak{S}$ will be said to **respect equality** iff for all $a, b \in Y$, the $\mathfrak{M} \models a = b$ if and only if $a = b$. Thus $\mathfrak{M}$ respects equality iff "equality in the model $\mathfrak{M}$" is the same as equality.

18.3 Soundness Theorem for $L^{=}(\mathfrak{S}, X)$. Let $\mathfrak{M}$ be a model which respects equality and **A** a sentence of $L^{=}(\mathfrak{S}, X)$. If $L^{=}(\mathfrak{S}, X) \vdash \mathbf{A}$, then $\mathfrak{M} \models \mathbf{A}$.

PROOF. Clearly $\mathfrak{M} \models \mathbf{C}$ if **C** is an instance of 18.1 or 18.2. Thus the same argument used in previous soundness theorems (6.1, 15.1, and 15.2) applies. ▌

Axiom 18.7 is a kind of converse of 18.3. Before proving it we state some theorems of $L^{=}(\mathfrak{S}, X)$. We shall write $\vdash \mathbf{A}$ instead of $L^{=}(\mathfrak{S}, X) \vdash \mathbf{A}$.

18.4 $\vdash \mathrm{x} = \mathrm{y} \supset \mathrm{y} = \mathrm{x}$

18.5 $\vdash \mathrm{x} = \mathrm{y} \supset . \, \mathrm{y} = \mathrm{z} \supset \mathrm{x} = \mathrm{z}$

18.6 $\vdash \mathrm{x}_1 = \mathrm{y}_1 \wedge \mathrm{x}_2 = \mathrm{y}_2 \wedge \ldots \wedge \mathrm{x}_n = \mathrm{y}_n \, . \supset . \, \mathbf{P}(\mathrm{x}_1, \mathrm{x}_2, \ldots, x_n) \equiv \mathbf{P}(\mathrm{y}_1, \mathrm{y}_2, \ldots, \mathrm{y}_n)$

where **P** is an n-place predicate symbol of $\mathfrak{S}$.

18.7 Equivalence Theorem. Let $\mathfrak{M}$ be a model of type $\mathfrak{S}$ and suppose that $\mathfrak{M} \models \mathbf{A}$ whenever $L^{=}(\mathfrak{S}, X) \vdash \mathbf{A}$ (namely $\mathfrak{M}$ models 18.1 and 18.2). Then there is a model $\mathfrak{M}'$ of type $\mathfrak{S}$ such that

(I) $\mathfrak{M}'$ respects equality; and

(II) For every sentence **A**, $\mathfrak{M}' \models \mathbf{A}$ if and only if $\mathfrak{M} \models \mathbf{A}$.

Proof. Let $\mathfrak{M} = (Y, V)$. In view of 18.1, 18.4, and 18.5 the relation $\mathfrak{M} \models a = b$ [that is, the relation $V(=)$] is an *equivalence relation* on Y namely for $a, b, c \in Y$ we have

(1) $\mathfrak{M} \models a = a$.

(2) If $\mathfrak{M} \models a = b$, then $\mathfrak{M} \models b = a$.

(3) If $\mathfrak{M} \models a = b$ and $\mathfrak{M} \models b = c$, then $\mathfrak{M} \models a = c$.

Furthermore, by 18.6, this equivalence relation respects the relations $V(\mathbf{P})$ on Y; that is,

(4) If $\mathfrak{M} \models a_i = b_i$ $(i = 1, 2, \ldots, n)$, then $\mathfrak{M} \models \mathbf{P}(a_1, a_2, \ldots, a_n)$ if and only if $\mathfrak{M} \models \mathbf{P}(b_1, b_2, \ldots, b_n)$.

(Here $\mathbf{P}$ is an n-place predicate letter of $\mathfrak{S}$.)

Now for $a \in Y$ we define the *equivalence class* $[a]$ of a by

$$[a] = \{b \in Y \mid \mathfrak{M} \models a = b\}$$

that is, $b \in [a]$ if and only if $\mathfrak{M} \models a = b$. By (1), (2), and (3), we derive

(5) $[a] = [b]$ if and only if $\mathfrak{M} \models a = b$.

We now define the model $\mathfrak{M}' = (Y', V')$ as follows: the Y' is the set of equivalence classes of Y; that is,

$$Y' = \{[a] \mid a \in Y\}$$

and for each n-place predicate letter $\mathbf{P}$ of $\mathfrak{S}$ and $[a_1], [a_2], \ldots, [a_n] \in Y'$ $([a_1], [a_2], \ldots, [a_n])$ satisfies $V'(\mathbf{P})$ iff $(a_1, a_2, \ldots, a_n)$ satisfies $V(\mathbf{P})$; that is,

(6) $\mathfrak{M}' \models \mathbf{P}([a_1], [a_2], \ldots, [a_n])$ iff $\mathfrak{M} \models \mathbf{P}(a_1, a_2, \ldots, a_n)$.

By (4) and (5), the relation $V'(\mathbf{P})$ is well defined; the definition of $V'(\mathbf{P})$ is independent of the choice of $a_i \in [a_i]$ $(i = 1, 2, \ldots, n)$.

In view of (5) and (6) (reading = for $\mathbf{P}$) conclusion (I) of the theorem is immediate; that is, $\mathfrak{M}'$ respects equality. For conclusion (II) we prove a slightly stronger statement.

For each sentence $\mathbf{A}$ of $L(\mathfrak{S}, Y)$ let $\mathbf{A}^*$ denote the sentence of $L(\mathfrak{S}, Y')$ which results from $\mathbf{A}$ by replacing each constant $a \in Y$ which appears in $\mathbf{A}$ by $[a] \in Y'$. Then

(7) $\mathfrak{M} \models \mathbf{A}$ if and only if $\mathfrak{M}' \models \mathbf{A}^*$.

Indeed if $\mathbf{A}$ contains no connectives or quantifiers [$\mathbf{A}$ is of form $\mathbf{P}(a_1, a_2, \ldots, a_n)$] then (7) becomes (6). The general case in (7) follows by induction on the length of $\mathbf{A}$. Then (7) clearly implies (II). ∎

A set of sentences $\mathbf{\Gamma}$ of $L^{=}(\mathfrak{S}, X)$ is **inconsistent** in $L^{=}(\mathfrak{S}, X)$ iff $\mathfrak{f}$ is provable from $\mathbf{\Gamma}$ in $L^{=}(\mathfrak{S}, X)$ and is **consistent** in $L^{=}(\mathfrak{S}, X)$ otherwise. A sentence $\mathbf{A}$ is

valid in $L^=(\mathfrak{S}, X)$ iff $\mathfrak{M} \models \mathbf{A}$ for every model $\mathfrak{M}$ which respects equality. A wff **A** is **valid** in $L^=(\mathfrak{S}, X)$ iff its universal closure is valid. Using 18.7 we may prove the following analogs of 17.2 and 17.3.

18.8 The Completeness Theorem for $L^=(\mathfrak{S}, X)$**.** A set of sentences $\mathbf{\Gamma}$ is consistent in $L^=(\mathfrak{S}, X)$ if and only if $\mathbf{\Gamma}$ has a model which respects equality.

18.9 Corollary. A wff **A** is valid in $L^=(\mathfrak{S}', X)$ if and only if $L^=(\mathfrak{S}, X) \vdash \mathbf{A}$.

To prove 18.9, form the set of sentences $\mathbf{\Gamma}'$ by adding to $\mathbf{\Gamma}$ all instances of 18.1 and 18.2. The $\mathbf{\Gamma}$ is consistent in $L^=(\mathfrak{S}, X)$ if and only if $\mathbf{\Gamma}'$ is consistent in $L(\mathfrak{S}, X)$. If $\mathbf{\Gamma}'$ is consistent, then by 17.2 it has a model, whence by 18.7 the $\mathbf{\Gamma}$ has a model which respects equality. Corollary 18.9 is proved from 18.8 as 17.3 was proved from 17.2.

EXERCISES

1. Prove 18.4–18.6.

2. For each $n = 1, 2, 3, \ldots$ construct a sentence $\mathbf{A}_n$ such that any model of $\mathbf{A}_n$ which respects equality has exactly n elements (but $\mathbf{A}_n$ has a model). *Hint:* $\mathbf{A}_2$ is $\exists x\, \exists y \centerdot x \neq y \wedge \forall z \centerdot x = z \vee y = z$.

3. Give an example of a model $\mathfrak{M}$ which does not respect equality and a model $\mathfrak{M}'$ which respects equality and is equivalent to $\mathfrak{M}$ in the sense of 18.7.

4. For each $n = 1, 2, 3, \ldots$ construct a sentence $\mathbf{B}_n$ of $L^=(\mathfrak{S}, X)$ such that a model $\mathfrak{M}$ respecting equality models $\mathbf{B}_n$ if and only if $\mathfrak{M}$ has n or more elements.

★5. Show that any sentence **A** which has arbitrarily large finite models respecting equality has an infinite model respecting equality. *Hint:* Let $\mathbf{B}_1, \mathbf{B}_2, \ldots$ be the sentences of Exercise 4 and let $\mathbf{\Gamma}$ be the set of sentences $\mathbf{A}, \mathbf{B}_1, \mathbf{B}_2 \ldots$. Show that $\mathbf{\Gamma}$ is consistent and use 18.8.

★6. Construct a sentence (containing predicates other than =) which has an infinite model but no finite model.

★7. Show that if the language $L^=(\mathfrak{S}, X)$ is modified by replacing of axiom schema 18.2 with 18.4–18.6, then the new language is equivalent to the old in the sense that both languages have exactly the same theorems.

★8. For each system of predicates $\mathfrak{S}$ and set of constants X the **intuitionistic first-order language** $L_i(\mathfrak{S}, X)$ is defined by adding to the primitive symbols of $L(\mathfrak{S}, X)$ the symbols $\vee$, $\wedge$, and $\exists$ and of modifying the definition of wff accordingly. The definition of bound variable also should be modified to include $\exists$

(for example, every occurrence of **x** in $\exists\mathbf{xA}$ is bound). The axiom schemas of $L_i(\mathfrak{S}, X)$ are those of the intuitionistic propositional calculus P_i (Exercise 9, §6), together with the following four schemas:

(1) $\forall\mathbf{xA} \supset \mathbf{S_a}^{\mathbf{x}}\mathbf{A}|$

(2) $\mathbf{S_a}^{\mathbf{x}}\mathbf{A}| \supset \exists\mathbf{xA}$

(3) $\forall\mathbf{x}[\mathbf{A} \supset \mathbf{B}] \supset . \mathbf{A} \supset \forall\mathbf{xB}$

(4) $\forall\mathbf{x}[\mathbf{B} \supset \mathbf{A}] \supset . \exists\mathbf{xB} \supset \mathbf{A}$.

[In (1) and (2) **a** is an individual variable or constant and is free for **x** in **A**. In (3) and (4) **x** is not free in **A**.] The rules of inference are *modus ponens* and generalization. The abbreviations $\sim\mathbf{A} \rightsquigarrow \mathbf{A} \supset \mathfrak{f}$ and $\mathbf{A} \equiv \mathbf{B} \rightsquigarrow [\mathbf{A} \supset \mathbf{B}] \wedge [\mathbf{B} \supset \mathbf{A}]$ are employed. The symbol $\vdash_i \mathbf{A}$ means **A** is a theorem of $L_i(\mathfrak{S}, X)$. Show that the deduction theorem (13.2) is valid for $L_i(\mathfrak{S}, X)$, and that 14.1–14.7 all are theorem schemas of $L_i(\mathfrak{S}, X)$.

★9. Show that substitutivity of equivalence (14.8) also holds for $L_i(\mathfrak{S}, X)$. *Hint:* You must first prove certain additional theorem schemas such as

$\vdash_i \forall\mathbf{x}[\mathbf{A} \equiv \mathbf{B}] \supset . \exists\mathbf{xA} \equiv \exists\mathbf{xB}$ and

$\vdash_i \mathbf{A}_1 \equiv \mathbf{A}_2 \supset . \mathbf{B}_1 \equiv \mathbf{B}_2 \supset . [\mathbf{A}_1 \vee \mathbf{B}_1] \equiv [\mathbf{A}_2 \vee \mathbf{B}_2]$.

★10. Prove the following theorem schemas in $L_i(\mathfrak{S}, X)$:

(1) $\vdash_i \exists\mathbf{x} \sim \mathbf{A} \supset \sim\forall\mathbf{xA}$

(2) $\vdash_i \sim \exists\mathbf{xA} \supset \forall\mathbf{x} \sim \mathbf{A}$

(3) $\vdash_i \exists\mathbf{x} \sim\sim \mathbf{A} \supset \sim\sim \exists\mathbf{xA}$

(4) $\vdash_i \sim\sim \forall\mathbf{xA} \supset \forall\mathbf{x} \sim\sim \mathbf{A}$

(5) $\vdash_i \forall\mathbf{xA} \supset \sim \exists\mathbf{x} \sim \mathbf{A}$

(6) $\vdash_i \exists\mathbf{xA} \supset \sim \forall\mathbf{x} \sim \mathbf{A}$

★11. Show that if any one of the schemas (1)–(5) of Exercise 10, §6 is added as an axiom schema to $L_i(\mathfrak{S}, X)$ then the resulting system is complete in the sense that every valid formula is a theorem. (You will have to modify the definition of validity to account for the additional connectives.)

★12. For each wff of $L(\mathfrak{S}, X)$ let $\mathbf{A}^*$ be the wff which results from **A** on replacing each wff part $\mathbf{P}(\mathbf{a}_1, \ldots, \mathbf{a}_n)$ (where **P** is an n-place predicate letter and each $\mathbf{a}_j$ $(j = 1, \ldots, n)$ is either an individual variable or an individual constant) by $\sim\sim \mathbf{P}(\mathbf{a}_1, \ldots, \mathbf{a}_n)$. Show that if $\vdash \mathbf{A}$, then $\vdash_i \mathbf{A}^*$. *Hint:* Apply * to each wff of a deduction of **A** in $L(\mathfrak{S}, X)$. Show that the resulting sequence of wffs can be transformed into a deduction in $L_i(\mathfrak{S}, X)$.

★13. A **Kripke model** for $L_i(\mathfrak{S}, X)$ is a triple $\mathfrak{M} = (\Omega, \leqslant, M)$ where Ω is a nonempty set, $\leqslant$ is a binary relation on Ω, and M is a function which assigns to each

$\alpha \in \Omega$ a model $M(\alpha) = (X_\alpha, V_\alpha)$ of type $\mathfrak{S}$ with $X \subseteq X_\alpha$. In addition $\mathfrak{M}$ must satisfy the following conditions for all $\alpha, \beta, \gamma \in \Omega$ and all predicate letters $\mathbf{P} \in \mathfrak{S}$.

(1) $\alpha \leqslant \alpha$

(2) $\alpha \leqslant \beta$ and $\beta \leqslant \gamma$ implies $\alpha \leqslant \gamma$

(3) $\alpha \leqslant \beta$ implies $X_\alpha \subseteq X_\beta$

(4) $\alpha \leqslant \beta$ implies $V_\alpha(\mathbf{P}) \subset V_\beta(\mathbf{P})$.

For each $\alpha \in \Omega$ and each sentence **A** of $\mathbf{L}_i(\mathfrak{S}, X_\alpha)$ the relation $\mathfrak{M} \models_\alpha \mathbf{A}$ (read **A** holds in $\mathfrak{M}$ at α) is defined by the following rules:

(KM1) $\mathfrak{M} \models_\alpha \mathbf{P}(a_1, \ldots, a_n)$ iff $M(\alpha) \models \mathbf{P}(a_1, \ldots, a_n)$ (here $\mathbf{P} \in \mathfrak{S}$ and $a_1, \ldots, a_n \in X_\alpha$).

(KM2) $\mathfrak{M} \models_\alpha \mathbf{A} \wedge \mathbf{B}$ iff $\mathfrak{M} \models_\alpha \mathbf{A}$ and $\mathfrak{M} \models_\alpha \mathbf{B}$.

(KM3) $\mathfrak{M} \models_\alpha \mathbf{A} \vee \mathbf{B}$ iff $\mathfrak{M} \vdash_\alpha \mathbf{A}$ or $\mathfrak{M} \models_\alpha \mathbf{B}$.

(KM4) $\mathfrak{M} \models_\alpha \mathbf{A} \supset \mathbf{B}$ iff for all β, if $\alpha \leqslant \beta$ and $\mathfrak{M} \models_\beta \mathbf{A}$, then $\mathfrak{M} \models_\beta \mathbf{B}$.

(KM5) $\mathfrak{M} \models_\alpha \exists \mathbf{x} \mathbf{A}$ iff for some $a \in X_\alpha$, we have $\mathfrak{M} \models_\alpha \mathbf{S}_a{}^{\mathbf{x}}\mathbf{A}|$.

(KM6) $\mathfrak{M} \models_\alpha \forall \mathbf{x} \mathbf{A}$ iff for all β such that $\alpha \leqslant \beta$ and all $a \in X_\beta$, we have $\mathfrak{M} \models_\beta \mathbf{S}_a{}^{\mathbf{x}}\mathbf{A}|$.

Let $\mathfrak{M} = (\Omega, \leqslant, M)$ be a Kripke model, $\alpha \in \Omega$, and **A** be a sentence of $\mathbf{L}_i(\mathfrak{S}, X_\alpha)$. Show that if $\mathfrak{M} \models_\alpha \mathbf{A}$ and $\alpha \leqslant \beta$, then $\mathfrak{M} \models_\beta \mathbf{A}$. Show that $\mathfrak{M} \models_\alpha \sim \mathbf{A}$ if and only if for every $\beta \geqslant \alpha$ not $\mathfrak{M} \models_\beta \mathbf{A}$ (where $\beta \geqslant \alpha$ means $\alpha \leqslant \beta$). When does $\mathfrak{M} \models_\alpha \sim\sim \mathbf{A}$?

★14. A sentence **A** is **intuitionistically valid** iff $\mathfrak{M} \models_\alpha \mathbf{A}$ for all Kripke models $\mathfrak{M} = (\Omega, \leqslant, M)$ and all $\alpha \in \Omega$. A wff is **intuitionistically valid** iff its universal closure is. Show that if $\vdash_i \mathbf{A}$, then **A** is intuitionistically valid.

★15. Consider the following Kripke model $\mathfrak{M} = (\Omega, \leqslant, M)$, of type $\mathfrak{S}$ where $\mathfrak{S}$ consists of a single one-place predicate **P**:

(1) Ω consists of exactly two elements α and β;

(2) $\alpha \leqslant \alpha$, $\beta \leqslant \beta$, and $\alpha \leqslant \beta$;

(3) X_α consists of a single element a, and X_β consists of two elements a and b (that is, $X_\alpha = \{a\}$ and $X_\beta = \{a, b\}$);

(4) P(a) holds in $M(\alpha)$ and $M(\beta)$, and P(b) does not hold in $M(\beta)$.

The model is schematically represented by the picture

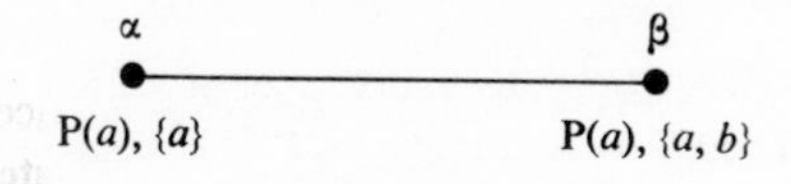

Show that $\sim \forall x P(x) \supset \exists x \sim P(x)$ does not hold in $\mathfrak{M}$ at α. Conclude that it is not a theorem of intuitionistic first order logic.

*16. Consider the Kripke model $\mathfrak{M} = (\Omega, \leqslant, M)$ where

(1) $\Omega = \{\alpha, \beta, \gamma\}$

(2) $\alpha \leqslant \alpha, \beta \leqslant \beta, \gamma \leqslant \gamma, \alpha \leqslant \beta, \alpha \leqslant \gamma$

(3) $X_\alpha = X_\beta = X_\gamma = \{a, b\}$

(4) $P(a)$ holds in (and only in) $M(\beta)$, and $P(b)$ holds in (and only in) $M(\gamma)$. The picture is

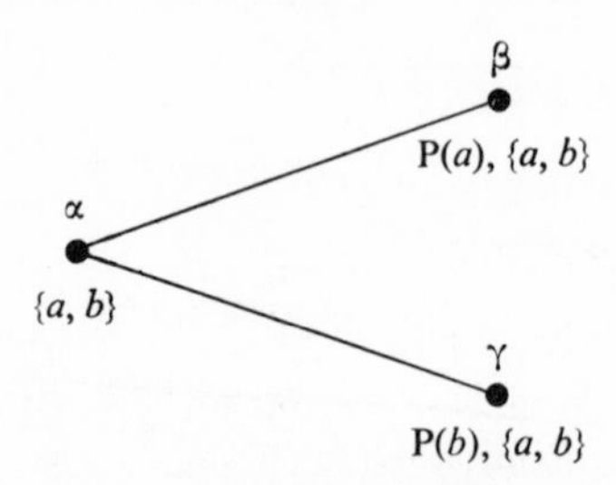

Show that $\forall x \forall y \,.\, [P(x) \supset P(y)] \vee [P(y) \supset P(x)]$ does not hold in $\mathfrak{M}$ at α.

*17. Consider the Kripke model $\mathfrak{M} = (\Omega, \leqslant, M)$ where

(1) Ω is the set of natural numbers 0, 1, 2, . . .;

(2) $\leqslant$ is the usual order relation;

(3) $X_{2n} = \{0, 1, 2, \ldots, n\}$ and $X_{2n+1} = \{0, 1, 2, \ldots, n, n+1\}$ for $n = 0, 1, 2, \ldots$.

(4) $P(a)$ holds in $M(2n)$ for $a = 0, 1, \ldots, n$; $P(a)$ holds in $M(2n+1)$ for $a = 0, 1, \ldots, n$ but not for $a = n+1$.

Show that $\sim . \forall x P(x) \vee \exists x \sim P(x)$ holds in $\mathfrak{M}$ at $\alpha = 0$. Show that $\sim\sim . \forall x P(x) \vee \exists x \sim P(x)$ does not hold in $\mathfrak{M}$ at $\alpha = 0$ and hence is not a theorem of $L_i(\mathfrak{S}, X)$. (Contrast this with Exercise 15, §6).

Show that if $\mathfrak{M} = (\Omega, \leqslant, M)$ is any Kripke model in which $\sim\sim . \forall x P(x) \vee \exists x \sim P(x)$ does not hold, then Ω is infinite. (Contrast this with Exercise 26 of §6.)

*18. Find a Kripke model in which $\forall x \sim\sim P(x) \supset \sim\sim \forall x P(x)$ does not hold. Conclude that it is not a theorem of P_i. (*Note:* The "converse" $\sim\sim \forall x P(x) \supset \forall x \sim\sim P(x)$ is a theorem of P_i.) Do the same for $P(a) \supset \exists x Q(x) \,.\supset.\, \exists x \,.\, P(a) \supset Q(x)$.

*19. Let **A** be a sentence of $L_i(\mathfrak{S}, X)$ and $\mathbf{\Gamma}$ a set of sentences of $L_i(\mathfrak{S}, X)$. The set $\mathbf{\Gamma}$ is **A inconsistent** iff $\mathbf{\Gamma} \vdash_i \mathbf{A}$; otherwise $\mathbf{\Gamma}$ is **A consistent**. The set $\mathbf{\Gamma}$ is **closed** in $L_i(\mathfrak{S}, X)$ iff $\mathbf{B} \in \mathbf{\Gamma}$ whenever $\mathbf{\Gamma} \vdash_i \mathbf{B}$ and $\mathbf{B}$ is a sentence of $L_i(\mathfrak{S}, X)$. The set $\mathbf{\Gamma}$ is **disjunctive** iff either $\mathbf{B} \in \mathbf{\Gamma}$ or $\mathbf{C} \in \mathbf{\Gamma}$ whenever $\mathbf{B} \vee \mathbf{C} \in \mathbf{\Gamma}$. The set is **existential** in $L_i(\mathfrak{S}, X)$ iff whenever $\exists \mathbf{x} \mathbf{B} \in \mathbf{\Gamma}$ there is an $\mathbf{a} \in X$ such that $\mathbf{S_a}^{\mathbf{x}}\mathbf{B}| \in \mathbf{\Gamma}$. The set $\mathbf{\Gamma}$ is **A complete** in $L_i(\mathfrak{S}, X)$ iff for every sentence $\mathbf{B}$ of $L_i(\mathfrak{S}, X)$ either $\mathbf{B} \in \mathbf{\Gamma}$ or $\mathbf{B} \supset \mathbf{A} \in \mathbf{\Gamma}$. The set $\mathbf{\Gamma}$ is **regular** in $L_i(\mathfrak{S}, X)$ iff it is $\mathfrak{f}$ consistent, and closed, disjunctive, and existential in $L_i(\mathfrak{S}, X)$. Prove that

(1) If $\mathbf{\Gamma}$ is $\mathbf{A}$ consistent, existential, and $\mathbf{A}$ complete in $L_i(\mathfrak{S}, X)$, then $\mathbf{\Gamma}$ is regular in $L_i(\mathfrak{S}, X)$.

(2) If $\mathbf{\Gamma}$ is $\mathbf{A}$ consistent, then there is a set Y of constants and a set $\mathbf{\Delta}$ of sentences such that $X \subseteq Y$, $\mathbf{\Gamma} \subseteq \mathbf{\Delta}$, and $\mathbf{\Delta}$ is $\mathbf{A}$ consistent, existential, and $\mathbf{A}$ complete (and hence regular) in $L_i(\mathfrak{S}, Y)$.

(3) If $\mathbf{\Gamma}$ is regular in $L_i(\mathfrak{S}, X)$ then

(3a) $\mathbf{A} \wedge \mathbf{B} \in \mathbf{\Gamma}$ if and only if $\mathbf{A} \in \mathbf{\Gamma}$ and $\mathbf{B} \in \mathbf{\Gamma}$

(3b) $\mathbf{A} \vee \mathbf{B} \in \mathbf{\Gamma}$ if and only if $\mathbf{A} \in \mathbf{\Gamma}$ or $\mathbf{B} \in \mathbf{\Gamma}$

(3c) $\mathbf{A} \supset \mathbf{B} \in \mathbf{\Gamma}$ if and only if for every set Y extending X and every set of sentences $\mathbf{\Delta}$ extending $\mathbf{\Gamma}$, if $\mathbf{\Delta}$ is regular in $L_i(\mathfrak{S}, Y)$ and $\mathbf{A} \in \mathbf{\Delta}$, then $\mathbf{B} \in \mathbf{\Delta}$.

(3d) $\exists \mathbf{x} \mathbf{A} \in \mathbf{\Gamma}$ if and only if for some $a \in X$, $\mathbf{S}_a{}^{\mathbf{x}}\mathbf{A}| \in \mathbf{\Gamma}$.

(3e) $\forall \mathbf{x} \mathbf{A} \in \mathbf{\Gamma}$ if and only if for every set Y extending X and every set of sentences $\mathbf{\Delta}$ extending $\mathbf{\Gamma}$, if $\mathbf{\Delta}$ is regular in $L_i(\mathfrak{S}, Y)$ and $a \in Y$, then $\mathbf{S}_a{}^{\mathbf{x}}\mathbf{A}| \in \mathbf{\Delta}$.
Hint: First do Exercise 18, §6, to get the idea.

*20. Consider the following Kripke model $\mathfrak{M} = (\Omega, \leqslant, M)$.

(1) Ω is the class of all sets of sentences $\mathbf{\Gamma}$ which are regular in $L_i(\mathfrak{S}, X)$ for some set X.

(2) $\mathbf{\Gamma} \leqslant \mathbf{\Delta}$ iff $\mathbf{\Gamma} \subseteq \mathbf{\Delta}$

(3) $X_{\mathbf{\Gamma}} =$ the set of constants which appear in some sentence of $\mathbf{\Gamma}$.

(4) For $a_1, \ldots, a_n \in X_{\mathbf{\Gamma}}$ and $\mathbf{P}$ an n-place predicate symbol in $\mathfrak{S}$, $\mathbf{P}(a_1, \ldots, a_n)$ holds in $M(\mathbf{\Gamma})$ iff $\mathbf{P}(a_1, \ldots, a_n) \in \mathbf{\Gamma}$.

Show that for each sentence $\mathbf{A}$, $\mathfrak{M} \models_{\mathbf{\Gamma}} \mathbf{A}$ if and only if $\mathbf{A} \in \mathbf{\Gamma}$. Conclude that a sentence $\mathbf{A}$ is intuitionistically valid if and only if $\vdash_i \mathbf{A}$. (This theorem is due to S. Kripke; the proof outlined above is due to P. Aczel.)

*21. Let $\mathbf{A}$ and $\mathbf{B}$ be sentences of $L_i(\mathfrak{S}, X)$. Show that if there is a Kripke model in which $\mathbf{A}$ does not hold and if there is a Kripke model in which $\mathbf{B}$ does not hold, then there is a Kripke model in which $\mathbf{A} \vee \mathbf{B}$ does not hold. Conclude that if $\vdash_i \mathbf{A} \vee \mathbf{B}$, then $\vdash_i \mathbf{A}$ or $\vdash_i \mathbf{B}$.

*22. Let $\mathfrak{S}$ be a system of predicates consisting of exactly n one-place predicate letters and no others. Let X be the empty set of individual constants. Show that a sentence $\mathbf{A}$ of $L(\mathfrak{S}, X)$ is valid if and only if $\mathfrak{M} \models \mathbf{A}$ for every model

$\mathfrak{M} = (Y, V)$ such that Y contains exactly 2^n elements. Show that there are exactly $2^{n(2^n)}$ essentially distinct models $\mathfrak{M} = (Y, V)$ where Y has exactly 2^n elements. Thus there is an algorithm for deciding when a sentence **A** of $L(\mathfrak{S}, X)$ is valid (and hence when $\vdash$ **A**). *Hint:* For the last part see Exercise 4, §9. For the first part proceed as follows. Let $\mathfrak{M} = (Y, V)$ be any model of type $\mathfrak{S}$ and let $P_1, P_2, \ldots, P_n$ be the predicate letters of $\mathfrak{S}$. Define a two place relation $\approx$ on Y by the rule that for $a, b \in Y$, the relation $a \approx b$ holds iff

$$\mathfrak{M} \models P_i(a) \equiv P_i(b)$$

for each $i = 1, 2, \ldots, n$. Show that $\approx$ is an equivalence relation, that the set of equivalence classes is less than or equal to 2^n, and that these equivalence classes form a model which is equivalent to $\mathfrak{M}$ in the sense of §18. Follow the argument of §18 closely.

*23 (*Skolem–Lowenheim Theorem*). Let $\mathfrak{S}$ be a (countable or finite) system of predicate letters and $\mathfrak{M} = (X, V)$ be a model of type $\mathfrak{S}$. A model $\mathfrak{M}' = (X', V')$ of type $\mathfrak{S}$ is a **submodel** of $\mathfrak{M}$ iff $X' \subseteq X$; and for each predicate letter **P** of $\mathfrak{S}$ and all $a_1, a_2, \ldots, a_n \in X'$ (where **P** is n-place), $\mathfrak{M} \models \mathbf{P}(a_1, a_2, \ldots, a_n)$ if and only if $\mathfrak{M}' \models \mathbf{P}(a_1, a_2, \ldots, a_n)$. The model $\mathfrak{M}'$ is an **elementary submodel** iff for each sentence **A** of $L(\mathfrak{S}, X')$, $\mathfrak{M} \models \mathbf{A}$ if and only if $\mathfrak{M}' \models \mathbf{A}$. The model $\mathfrak{M}'$ is **countable** iff X' is countable. Prove that every infinite model $\mathfrak{M}$ has a countable elementary submodel $\mathfrak{M}'$. *Hint:* It suffices to find a countable subset X' of X such that $\exists \mathbf{x} \mathbf{A}$ is a sentence of $L(\mathfrak{S}, X')$ and $\mathfrak{M} \models \exists \mathbf{x} \mathbf{A}$, then $\mathfrak{M} \models \mathbf{S}_b{}^{\mathbf{x}} \mathbf{A}|$ for some $b \in X'$.

*24. Let $\mathfrak{S}$ and $\mathfrak{S}'$ be systems of predicate letters and X and X' be sets of individual constants. Suppose $\mathfrak{S} \subseteq \mathfrak{S}'$ and $X \subseteq X'$. Let $\mathbf{\Gamma}$ be a set of sentences of $L(\mathfrak{S}, X)$, $\mathbf{\Gamma}_1$ be a set of sentences of $L(\mathfrak{S}, X')$, and $\mathbf{\Gamma}_2$ be a set of sentences of $L(\mathfrak{S}', X)$. Show that if $\mathbf{\Gamma}$ is complete in $L(\mathfrak{S}, X)$, $\mathbf{\Gamma} \subseteq \mathbf{\Gamma}_1 \cap \mathbf{\Gamma}_2$, and $\mathbf{\Gamma}_1$ and $\mathbf{\Gamma}_2$ are consistent, then $\mathbf{\Gamma}_1 \cup \mathbf{\Gamma}_2$ is consistent. *Hint:* If $\mathbf{\Gamma}_1 \cup \mathbf{\Gamma}_2$ is not consistent, then $\vdash \mathbf{A} \supset \sim \mathbf{B}$ where **A** is a conjunction of sentences of $\mathbf{\Gamma}_1$ and **B** is a conjunction of sentences of $\mathbf{\Gamma}_2$. Let **A′** result from **A** by replacing each constant of **A** which is in X' and not in X with a suitable individual variable and by existentially quantifying on these variables. Then **A′** is a sentence of $L(\mathfrak{S}, X)$ and $\mathbf{\Gamma}_1 \vdash \mathbf{A}'$. Hence as $\mathbf{\Gamma}_1$ is consistent and $\mathbf{\Gamma}$ is complete, $\mathbf{\Gamma} \vdash \mathbf{A}'$ so that $\mathbf{\Gamma} \vdash \sim \mathbf{B}$ and hence $\mathbf{\Gamma}_2 \vdash \sim \mathbf{B}$ contradicting the consistency of $\mathbf{\Gamma}_2$.

*25. (*The Consistency Lemma*). Let $\mathfrak{S}_1, \mathfrak{S}_2$ be systems of predicate letters and X_1, X_2 be sets of individual constants. Let $\mathbf{A}_1$ be a sentence of $L(\mathfrak{S}_1, X_1)$, $\mathbf{A}_2$ be a sentence of $L(\mathfrak{S}_2, X_2)$, and $\mathbf{\Gamma}_0$ be a set of sentences of $L(\mathfrak{S}_1 \cap \mathfrak{S}_2, X_1 \cap X_2)$. Show that if $\mathbf{\Gamma}_0$ is complete in $L(\mathfrak{S}_1 \cap \mathfrak{S}_2, X_1 \cap X_2)$ and $\mathbf{\Gamma}_0 \cup \{\mathbf{A}_1\}$ and $\mathbf{\Gamma}_0 \cup \{\mathbf{A}_2\}$ both are consistent, then $\mathbf{\Gamma}_0 \cup \{\mathbf{A}_1 \wedge \mathbf{A}_2\}$ also is consistent. *Hint:* Show first that we may assume $X_1 = X_2$. Then if $\mathbf{\Gamma}$ is any set of sentences, let $\mathbf{\Gamma}^*$ denote those sentences of $\mathbf{\Gamma}$ containing only predicate letters from $\mathfrak{S}_1 \cap \mathfrak{S}_2$. By 16.1 let $\mathbf{\Gamma}_1$ be a consistent, complete, and universal set extending $\mathbf{\Gamma} \cup \{\mathbf{A}_1\}$. By the previous exercise $\mathbf{\Gamma}_1^* \cup \{\mathbf{A}_2\} = \mathbf{\Gamma}_1^* \cup (\mathbf{\Gamma} \cup \{\mathbf{A}_2\})$ is consistent; let $\mathbf{\Gamma}_2$ be a consistent, complete, and universal set extending it.

Using Exercise 24 and 16.1 repeatedly, define inductively a sequence of consistent, complete, and universal sets $\mathbf{\Gamma}_1, \mathbf{\Gamma}_2, \mathbf{\Gamma}_3, \mathbf{\Gamma}_4, \ldots$ such that $\mathbf{\Gamma}_{2k-1} \cup \mathbf{\Gamma}_{2k}^* \subseteq \mathbf{\Gamma}_{2k+1}$ and $\mathbf{\Gamma}_{2k} \cup \mathbf{\Gamma}_{2k+1}^* \subseteq \mathbf{\Gamma}_{2k+2}$. Let $\mathbf{\Delta}_0 = \bigcup_{n=0}^{\infty} \mathbf{\Gamma}_n^*$, $\mathbf{\Delta}_1 = \bigcup_{k=0}^{\infty} \mathbf{\Gamma}_{2k+1}$, $\mathbf{\Delta}_2 = \bigcup_{k=1}^{\infty} \mathbf{\Gamma}_{2k}$, and $\mathbf{\Delta} = \mathbf{\Delta}_1 \cup \mathbf{\Delta}_2$. Then $\mathbf{\Delta}_0$, $\mathbf{\Delta}_1$ and $\mathbf{\Delta}_2$ are consistent, complete, and universal. Consider the models $\mathfrak{M}_{\mathbf{\Delta}_0}$, $\mathfrak{M}_{\mathbf{\Delta}_1}$, $\mathfrak{M}_{\mathbf{\Delta}_2}$, and $\mathfrak{M}_{\mathbf{\Delta}}$ of types $\mathfrak{S}_1 \cap \mathfrak{S}_2$, $\mathfrak{S}_1$, $\mathfrak{S}_2$, and $\mathfrak{S}_1 \cup \mathfrak{S}_2$, respectively. (See §17.) Any two of these models agree on their common predicate letters and $\mathfrak{M}_{\mathbf{\Delta}_0} \models \mathbf{\Gamma}_0$, $\mathfrak{M}_{\mathbf{\Delta}_1} \models \mathbf{A}_1$, and $\mathfrak{M}_{\mathbf{\Delta}_2} \models \mathbf{A}_2$. Hence $\mathfrak{M}_{\mathbf{\Delta}} \models \mathbf{\Gamma}_0 \cup \{\mathbf{A}_1\} \cup \{\mathbf{A}_2\}$.

*26 (*Craig Interpolation Lemma*). Let $\mathbf{A}_1$ be a sentence of $L(\mathfrak{S}_1, X_1)$ and $\mathbf{A}_2$ a sentence of $L(\mathfrak{S}_2, X_2)$. Show that if $\vdash \mathbf{A}_1 \supset \mathbf{A}_2$, then there is a sentence $\mathbf{B}$ of $L(\mathfrak{S}_1 \cap \mathfrak{S}_2, X_1 \cap X_2)$ such that $\vdash \mathbf{A}_1 \supset \mathbf{B}$ and $\vdash \mathbf{B} \supset \mathbf{A}_2$. *Hint:* Let $\mathbf{\Gamma}$ be the set of all sentences $\mathbf{C}$ of $L(\mathfrak{S}_1 \cap \mathfrak{S}_2, X_1 \cap X_2)$ such that $\vdash \mathbf{A}_1 \supset \mathbf{C}$. If $\mathbf{\Gamma}$ is inconsistent, let $\mathbf{B}$ be $\mathfrak{f}$. Suppose $\mathbf{\Gamma}$ is consistent. Then $\mathbf{\Gamma} \vdash \mathbf{A}_2$, for if not, $\mathbf{\Gamma} \cup \{\sim\mathbf{A}_2\}$ is consistent and extends to a consistent, complete set $\mathbf{\Delta}$. The sets $\mathbf{\Delta}^* \cup \{\mathbf{A}_1\}$ and $\mathbf{\Delta}^* \cup \{\sim\mathbf{A}_2\}$ are consistent ($\mathbf{\Delta}^*$ is defined as in Exercise 25) and hence by Exercise 25, $\mathbf{\Delta}^* \cup \{\mathbf{A}_1 \wedge \sim \mathbf{A}_2\}$ is consistent contradicting $\vdash \mathbf{A}_1 \supset \mathbf{A}_2$. From $\mathbf{A}_1 \vdash \mathbf{\Gamma}$ and $\mathbf{\Gamma} \vdash \mathbf{A}_2$ the theorem follows easily. (*Note:* When $\mathfrak{S}_1 \cap \mathfrak{S}_2$ is empty, each sentence of $L(\mathfrak{S}_1 \cap \mathfrak{S}_2, X_1 \cap X_2)$ is either a theorem or the negation of a theorem. Hence in this case we may conclude that either $\vdash \sim \mathbf{A}_1$ or $\vdash \mathbf{A}_2$.)

*27 (*Beth Definability Theorem*). Let $\mathbf{A(P)}$ be a sentence containing an n-place predicate letter $\mathbf{P}$ (and possibly other predicate letters), let $\mathbf{P}'$ be an n-place predicate letter not occurring in $\mathbf{A(P)}$, and let $\mathbf{A(P')}$ result from $\mathbf{A(P)}$ by replacing $\mathbf{P}$ by $\mathbf{P}'$. The sentence $\mathbf{A(P)}$ **implicitly defines P** iff

$$\vdash \mathbf{A(P)} \wedge \mathbf{A(P')} \,.\!\supset \forall \mathrm{x}_1 \ldots \forall \mathrm{x}_n\, [\mathbf{P}(\mathrm{x}_1, \ldots, \mathrm{x}_n) \equiv \mathbf{P}'(\mathrm{x}_1, \ldots, \mathrm{x}_n)].$$

The sentence $\mathbf{A(P)}$ **explicitly defines P** iff there is a wff $\mathbf{B}(\mathrm{x}_1, \ldots, x_n)$ not containing $\mathbf{P}$, having $\mathrm{x}_1, \ldots, \mathrm{x}_n$ as its only free variables, and containing no predicate letters or individual constants not occurring in $\mathbf{A(P)}$, such that

$$\vdash \mathbf{A(P)} \supset \forall \mathrm{x}_1 \ldots \forall \mathrm{x}_n\, [\mathbf{P}(\mathrm{x}_1, \ldots, \mathrm{x}_n) \equiv \mathbf{B}(\mathrm{x}_1, \ldots, \mathrm{x}_n)].$$

Show that if $\mathbf{A(P)}$ implicitly defines $\mathbf{P}$, then $\mathbf{A(P)}$ explicitly defines $\mathbf{P}$. *Hint*: Let $a_1, \ldots, a_n$ be distinct individual constants not occurring in $\mathbf{A(P)}$. As

$$\vdash \mathbf{A(P)} \wedge \mathbf{P}(a_1, \ldots, a_n) \,.\!\supset\!.\, \mathbf{A(P')} \supset \mathbf{P}'(a_1, \ldots, a_n)$$

there is by Exercise 26 above a sentence $\mathbf{B}(a_1, \ldots, a_n)$ containing neither $\mathbf{P}$ nor $\mathbf{P}'$ such that

$$\vdash \mathbf{A(P)} \wedge \mathbf{P}(a_1, \ldots, a_n) \supset \mathbf{B}(a_1, \ldots, a_n)$$

and

$$\vdash \mathbf{B}(a_1, \ldots, a_n) \supset\!.\, \mathbf{A(P')} \supset \mathbf{P}'(a_1, \ldots, a_n).$$

[Here $\mathbf{B}(a_1, \ldots, a_n)$ denotes the result of replacing $\mathrm{x}_1, \ldots, \mathrm{x}_n$ by $a_1, \ldots, a_n$ in $\mathbf{B}(\mathrm{x}_1, \ldots, \mathrm{x}_n)$.]

Chapter 3 FIRST-ORDER RECURSIVE ARITHMETIC

In this chapter we study a language RA called *first-order primitive recursive arithmetic*. This language is adequate for the formalization of a large portion of that branch of mathematics known as elementary number theory.

In mathematical logic there are always at least two languages present: the *object language* which is the language being studied and the *metalanguage* which is the language in which we speak. In Chapter 3 RA is the object language and English is the metalanguage. We shall see in Chapter 4 that, to a limited extent, RA may serve as its own metalanguage.

The language RA has, in addition to all of the apparatus of first order logic, names for the natural numbers 0, 1, 2, . . . (these names are called "numerals") and names for certain numerical functions called "primitive recursive functions" (these names will be called "function constants"). The first two sections of this chapter are devoted to the primitive recursive functions, and then the syntax and semantics of the language RA is given.

§19 Primitive Recursive Functions

The set $\{0, 1, 2, \ldots\}$ of **natural numbers** is denoted by the symbol $\mathbf{N}$. An **n-place numerical function** ($n = 1, 2, \ldots$) is a rule f which assigns to each n-tuple $(x_1, x_2, \ldots, x_n)$ of natural numbers another natural number $f(x_1, x_2, \ldots, x_n)$. (For a more set theoretic definition see Appendix A1.)

Theorem. Let g be an n-place numerical function and h be an $(n + 2)$-place numerical function. Then there is a unique $(n + 1)$-place numerical function f which satisfies the equations

(1) $f(x_1, \ldots, x_n, 0) = g(x_1, \ldots, x_n)$

(2) $f(x_1, \ldots, x_n, y + 1) = h(x_1, \ldots, x_n, y, f(x_1, \ldots, x_n, y))$

for all $x_1, \ldots, x_n, y \in \mathbf{N}$.

The function f in the theorem is called the **function defined from g and h by primitive recursion.**

The theorem may seem obvious to the reader. Indeed, if we take $n = 1$, then

$$\begin{aligned} f(x, 0) &= g(x) \\ f(x, 1) &= h(x, 0, f(x, 0)) \\ &= h(x, 0, g(x)) \\ f(x, 2) &= h(x, 1, f(x, 1)) \\ &= h(x, 1, h(x, 0, g(x))) \end{aligned}$$

and so on. However, the theorem can be proven from more basic principles. This is done in Appendix A3.

There is another way of making new functions from old. If h is an m-place numerical function and $g_1, \ldots, g_m$ are n-place numerical functions, then the n-place numerical function f defined by the equation

(3) $f(x_1, \ldots, x_n) = h(g_1(x_1, \ldots, x_n), \ldots, g_m(x_1, \ldots, x_n))$

(for all $x_1, \ldots, x_n \in \mathbf{N}$) is called the **function defined from $g_1, \ldots, g_m$ and h by composition.**

Next we define some specific functions. The 1-place function Z defined by the equation

$$Z(x) = 0$$

(for all $x \in \mathbf{N}$) is called the **zero function**. The 1-place function S defined by the equation

$$S(x) = x + 1$$

(for all $x \in \mathbf{N}$) is called the **successor function**. For each $n = 1, 2, \ldots$ and each $i = 1, 2, \ldots, n$ the n-place function I_i^n defined by the equation

$$I_i^n(x_1, \ldots, x_n) = x_i$$

(for all $x_1, \ldots, x_n \in \mathbf{N}$) is called a **projection function.**

The class of **primitive recursive functions** is defined inductively by the following set of rules:

(PR1) The zero function Z is primitive recursive;

(PR2) The successor function S is primitive recursive;

(PR3) The projection functions I_i^n ($n = 1, 2, \ldots; i = 1, 2, \ldots, n$) are primitive recursive;

(PR4) If g is an n-place primitive recursive function and h is an $(n + 2)$-place primitive recursive function, then the $(n + 1)$-place function f defined from g and h by primitive recursion is also a primitive recursive function; that is, if g and h are primitive recursive, then so is the function f defined by the equations (1) and (2);

(PR5) If h is an m-place primitive recursive function, and $g_1, \ldots, g_m$ are n-place primitive recursive functions, then the n-place function f defined from $g_1, \ldots, g_m$ and h by composition is also a primitive recursive function; that is, if $g_1, \ldots, g_m$, and h are all primitive recursive, then so is the function f defined by equation (3);

(PR6) A function is primitive recursive only if it is required to be so by (PR1)–(PR5).

EXERCISES

1. Let g be the one-place numerical function given by

$$g(x) = (x + 1)^2$$

and h the three-place numerical function given by

$$h(x, y, z) = x + 3y + z.$$

Let f be the two-place numerical function defined from g and h by primitive recursion. Compute $f(2, 0), f(2, 1), f(2, 2), f(2, 3)$. Compute $f(3, 2)$.

2. Let g be the two-place numerical function given by

$$g(x_1, x_2) = x_1 x_2$$

and h the four-place numerical function given by

$$h(x_1, x_2, y, z) = z + y + 1.$$

Let f be the three-place numerical function defined from g and h by primitive recursion. Compute $f(3, 4, 0)$, $f(3, 4, 1)$, $f(3, 4, 2)$. Compute $f(2, 6, 3)$. Find a formula for $f(x_1, x_2, y)$.

3. Let g_1, g_2, g_3 be the two-place numerical functions given by

$$g_1(x, y) = x + y$$

$$g_2(x, y) = xy$$

$$g_3(x, y) = (x + 1)^y$$

and h be the three-place function given by

$$h(z_1, z_2, z_3) = z_1 z_2 + z_1 z_3 + z_2 z_3.$$

Let f be the two-place function defined from g_1, g_2, g_3, and h by composition. Compute $f(3, 2)$ and $f(2, 3)$. Find a formula for $f(x, y)$.

§20 Some Primitive Recursive Functions

For each $n = 0, 1, 2, \ldots$ the function Z_n defined by the equation

$$Z_n(x) = n$$

(for all $x \in \mathbf{N}$) is called the *constant function whose value is* n.

20.1 Proposition. For each $n = 0, 1, 2, \ldots$ the 1-place function Z_n is primitive recursive.

PROOF. By induction on n. Since $Z_0 = Z$, the case $n = 0$ follows from PR1. Suppose Z_n is primitive recursive. Since

$$Z_{n+1}(x) = S(Z_n(x)),$$

Z_{n+1} is primitive recursive by (PR5). ∎

20.2 Proposition. The two-place numerical function σ defined by

$$\sigma(x, y) = x + y$$

(for all $x, y \in \mathbf{N}$) is primitive recursive.

PROOF. Define the three-place function S_3 by the equation

$$S_3(x, y, z) = S(I_3{}^3(x, y, z))$$

(for all $x, y, z \in \mathbf{N}$). Then S_3 is primitive recursive by (PR5). But

$$\sigma(x, 0) = I_1{}^1(x)$$

and

$$\sigma(x, y + 1) = S_3(x, y, \sigma(x, y)).$$

Hence σ is primitive recursive by (PR3) and (PR4). ∎

The last two equations may be written

$$x + 0 = x$$

$$x + (y + 1) = (x + y) + 1.$$

20.3 Proposition. The two-place numerical function π defined by

$$\pi(x, y) = xy$$

(for $x, y \in \mathbf{N}$) is primitive recursive.

PROOF. Of course, xy denotes the product of x and y. Define the 3-place numerical function σ_{13} by the equation

$$\sigma_{13}(x, y, z) = \sigma(I_1^3(x, y, z), I_3^3(x, y, z)).$$

Then σ_{13} is primitive recursive by (PR3), 20.2, and (PR5). But

$$\pi(x, 0) = Z(x)$$
$$\pi(x, y + 1) = \sigma_{13}(x, y, \pi(x, y))$$

so that π is primitive recursive by (PR4) and (PR1). ▮

The last two equations may be written

$$x0 = 0$$
$$x(y + 1) = x + xy.$$

20.4 Proposition. If g is a two-place primitive recursive function, then the two-place numerical function f defined by the equation

$$f(x, y) = g(y, x)$$

(for $x, y \in \mathbf{N}$) is also primitive recursive.

PROOF. $f(x, y) = g(I_2^2(x, y), I_1^2(x, y))$
for $x, y \in \mathbf{N}$. Use (PR5). ▮

20.5 Proposition. If g is a three-place recursive function and $b \in \mathbf{N}$ is a natural number, then the two-place numerical function f defined by the equation

$$f(x, y) = g(x, y, b)$$

(for $x, y \in \mathbf{N}$) is also primitive recursive.

PROOF. The two-place function Z_b^2 defined by

$$Z_b^2(x, y) = b$$

is primitive recursive by 20.1 and (PR5) since

$$Z_b^2(x, y) = Z_b(I_1^2(x, y))$$

$(x, y \in \mathbf{N})$. Then, since

$$f(x, y) = g(I_1^2(x, y), I_2^2(x, y), Z_b^2(x, y))$$

$(x, y \in \mathbf{N})$, f is primitive recursive by (PR5). ▮

In the sequel we shall have to construct a great many primitive recursive functions. The work will be easier to follow if we streamline our language somewhat. This we shall do in three ways. First, we shall avoid giving names (even temporary names) to functions which we are defining; rather we shall talk about the defining expression itself. Thus instead of saying

"The three-place numerical function f defined by the equation

$f(x, y, z) = x + y + z$ $(x, y, z \in \mathbf{N})$ is primitive recursive."

we shall say more simply

"$x + y + z$ is a primitive recursive function of x, y, and z."

Second, we shall avoid writing expressions like $I_i^n(x_1, \ldots, x_n)$, $Z_b(x)$, and $S(x)$ writing instead x_i, b, and $x + 1$ respectively. The reader may always (if he likes) provide the longer notations to justify the argument by (PR1)–(PR5) by using methods similar to those of Propositions 20.1–20.5. Thirdly, we shall often avoid mentioning (PR1)–(PR5), leaving the reader to supply the justification for the argument.

20.6 Proposition. x^y is a primitive recursive function of x and y.

PROOF. $x^0 = 1 \qquad x^{y+1} = x(x^y)$. ▌ [1]

Subtraction is not a numerical function because the difference of two numbers may be negative (for example, $2 \in \mathbf{N}$ and $4 \in \mathbf{N}$ but $2 - 4 \notin \mathbf{N}$). To circumvent this difficulty we define **limited subtraction** by the equations

$$\begin{aligned} x \dot{-} y &= x - y \quad &\text{if } y \leqslant x; \\ &= 0 \quad &\text{if } x < y \end{aligned}$$

(for $x, y \in \mathbf{N}$).

20.7 Proposition. $x \dot{-} y$ is a primitive recursive function of x and y.

PROOF. $0 \dot{-} 1 = 0$; $(x + 1) \dot{-} 1 = x$. Hence by Exercise 1 below, $x \dot{-} 1$ is a primitive recursive function of x. (Don't be troubled by the fact that $x \dot{-} 1$ does not appear on the right side in the second equation; the equation could have been written $(x + 1) \cdot 1 = I_1^2(x, x \dot{-} 1)$.) Now $x \dot{-} y$ may be defined by primitive recursion: $x \cdot 0 = x$ and $x \dot{-} (y + 1) = (x \dot{-} y) \dot{-} 1$. ▌

---

[1] Mathematicians usually do not define 0^0, roughly for the same reasons that they do not divide by 0. We have arbitrarily defined $0^0 = 1$.

EXERCISES

1. Justify the proof of Proposition 20.7 by showing that if h is a primitive recursive function and if a is a natural number then the function f defined by the equations

$$f(0) = a$$
$$f(x+1) = h(x, f(x))$$

is also primitive recursive.

2. Show that $x!$ is a primitive recursive function of x. ($x!$ is read "x factorial" and is defined by $x! = x(x-1)(x-2)\ldots\cdot 2\cdot 1$ with $0! = 1$.)

3. Let e be the one-place numerical function defined by

$$\begin{aligned} e(x) &= 0 \quad \text{if} \quad x \text{ is even} \\ &= 1 \quad \text{if} \quad x \text{ is odd.} \end{aligned}$$

Show that e is primitive recursive. *Hint:* $e(1) = 1 \dot{-} e(0)$ and $e(2) = 1 \dot{-} e(1)$.

4. If α is a nonnegative real number, then $[\alpha]$ is defined to be the largest natural number n such that $n \leqslant \alpha$. (e.g. $[1/2] = 0$, $[16/5] = 3$, $[3.14159\ldots] = 3$, $[4] = 4$.) Show that $[x/2]$ is a primitive recursive function of the natural number x. *Hint:* Use the function e defined in the previous exercise.

§21 Formation Rules for RA

In this section we give the formation rules for the formal language RA called **first-order primitive recursive arithmetic**. The language will have individual variables (intended to assume values in the set of natural numbers) and names for the primitive recursive functions.

For technical reasons it is convenient not to have an infinite list of variables. Accordingly, we will introduce the variables as abbreviations for formulas of the language.

The primitive symbols of RA are the following sixteen symbols:

Z S I | R C **0** v

= ⊃ f ∀ ( ) [ ].

The names of the first nine symbols are (respectively) the **zero-function letter**, the **successor-function letter**, the **atomic projection-function letter**, the **stroke**, the **recursion functor**, the **composition functor**, the **constant zero**, the **atomic variable**, and the **equal sign**. The remaining symbols have the same names as in Chapter 2.

As usual, any finite sequence of primitive symbols is called a **formula**. We will single out those formulas which are of interest:

A formula which consists of a finite sequence of strokes is called an **index**. If **i** is an index, then (v **i**) is an **individual variable.** We immediately introduce more familiar notations via a definition schema:

(D6) $$\mathrm{x}_n \rightsquigarrow (\mathrm{v}\underbrace{||\ldots|}_{n})$$

(for $n = 0, 1, 2, \ldots$). Thus the individual variables are the formulas $\mathrm{x}_0, \mathrm{x}_1, \mathrm{x}_2$, . . . and so on.

We introduce a further definition schema:

(D7) $$\mathrm{I}_i^n \rightsquigarrow (\underbrace{||\ldots|}_{n}\mathrm{I}\underbrace{||\ldots|}_{i})$$

(for $n, i = 0, 1, 2, \ldots$). In case $n = 1, 2, 3, \ldots$ and $i = 1, 2, \ldots, n$ the formula I_i^n is called a *projection-function letter*.

The class of **function constants** is the class of formulas inductively defined by the six following rules:

(Fcn1) The symbol Z is a one-place function constant.

(Fcn2) The symbol S is a one-place function constant.

(Fcn3) For each $n = 1, 2, 3, \ldots$ and each $i = 1, 2, \ldots, n$, I_i^n is an n-place function constant.

(Fcn4) If **g** is an n-place function constant and **h** is an $(n+2)$-place function constant, then (R**gh**) is an $(n+1)$-place function constant.

(Fcn5) If **h** is an m-place function constant and $\mathbf{g}_1, \mathbf{g}_2, \ldots, \mathbf{g}_m$ are n-place function constants, then $(\mathrm{C}\mathbf{h}\mathbf{g}_1\,\mathbf{g}_2 \ldots \mathbf{g}_m)$ is an n-place function constant.

(Fcn6) A formula is a function constant only as required by (Fcn1)–(Fcn5).

To make our formulas more readable we shall adopt the convention of omitting parentheses from function constants. Thus we write

$$\mathrm{CCSI}_1{}^3\,\mathrm{RSI}_2{}^3\mathrm{RZI}_1{}^3\,\mathrm{CZI}_2{}^3$$

instead of

$$(\mathrm{C}(\mathrm{CSI}_1{}^3)(\mathrm{RSI}_2{}^3)(\mathrm{RZI}_1{}^3)(\mathrm{CZI}_2{}^3)).$$

The class of **terms** is the class of formulas defined inductively by the following four rules:

(Term 1) The symbol **0** is a term.

(Term 2) If **x** is an individual variable, **x** is a term.

(Term 3) If $\mathbf{f}$ is an n-place function constant and $\mathbf{t}_1, \mathbf{t}_2, \ldots, \mathbf{t}_n$ are terms, then $\mathbf{f}(\mathbf{t}_1 \mathbf{t}_2 \ldots \mathbf{t}_n)$ is a term.

(Term 4) A formula is a term only as required by (Term 1)–(Term 3).

Note that we have omitted the comma from our language. This is because its position in a term (were it included as a primitive symbol) can always be determined by matching parentheses. To make our formulas easier to read, we now introduce commas via a definition schema:

(D8) $$\mathbf{f}(\mathbf{t}_1, \mathbf{t}_2, \ldots, \mathbf{t}_n) \rightsquigarrow \mathbf{f}(\mathbf{t}_1 \mathbf{t}_2 \ldots \mathbf{t}_n).$$

The class of **wffs (well-formed formulas)** is the class of formulas defined inductively by the following five rules:

(Wff1) If $\mathbf{t}$ and $\mathbf{s}$ are terms, $\mathbf{t} = \mathbf{s}$ is a wff.

(Wff2) The symbol $\mathfrak{f}$ is a wff.

(Wff3) If $\mathbf{A}$ and $\mathbf{B}$ are wffs, then $[\mathbf{A} \supset \mathbf{B}]$ is a wff.

(Wff4) If $\mathbf{A}$ is a wff and $\mathbf{x}$ is an individual variable, then $\forall \mathbf{x} \mathbf{A}$ is a wff.

(Wff5) A formula is a wff only as required by (Wff1)–(Wff4).

The conventions on omission of brackets which were introduced in Chapters 1 and 2 remain in force here as well as the definition schemas (D1)–(D5).

An occurrence of a variable $\mathbf{x}$ in a wff $\mathbf{A}$ is called **bound** iff it is in a well-formed part of $\forall \mathbf{x} \mathbf{B}$ and **free** otherwise. A term $\mathbf{t}$ is **free for a variable x** in the wff $\mathbf{A}$ iff there is no occurrence of $\mathbf{x}$ in a well-formed part of $\mathbf{A}$ of form $\forall \mathbf{y} \mathbf{B}$ where $\mathbf{y}$ is a variable occurring in $\mathbf{t}$.

The notation

$$\mathbf{S}_{\mathbf{t}}^{\mathbf{x}} \mathbf{A}|$$

denotes the wff which results from $\mathbf{A}$ by replacing the variable $\mathbf{x}$ by the term $\mathbf{t}$ at each free occurrence of $\mathbf{x}$ in $\mathbf{A}$.

If $n = 0, 1, 2, \ldots$, the **numeral corresponding to the natural number** n is denoted by $\mathbf{k}_n$ and is defined by the definition schema

(D9) $$\mathbf{k}_n \rightsquigarrow \underbrace{\mathrm{S}(\mathrm{S}(\ldots \mathrm{S}}_{n}(\mathbf{0}))\ldots).$$

Thus, $\mathbf{k}_0$ is an abbreviation for $\mathbf{0}$.

Our last definition schema is

(D10) $$\mathbf{t} \neq \mathbf{s} \rightsquigarrow \sim \mathbf{t} = \mathbf{s}.$$

EXERCISES

1. Which of the following formulas are function constants or abbreviations for function constants? For each of the formulas which is a function constant compute the number of places (i.e. the number n such that it is an n-place function constant).

(1) Z
(2) $Z(\mathbf{0})$
(3) $(||I|)$
(4) $(|I||)$
(5) $(||I||)$
(6) $(||I)$
(7) $(I||)$
(8) I_3^4
(9) I_4^3
(10) I_4^4
(11) (CZS)
(12) CZS
(13) $RCZSI_1^3$
(14) $RCZSI_1^2$
(15) $RCZSI_1^3(\mathbf{0}, S(\mathbf{0}))$
(16) $RCZSI_1^3(S(\mathbf{0}), S(S(\mathbf{0})))$
(17) $RCZSI_1^3(\mathbf{k}_1, \mathbf{k}_2)$
(18) $(RI_1^1(CSI_3^3))$
(19) $RI_1^1 CSI_3^3$
(20) $(C(RI_1^1(CSI_3^3))I_1^3 I_3^3)$
(21) $CRI_1^1 CSI_3^3 I_1^3 I_3^3$ *Hint:* (21) is (20) without parentheses.
(22) $RZCRI_1^1 CSI_3^3 I_1^3 I_3^3$ *Hint:* If the first two symbols of (22) are deleted, the result is (21).
(23) $S(\mathbf{k}_0)$
(24) $CZS(\mathbf{0})$
(25) $C(\mathbf{0})$
(26) $CZS(\mathbf{0}, \mathbf{0})$
(27) $RI_1^1 CSI_3^3(\mathbf{k}_0)$
(28) $RI_1^1 CSI_3^3(x_2, \mathbf{k}_5)$
(29) $RI_1^1 CSI_3^3(S(\mathbf{0}), S(S(\mathbf{0})))$
(30) $RI_1^1 CSI_3^3(\mathbf{k}_1, \mathbf{k}_2)$

2. Which of the formulas (and abbreviations for formulas) in the preceding exercise are terms?

3. Which of the abbreviations in Exercise 1 stand for the same formula?

4. What kind of formula (that is, index, variable, function constant, term, wff) is (or is abbreviated by) each of the following?

(1) $||||$
(2) (v)
(3) $(v|||)$
(4) x_0
(5) x_3
(6) $S(x_1)$
(7) $S(x_1) = Z(x_2)$
(8) $S(x_1) = \mathbf{0}$
(9) $S(x_1) = \mathbf{0} \supset \mathfrak{f}$
(10) $\exists x_1 \, S(x_1) = \mathbf{k}_0$
(11) $\exists x_1 \, S(x_1) = \mathbf{k}_1$
(12) $\forall x_1 \forall x_2 \,.\, S(x_1) = S(x_2) \supset x_1 = x_2$
(13) I_2^3
(14) $I_2^3(x_1, x_2, x_1) = x_2$
(15) $\forall x_1 \forall x_2 I_2^3(x_1, x_1, x_2) = x_1$
(16) $\mathfrak{f} \supset S(x_0) = \mathbf{0}$
(17) $I_3^3(\mathbf{k}_7, \mathbf{k}_6 \, \mathbf{k}_2) = \mathbf{k}_6$

§22 Semantics

For each function constant **f**, *val* (**f**) denotes the numerical function defined inductively by the following five rules:

(Valfcn 1) *val* (Z) = Z, the zero function.

(Valfcn 2) *val* (S) = S, the successor function.

(Valfcn 3) For each $n = 1, 2, \ldots$ and $i = 1, 2, \ldots, n$, *val* (I_i^n) = I_i^n.

(Valfcn 4) *val* (R**gh**) = f where f is the function defined from *val* (**g**) and *val* (**h**) by primitive recursion.

(Valfcn 5) *val* (C**h**$\mathbf{g}_1 \mathbf{g}_2 \ldots \mathbf{g}_m$) = f where f is the function defined from *val* ($\mathbf{g}_1$), *val* ($\mathbf{g}_2$), . . . , *val* ($\mathbf{g}_m$), and *val* (**h**) by composition.

Clearly a numerical function f is primitive recursive if and only if there is a function constant **f** such that f = *val* (**f**).

A **variable-free term** is a term which contains no variable. Semantically, variable-free terms are to terms what sentences are to wffs; that is, a variable-free term has a value, but a term with variables has no value until values are assigned to the variables in the term.

If **t** is a variable-free term, $v(\mathbf{t})$ is the natural number inductively defined by the following two rules:

(Valtm 1) $v(\mathbf{0}) = 0$.

(Valtm 2) $v(\mathbf{f}(\mathbf{t}_1, \ldots, \mathbf{t}_n)) = val\,(\mathbf{f})(v(\mathbf{t}_1), \ldots, v(\mathbf{t}_n))$.

[In (Valtm 2) **f** is an n-place function constant and $\mathbf{t}_1, \ldots, \mathbf{t}_n$ are variable-free terms.]

Let **N** denote the set of natural numbers; namely, $\mathbf{N} = \{0, 1, 2, \ldots\}$. If a sentence **A** is true in **N** we write $\mathbf{N} \models \mathbf{A}$; if **A** is false in **N** we write $\mathbf{N} \not\models \mathbf{A}$. This is defined inductively by the following rules:

(Valsen 1) If **t** and **s** are variable free terms, then

$\mathbf{N} \models \mathbf{t} = \mathbf{s}$ if $v(\mathbf{t}) = v(\mathbf{s})$

$\mathbf{N} \not\models \mathbf{t} = \mathbf{s}$ if $v(\mathbf{t}) \neq v(\mathbf{s})$.

(Valsen 2) $\mathbf{N} \not\models \mathfrak{f}$.

(Valsen 3) $\mathbf{N} \not\models \mathbf{A} \supset \mathbf{B}$ if $\mathbf{N} \models \mathbf{A}$ and $\mathbf{N} \not\models \mathbf{B}$

$\mathbf{N} \models \mathbf{A} \supset \mathbf{B}$ otherwise.

(Valsen 4) $\mathbf{N} \models \forall \mathbf{x} \mathbf{A}$ if $\mathbf{N} \models \mathbf{S}^{\mathbf{x}}_{\mathbf{k}_n} \mathbf{A}|$ for all natural numbers n,

$\mathbf{N} \not\models \forall \mathbf{x} \mathbf{A}$ otherwise.

We have defined $\mathbf{N} \models \mathbf{A}$ only when **A** is a sentence of RA (that is, a wff with no free variables). If **A** is a wff of RA which is not a sentence, we say **A** is **valid** in **N** iff $\mathbf{N} \vdash \mathbf{A}'$ where $\mathbf{A}'$ is the universal closure of **A**.

EXERCISES

1. Let $\boldsymbol{\sigma}$ be the two-place function constant $\mathrm{RI_1{}^1(CSI_3{}^3)}$. Show that for $a, b \in \mathbf{N}$,

$$val(\boldsymbol{\sigma})(a, b) = a + b.$$

2. Let $\boldsymbol{\pi}$ be the two-place function constant $\mathrm{RZ(C\boldsymbol{\sigma}I_1{}^3I_3{}^3)}$ where $\boldsymbol{\sigma}$ is the two-place function constant defined above. Show that

$$val(\boldsymbol{\pi})(a, b) = ab.$$

3. Construct a two-place function constant $\boldsymbol{\epsilon}$ such that

$$val(\boldsymbol{\epsilon})(a, b) = a^b$$

for $a, b \in \mathbf{N}$. (See 20.6.)

4. Construct a three-place function constant $\mathbf{f}$ such that for $a, b, c \in \mathbf{N}$,

$$val(\mathbf{f})(a, b, c) = a + b + c.$$

5. Where $\boldsymbol{\sigma}$ and $\boldsymbol{\pi}$ are the two-place function constants defined in Exercises 1 and 2, compute the value $v(\mathbf{t})$ of each of the following variable free terms $\mathbf{t}$:

(1) $\boldsymbol{\sigma}(\mathbf{k}_3, \mathbf{k}_2)$
(2) $\boldsymbol{\pi}(\boldsymbol{\sigma}(\mathbf{k}_3, \mathbf{k}_2), \mathrm{I}_2{}^3(\mathbf{k}_4, \mathbf{k}_5, \mathbf{0}))$
(3) $\mathrm{I}_3{}^4(\mathbf{k}_2, \boldsymbol{\sigma}(\mathbf{k}_3, \mathbf{k}_2), \mathbf{k}_4, \boldsymbol{\sigma}(\mathbf{k}_2, \mathbf{k}_3))$
(4) $(\mathrm{C}\boldsymbol{\sigma}\boldsymbol{\pi}\mathrm{I}_1{}^2)(\boldsymbol{\sigma}(\mathbf{k}_1, \mathbf{k}_2), \mathrm{I}_1{}^3(\mathbf{k}_4, \mathbf{k}_5, \mathbf{k}_5))$
(5) $(\mathrm{C}\boldsymbol{\pi}\boldsymbol{\sigma}\mathrm{I}_1{}^2)(\boldsymbol{\sigma}(\mathbf{k}_4, \mathbf{k}_5), \mathbf{k}_5)$
(6) $(\mathrm{CS}\boldsymbol{\sigma})(\boldsymbol{\sigma}(\mathbf{k}_1, \mathbf{k}_2), \boldsymbol{\pi}(\mathbf{k}_1, \mathbf{k}_2))$
(7) $(\mathrm{CS}\boldsymbol{\sigma})(\mathrm{S}(\boldsymbol{\pi}(\mathbf{k}_1, \mathbf{k}_2)), \mathbf{k}_3)$
(8) $(\mathrm{CS}\boldsymbol{\sigma})(\boldsymbol{\pi}(\mathbf{k}_1, \boldsymbol{\sigma}(\mathbf{k}_3, \mathbf{k}_2)), \mathbf{0})$

6. Compute $v(\mathbf{t})$ for each of the following terms $\mathbf{t}$:

(1) $\mathrm{RSI}_3{}^3(\mathbf{k}_1, \mathbf{0})$
(2) $\mathrm{RSI}_3{}^3(\mathbf{k}_1, \mathbf{k}_1)$
(3) $\mathrm{RSI}_3{}^3(\mathbf{k}_1, \mathbf{k}_2)$
(4) $\mathrm{RSI}_3{}^3(\mathbf{0}, \mathbf{k}_3)$
(5) $\mathrm{CSI}_3{}^3(\mathbf{k}_4, \mathrm{S}(\mathrm{Z}(\mathbf{k}_2)), \mathrm{Z}(\mathrm{S}(\mathbf{0})))$
(6) $\mathrm{RSI}_3{}^3(\mathrm{RSI}_3{}^3(\mathbf{0}, \mathbf{k}_3), \mathrm{I}_3{}^3(\mathbf{0}, \mathbf{0}, \mathbf{0}))$.

7. For each of the following sentences $\mathbf{A}$ state whether or not $\mathbf{N} \models \mathbf{A}$:

(1) $\exists \mathrm{x}_0\, \mathrm{S}(\mathrm{x}_0) = \mathbf{0}$
(2) $\forall \mathrm{x}_0\, \mathrm{S}(\mathrm{x}_0) = \mathbf{0}$
(3) $\forall \mathrm{x}_0\, \mathrm{S}(\mathrm{x}_0) \neq \mathbf{0}$
(4) $\forall \mathrm{x}_0\, \mathrm{S}(\mathrm{x}_0) = \mathbf{0} \supset \forall \mathrm{x}_0\, \mathrm{Z}(\mathrm{x}_0) = \mathbf{0}$
(5) $\forall \mathrm{x}_0 \,.\, \mathrm{S}(\mathrm{x}_0) = \mathbf{0} \supset \mathrm{Z}(\mathrm{x}_0) = \mathbf{k}_1$
(6) $\forall \mathrm{x}_0 \,.\, \mathrm{Z}(\mathrm{x}_0) = \mathbf{0} \supset \mathrm{S}(\mathrm{x}_0) = \mathbf{k}_1$
(7) $\forall \mathrm{x}_0 \,.\, \mathrm{S}(\mathrm{x}_0) = \mathbf{k}_2 \supset \mathrm{Z}(\mathrm{x}_0) = \mathbf{k}_2$
(8) $\exists \mathrm{x}_0 \,.\, \mathrm{S}(\mathrm{x}_0) = \mathbf{k}_2 \supset \mathrm{Z}(\mathrm{x}_0) = \mathbf{k}_2$
(9) $\forall \mathrm{x}_1 \forall \mathrm{x}_2 \forall \mathrm{x}_3 \,.\, \mathrm{S}(\mathrm{I}_2{}^3(\mathrm{x}_1, \mathrm{x}_2, \mathrm{x}_3)) = \mathrm{S}(\mathrm{x}_2)$
(10) $\exists \mathrm{x}_1 \exists \mathrm{x}_2 \,.\, \mathrm{S}(\mathrm{I}_1{}^2(\mathrm{x}_1, \mathrm{x}_2)) = \mathrm{x}_2$.

8. For each of the wffs of Exercise 4, §21, decide whether or not it is valid in $\mathbf{N}$.

§23 Axiomatics

Any wff of RA of one of the seventeen following forms is an **axiom of** RA:

23.1 $\mathbf{A} \supset . \mathbf{B} \supset \mathbf{A}$

23.2 $\mathbf{A} \supset [\mathbf{B} \supset \mathbf{C}] . \supset . [\mathbf{A} \supset \mathbf{B}] \supset [\mathbf{A} \supset \mathbf{C}]$

23.3 $\sim \sim \mathbf{A} \supset \mathbf{A}$

23.4 $\forall \mathbf{x}\mathbf{A} \supset \mathrm{S}_{\mathbf{t}}^{\mathbf{x}}\mathbf{A}|$ where $\mathbf{x}$ is any individual variable and $\mathbf{t}$ is any term which is free for $\mathbf{x}$ in $\mathbf{A}$.

23.5 $\forall \mathbf{x}[\mathbf{A} \supset \mathbf{B}] \supset . \mathbf{A} \supset \forall \mathbf{x}\mathbf{B}$ where $\mathbf{x}$ is any individual variable having no free occurrences in $\mathbf{A}$.

23.6 $\mathrm{x}_1 = \mathrm{x}_1$

23.7 $\mathrm{x}_1 = \mathrm{x}_2 \supset \mathrm{x}_2 = \mathrm{x}_1$

23.8 $\mathrm{x}_1 = \mathrm{x}_2 \supset . \mathrm{x}_2 = \mathrm{x}_3 \supset \mathrm{x}_1 = \mathrm{x}_3$

23.9 $\mathrm{x}_i = \mathrm{x}_0 \supset \mathbf{f}(\mathrm{x}_1, \ldots, \mathrm{x}_i, \ldots, \mathrm{x}_n) = \mathbf{f}(\mathrm{x}_1, \ldots, \mathrm{x}_0, \ldots, \mathrm{x}_n)$ where $i = 1, 2, \ldots, n$

23.10 $\mathrm{Z}(\mathrm{x}_0) = \mathbf{0}$

23.11 $\mathrm{S}(\mathrm{x}_0) \neq \mathbf{0}$

23.12 $\mathrm{S}(\mathrm{x}_1) = \mathrm{S}(\mathrm{x}_2) \supset \mathrm{x}_1 = \mathrm{x}_2$

23.13 $\mathrm{I}_i^n(\mathrm{x}_1, \ldots, \mathrm{x}_n) = \mathrm{x}_i$

23.14 $\mathrm{R}\mathbf{gh}(\mathrm{x}_1, \ldots, \mathrm{x}_n, \mathbf{0}) = \mathbf{g}(\mathrm{x}_1, \ldots, \mathrm{x}_n)$

23.15 $\mathrm{R}\mathbf{gh}(\mathrm{x}_1, \ldots, \mathrm{x}_n, \mathrm{S}(\mathrm{x}_0)) = \mathbf{h}(\mathrm{x}_1, \ldots, \mathrm{x}_n, \mathrm{x}_0, \mathrm{R}\mathbf{gh}(\mathrm{x}_1, \ldots, \mathrm{x}_n, \mathrm{x}_0))$

23.16 $\mathrm{C}\mathbf{hg}_1 \ldots \mathbf{g}_m(\mathrm{x}_1, \ldots, \mathrm{x}_n) = \mathbf{h}(\mathbf{g}_1(\mathrm{x}_1, \ldots, \mathrm{x}_n), \ldots, \mathbf{g}_m(\mathrm{x}_1, \ldots, \mathrm{x}_n))$

23.17 $\mathrm{S}_{\mathbf{0}}^{\mathbf{x}}\mathbf{A}| \supset . \forall \mathbf{x}[\mathbf{A} \supset \mathrm{S}_{\mathrm{S}(\mathbf{x})}^{\mathbf{x}}\mathbf{A}|] \supset \forall \mathbf{x}\mathbf{A}$

Schema 23.17 is called the *schema of mathematical induction*.

The rules of inference are *modus ponens* (11.6) and generalization (11.7). As usual, a sequence of wffs of RA is a **deduction** (in RA) iff each member of the sequence is either an axiom or is obtained from an earlier member (or earlier members) of the sequence by a rule of inference. A wff is a **theorem** of RA iff it is the last member of some deduction. The notation RA $\vdash \mathbf{A}$ or simply $\vdash \mathbf{A}$ (where no confusion would result) shall mean that the wff $\mathbf{A}$ is a theorem of RA.

Notice that 23.6–23.8 and 23.10–23.12 are not schemas but are in fact particular wffs of RA. Also notice that in 23.6–23.13 the axioms contain variables although the axioms would remain "reasonable" (valid in **N** in the sense of the next section) if these variables are replaced by terms. The following rule says that these more general schemas are theorem schemas:

23.18 Derived Rule of Substitution for individual variables. Let **A** be a wff of RA, **x** an individual variable, and **t** a term which is free for **x** in **A**. If $\vdash \mathbf{A}$, then $\vdash \mathbf{S_t{}^x A}|$.

PROOF. Suppose $\vdash \mathbf{A}$. By generalization, $\vdash \forall\mathbf{xA}$. Now use 23.4 and *modus ponens.* ▮

We now may use 23.18 to "generalize" axioms 23.6–23.16:

23.19 $\vdash \mathbf{t} = \mathbf{t}$

23.20 $\vdash \mathbf{t}_1 = \mathbf{t}_2 \supset \mathbf{t}_2 = \mathbf{t}_1$

23.21 $\vdash \mathbf{t}_1 = \mathbf{t}_2 \supset \centerdot\, \mathbf{t}_2 = \mathbf{t}_3 \supset \mathbf{t}_1 = \mathbf{t}_3$

23.22 $\vdash \mathbf{t}_1 = \mathbf{t}_2 \supset \mathbf{t} = \mathbf{t}^*$ where $\mathbf{t}^*$ results from **t** by replacing one (or more) occurrences of $\mathbf{t}_1$ in **t** by $\mathbf{t}_2$.

23.23 $Z(\mathbf{t}) = 0$

23.24 $S(\mathbf{t}) \neq 0$

23.25 $S(\mathbf{t}_1) = S(\mathbf{t}_2) \supset \mathbf{t}_1 = \mathbf{t}_2$

23.26 $I_i{}^n(\mathbf{t}_1, \ldots, \mathbf{t}_n) = \mathbf{t}_i$

23.27 $R\mathbf{gh}(\mathbf{t}_1, \ldots, \mathbf{t}_n, 0) = \mathbf{g}(\mathbf{t}_1, \ldots, \mathbf{t}_n)$

23.28 $R\mathbf{gh}(\mathbf{t}_1, \ldots, \mathbf{t}_n, S(\mathbf{t}_0)) = \mathbf{h}(\mathbf{t}_1, \ldots, \mathbf{t}_n, \mathbf{t}_0, R\mathbf{gh}(\mathbf{t}_1, \ldots, \mathbf{t}_n, \mathbf{t}_0))$

23.29 $C\mathbf{hg}_1 \ldots \mathbf{g}_m(\mathbf{t}_1, \ldots, \mathbf{t}_n) = \mathbf{h}(\mathbf{g}_1(\mathbf{t}_1, \ldots, \mathbf{t}_n), \ldots, \mathbf{g}_m(\mathbf{t}_1, \ldots, \mathbf{t}_n))$

The method of proof of all these except 23.22 is the same. By repeated use of the substitution rule (23.18) we change the variables in the axiom to new variables which do not occur in any of the terms to be substituted in; then by repeated use of the substitution rule again, we obtain the theorem schema. For illustration, the proof of 23.20 follows:

PROOF OF 23.20. By 23.7 we have $\vdash x_1 = x_2 \supset x_2 = x_1$. Let **y** be a variable which does not occur in $\mathbf{t}_1$. By 23.18, we have $\vdash x_1 = \mathbf{y} \supset \mathbf{y} = x_1$. By 23.18 again, $\vdash \mathbf{t}_1 = \mathbf{y} \supset \mathbf{y} = \mathbf{t}_1$. Finally, by 23.18 once more, $\vdash \mathbf{t}_1 = \mathbf{t}_2 \supset \mathbf{t}_2 = \mathbf{t}_1$. (Note that 23.18 would not yield this last statement had we not taken care that **y** not occur in $\mathbf{t}_1$ because $\mathbf{t}_1$ would be changed by the substitution.) ▮

To prove 23.22 we first prove 23.9′.

23.9′ $\vdash \mathbf{x} = \mathbf{y} \supset \mathbf{t} = \mathbf{t}^*$ where $\mathbf{x}$ and $\mathbf{y}$ are individual variables and $\mathbf{t}^*$ results from $\mathbf{t}$ by replacing zero or more occurrences of $\mathbf{x}$ in $\mathbf{t}$ by $\mathbf{y}$.

PROOF OF 23.9′. We use induction (in the metalanguage) on the length of $\mathbf{t}$. If $\mathbf{t}$ is $\mathbf{x}$ then $\mathbf{t}^*$ is $\mathbf{y}$ and 23.9′ becomes $\mathbf{x} = \mathbf{y} \supset \mathbf{x} = \mathbf{y}$ which is a theorem by the propositional calculus. If the replacement is at zero places then $\mathbf{t}$ is $\mathbf{t}^*$ and 23.9′ becomes $\mathbf{x} = \mathbf{y} \supset \mathbf{t} = \mathbf{t}$ which follows by the propositional calculus, 23.6, and 23.18. If $\mathbf{t}$ is $\mathbf{f}(\mathbf{t}_1, \ldots, \mathbf{t}_n)$ then $\mathbf{t}^*$ is $\mathbf{f}(\mathbf{t}_1^*, \ldots, \mathbf{t}_n^*)$. By the induction hypothesis, $\vdash \mathbf{x} = \mathbf{y} \supset \mathbf{t}_i = \mathbf{t}_i^*$ for $i = 1, 2, \ldots, n$. By 23.9 and 23.18

$$\vdash \mathbf{t}_i = \mathbf{t}_i^* \supset \mathbf{f}(\mathbf{t}_1^*, \ldots, \mathbf{t}_{i-1}^*, \mathbf{t}_i, \mathbf{t}_{i+1}, \ldots, \mathbf{t}_n) = \mathbf{f}(\mathbf{t}_1^*, \ldots, \mathbf{t}_{i-1}^*, \mathbf{t}_i^*, \mathbf{t}_{i+1}, \ldots, \mathbf{t}_n)$$

for $i = 1, 2, \ldots, n$. Now repeatedly use 23.21 (and the propositional calculus). This proves 23.9′. ▮

Schema 23.22 follows from 23.9′ by the same argument used to prove 23.20. ▮

EXERCISE

1. Show that if the axiom schemas 23.7–23.9 are replaced by 23.9′, then the resulting formal language has exactly the same theorems as RA.

§24 Soundness

A deductive system is *sound* iff its theorems are all true in the intended interpretation. The following theorem parallels previous soundness theorems (6.1, 15.1, and 15.2).

24.1 Soundness Theorem. Let $\mathbf{A}$ be a sentence of RA. If $\vdash \mathbf{A}$, then $\mathbf{N} \models \mathbf{A}$.

PROOF. We shall prove a slightly different (but equivalent) assertion. A wff $\mathbf{B}$ of RA is **valid in N** iff $\mathbf{N} \models \mathbf{B}'$ where $\mathbf{B}'$ is the universal closure of $\mathbf{B}$. We shall show that if $\vdash \mathbf{B}$, then $\mathbf{B}$ is valid in $\mathbf{N}$. Theorem 24.1 is a special case of this.

A rigorous proof proceeds in the following way. Suppose $\vdash \mathbf{B}$. Then there is a deduction $\mathbf{B}_1, \mathbf{B}_2, \ldots, \mathbf{B}_m$ in RA such that $\mathbf{B}_m$ is $\mathbf{B}$. One shows by induction on k (where $k = 1, 2, \ldots, m$) that $\mathbf{B}_k$ is valid in $\mathbf{N}$. This is true since the axioms are all valid in $\mathbf{N}$ and the rules of inference yield wffs valid in $\mathbf{N}$ when applied to wffs valid in $\mathbf{N}$. We leave the details to the reader.

The converse of 24.1 is false as we shall see. This contrasts with the earlier soundness theorems (6.1 and 15.2) which both had true converses: namely, the completeness theorems for propositional calculus and for first-order logic.

We shall say that RA is **consistent** iff $\mathfrak{f}$ is not a theorem of RA. In view of the theorem schema $\vdash \mathfrak{f} \supset \mathbf{A}$, this is equivalent to saying that some wff is not a theorem of RA, and in view of the fact that $\sim\mathbf{A}$ is simply an abbreviation for $\mathbf{A} \supset \mathfrak{f}$ this is equivalent to saying that for no wff **A** of RA are both **A** and $\sim\mathbf{A}$ theorems of RA.

24.2 Corollary. RA is consistent.

This is immediately apparent since if $\vdash \mathfrak{f}$, then (by 24.1) $\mathbf{N} \models \mathfrak{f}$ which is not the case. We shall see later that 24.2 cannot be proven without using principles which are stronger than those principles which are formalized in the formal language RA.

§25 Sentences without Variables

A sentence without variables is, a fortiori, a sentence without quantifiers. For such sentences the converse of 24.1 holds. This is a kind of weak completeness of RA. We break up the proof into a series of lemmas.

25.1 Lemma. Let **f** be an n-place function constant, and let $f = val\,(\mathbf{f})$ be the corresponding primitive recursive function. Let $a_1, a_2, \ldots, a_n$ be natural numbers and let $b = f(a_1, \ldots, a_n)$. Then

$$\vdash \mathbf{f}(\mathbf{k}_{a_1}, \mathbf{k}_{a_2}, \ldots, \mathbf{k}_{a_n}) = \mathbf{k}_b.$$

Proof. This lemma is proved by induction on the number of symbols in **f**.

Case 1. **f** is Z. Then $n = 1$ and $b = 0$. Use 23.23.

Case 2. **f** is S. Then $n = 1$ and $b = a + 1$ (where $a = a_1$). Then $\mathbf{k}_b$ is $\mathrm{S}(\mathbf{k}_a)$ by definition schema (D9). Use 23.19.

Case 3. **f** is I_i^n. Use 23.26.

Case 4. **f** is R**gh**. We prove Case 4 by induction on a_n (an induction within an induction).

Subcase 4*a*. Assume $a_n = 0$. Then by 23.27

$$\vdash \mathbf{f}(\mathbf{k}_{a_1}, \ldots, \mathbf{k}_{a_n}) = \mathbf{g}(\mathbf{k}_{a_1}, \ldots, \mathbf{k}_{a_{n-1}}).$$

By the induction hypothesis (of the whole proof)

$$\vdash \mathbf{g}(\mathbf{k}_{a_1}, \ldots, \mathbf{k}_{a_{n-1}}) = \mathbf{k}_b.$$

Now use 23.21 and *modus ponens*.

Subcase 4*b*. Assume $a_n > 0$. Let $a = a_n - 1$. By 23.28

$$\vdash \mathbf{f}(\mathbf{k}_{a_1}, \ldots, \mathbf{k}_{a_n}) = \mathbf{h}(\mathbf{k}_{a_1}, \ldots, \mathbf{k}_{a_{n-1}}, \mathbf{k}_a, \mathbf{f}(\mathbf{k}_{a_1}, \ldots, \mathbf{k}_{a_{n-1}}, \mathbf{k}_a)).$$

By the induction hypothesis (for Case 4)

$$\vdash \mathbf{f}(\mathbf{k}_{a_1}, \ldots, \mathbf{k}_{a_{n-1}}, \mathbf{k}_a) = \mathbf{k}_c$$

where $c = f(a_1, \ldots, a_{n-1}, a)$. By 23.20–23.22 and *modus ponens*

$$\vdash \mathbf{f}(\mathbf{k}_{a_1}, \ldots, \mathbf{k}_{a_n}) = \mathbf{h}(\mathbf{k}_{a_1}, \ldots, \mathbf{k}_{a_{n-1}}, \mathbf{k}_a, \mathbf{k}_c).$$

By the induction hypothesis for the whole proof

$$\vdash \mathbf{h}(\mathbf{k}_{a_1}, \ldots, \mathbf{k}_{a_{n-1}}, \mathbf{k}_a, \mathbf{k}_c) = \mathbf{k}_b.$$

Now use 23.21 and *modus ponens*.

CASE 5. $\mathbf{f}$ is $\mathbf{Chg}_1 \ldots \mathbf{g}_m$. Let $c_i = g_i(a_1, \ldots, a_n)$ for $i = 1, \ldots, m$. By the hypothesis of induction

$$\vdash \mathbf{g}_i(\mathbf{k}_{a_1}, \ldots, \mathbf{k}_{a_n}) = \mathbf{k}_{c_i}$$

for $i = 1, \ldots, m$. Hence by 23.22 and *modus ponens* (repeatedly)

$$\vdash \mathbf{h}(\mathbf{g}_1(\mathbf{k}_{a_1}, \ldots, \mathbf{k}_{a_n}), \ldots, \mathbf{g}_m(\mathbf{k}_{a_1}, \ldots, \mathbf{k}_{a_n})) = \mathbf{h}(\mathbf{k}_{c_1}, \ldots, \mathbf{k}_{c_m}).$$

By 23.29, 23.21 and *modus ponens*

$$\vdash \mathbf{f}(\mathbf{k}_{a_1}, \ldots, \mathbf{k}_{a_n}) = \mathbf{h}(\mathbf{k}_{c_1}, \ldots, \mathbf{k}_{c_m}).$$

By the induction hypothesis

$$\vdash \mathbf{h}(\mathbf{k}_{c_1}, \ldots, \mathbf{k}_{c_m}) = \mathbf{k}_b.$$

Now use 23.21 and *modus ponens*. This completes the proof of Lemma 25.1. ∎

25.2 Lemma. Let $\mathbf{t}$ be a variable-free term and let $a = v(\mathbf{t})$ be its value (see §22). Then $\vdash \mathbf{t} = \mathbf{k}_a$.

PROOF. By induction on the length of $\mathbf{t}$.

CASE 1. $\mathbf{t}$ is $\mathbf{0}$. Then $v(\mathbf{t}) = 0$. Use 23.19.

CASE 2. $\mathbf{t}$ is $\mathbf{f}(\mathbf{t}_1, \ldots, \mathbf{t}_n)$. Let $b_i = v(\mathbf{t}_i)$ for $i = 1, \ldots, n$. By the induction hypothesis we have $\vdash \mathbf{t}_i = \mathbf{k}_{b_i}$ where $i = 1, \ldots, n$. Hence by n applications of 23.22 and *modus ponens*

$$\vdash \mathbf{f}(\mathbf{t}_1, \ldots, \mathbf{t}_n) = \mathbf{f}(\mathbf{k}_{b_1}, \ldots, \mathbf{k}_{b_n}).$$

By 23.1

$$\vdash \mathbf{f}(\mathbf{k}_{b_1}, \ldots, \mathbf{k}_{b_n}) = \mathbf{k}_a.$$

Now use 23.21 and *modus ponens.* ▌

25.3 Lemma. Let a and b be natural numbers. Then

$$\vdash \mathbf{k}_a = \mathbf{k}_b \text{ if } a = b \text{ and}$$

$$\vdash \mathbf{k}_a \neq \mathbf{k}_b \text{ if } a \neq b.$$

PROOF. If $a = b$, then $\vdash \mathbf{k}_a = \mathbf{k}_b$ by 23.19. Suppose $a \neq b$. Then either $a < b$ or $b < a$. Suppose $a < b$. Let $c = b - a - 1$. By 23.24, we find $\vdash \mathrm{S}(\mathbf{k}_c) \neq \mathbf{0}$. By 23.25 and propositional calculus

$$\vdash \mathbf{t}_1 \neq \mathbf{t}_2 \supset \mathrm{S}(\mathbf{t}_1) \neq \mathrm{S}(\mathbf{t}_2)$$

for all terms $\mathbf{t}_1$, $\mathbf{t}_2$. Reading $\mathbf{k}_c$ for $\mathbf{t}_1$ and $\mathbf{0}$ for $\mathbf{t}_2$ we get by *modus ponens*

$$\vdash \mathrm{S}(\mathrm{S}(\mathbf{k}_c)) \neq \mathrm{S}(\mathbf{0})$$

and repeating we get $\vdash \mathrm{S}(\mathrm{S}(\mathrm{S}(\mathbf{k}_c))) \neq \mathrm{S}(\mathrm{S}(\mathbf{0}))$ and so on. Repeating exactly a times we get $\vdash \mathbf{k}_b \neq \mathbf{k}_a$ from which $\vdash \mathbf{k}_a \neq \mathbf{k}_b$ follows by 23.20 and propositional calculus. The case $b < a$ is exactly the same. ▌

25.4 Lemma. Let $\mathbf{t}_1$ and $\mathbf{t}_2$ be variable-free terms. Then

$$\vdash \mathbf{t}_1 = \mathbf{t}_2 \quad \text{if} \quad \mathbf{N} \models \mathbf{t}_1 = \mathbf{t}_2$$

$$\vdash \mathbf{t}_1 \neq \mathbf{t}_2 \quad \text{otherwise.}$$

PROOF. This is immediate from 25.2 and 25.3. ▌

25.5 Weak Completeness Theorem. Let $\mathbf{A}$ be a sentence of RA containing no variables. Then $\vdash \mathbf{A}$ if and only if $\mathbf{N} \models \mathbf{A}$.

PROOF. The direction "only if" follows from the soundness theorem (24.1). To prove "if" suppose $\mathbf{N} \models \mathbf{A}$. Let $\mathbf{p}_1, \mathbf{p}_2, \ldots, \mathbf{p}_n$ be the well-formed parts of

$\mathbf{A}$ of form $\mathbf{t}_1 = \mathbf{t}_2$. For each $i = 1, 2, \ldots, n$ let $\mathbf{p}_i'$ be $\mathbf{p}_i$ if $\mathbf{N} \models \mathbf{p}_i$ and $\sim\mathbf{p}_i$ otherwise. By 25.4 we have $\vdash \mathbf{p}_i'$ for $i = 1, \ldots, n$. On the other hand,

$$\vdash \mathbf{p}_1' \supset . \, \mathbf{p}_2' \supset . \ldots \supset . \, \mathbf{p}_n' \supset \mathbf{A}$$

since this formula is a substitution instance of a tautology (compare with 6.2). Hence $\vdash \mathbf{A}$ by n applications of *modus ponens.* ▌

We give here for future reference a very useful derived rule of RA.

25.6 Substitutivity of Equality. Let $\mathbf{t}_1$ and $\mathbf{t}_2$ be terms and $\mathbf{A}$ a wff. Suppose $\mathbf{A}^*$ results from $\mathbf{A}$ by replacing an occurrence of $\mathbf{t}_1$ in $\mathbf{A}$ by $\mathbf{t}_2$. Suppose further that this occurrence of $\mathbf{t}_1$ in $\mathbf{A}$ is *not* in a well-formed part of $\mathbf{A}$ of form $\forall\mathbf{x}\mathbf{B}$ where $\mathbf{x}$ is a variable occurring in either $\mathbf{t}_1$ or $\mathbf{t}_2$. Then

$$\vdash \mathbf{t}_1 = \mathbf{t}_2 \supset . \, \mathbf{A} \equiv \mathbf{A}^*.$$

PROOF. The proof is by induction on the length of $\mathbf{A}$. If $\mathbf{A}$ contains no occurrence of $\supset$ or $\forall$, then this is simply 23.22, for $\mathbf{A}$ then has the form $\mathbf{s}_1 = \mathbf{s}_2$. If $\mathbf{A}$ is $\mathbf{A}_1 \supset \mathbf{A}_2$, then $\mathbf{A}^*$ is $\mathbf{A}_1^* \supset \mathbf{A}_2^*$ where $\mathbf{A}_i^*$ $(i = 1, 2)$ is either $\mathbf{A}_i$ or results from $\mathbf{A}_i$ by replacing an occurrence of $\mathbf{t}_1$ by $\mathbf{t}_2$. By the induction hypothesis in the latter case and the propositional calculus in the former

$$\vdash \mathbf{t}_1 = \mathbf{t}_2 \supset . \, \mathbf{A}_1 \equiv \mathbf{A}_1^*$$

and

$$\vdash \mathbf{t}_1 = \mathbf{t}_2 \supset . \, \mathbf{A}_2 \equiv \mathbf{A}_2^*.$$

The theorem now follows by the propositional calculus. Finally, if $\mathbf{A}$ is $\forall\mathbf{x}\mathbf{B}$, then by the induction hypothesis

$$\vdash \mathbf{t}_1 = \mathbf{t}_2 \supset \mathbf{B} \equiv \mathbf{B}^*.$$

Hence by generalization, 23.5, and the hypothesis of the theorem

$$\vdash \mathbf{t}_1 = \mathbf{t}_2 \supset . \, \forall\mathbf{x}[\mathbf{B} \equiv \mathbf{B}^*].$$

(This is where we use the fact that $\mathbf{x}$ does not occur in $\mathbf{t}_1$ or $\mathbf{t}_2$.) Now by 14.6

$$\vdash \forall\mathbf{x}[\mathbf{B} \equiv \mathbf{B}^*] \supset . \, \forall\mathbf{x}\mathbf{B} \equiv \forall\mathbf{x}\mathbf{B}^*.$$

Hence by the propositional calculus

$$\vdash \mathbf{t}_1 = \mathbf{t}_2 \supset . \, \forall\mathbf{x}\mathbf{B} \equiv \forall\mathbf{x}\mathbf{B}^*.$$

In other words,

$$\vdash \mathbf{t}_1 = \mathbf{t}_2 \supset . \, \mathbf{A} \equiv \mathbf{A}^*. \quad ▌$$

EXERCISES

1. Let $\boldsymbol{\sigma}$ be the two-place function constant given by

$$\boldsymbol{\sigma} \rightsquigarrow \mathrm{RI}_1{}^1\,\mathrm{CSI}_3{}^3.$$

For terms **t** and **s** let $(\mathbf{t} + \mathbf{s})$ be the term given by

$$(\mathbf{t} + \mathbf{s}) \rightsquigarrow \boldsymbol{\sigma}(\mathbf{t}, \mathbf{s})$$

and let $\mathbf{t}^+$ be the term given by

$$\mathbf{t}^+ \rightsquigarrow \mathrm{S}(\mathbf{t}).$$

We write x, y, and z instead of x_1, x_2, and x_3. Prove the following theorems of RA.

(1) $\vdash (x + \mathbf{0}) = x$

(2) $\vdash (x + y^+) = (x + y)^+$

(3) $\vdash ((x + y) + z) = (x + (y + z))$

(4) $\vdash (\mathbf{0} + x) = x$

(5) $\vdash (x^+ + y) = (x + y)^+$

(6) $\vdash (x + y) = (y + x)$

(7) $\vdash x^+ = (x + \mathbf{k}_1)$

Hints: Expression (1) is essentially an instance of 23.27 and (2) is essentially 23.28. [Use 23.26 and substitutivity of equality (25.6) also in (1).] For (3)–(8) use mostly (1) and (2) and the schema of mathematical induction (23.17). For example, if $\mathbf{A}_{xy}(z)$ stands for the wff

$$((x + y) + z) = (x + (y + z))$$

then the wff

$$\mathbf{A}_{xy}(\mathbf{0}) \supset \centerdot\, \forall z[\mathbf{A}_{xy}(z) \supset \mathbf{A}_{xy}(z^+)] \supset \forall z\mathbf{A}_{xy}(z)$$

is an instance of 23.17. By (1) and (2), substitution (23.18), and substitutivity of equality (25.6) we obtain

$$\vdash \mathbf{A}_{xy}(\mathbf{0}) \qquad \text{and} \qquad \vdash \mathbf{A}_{xy}(z) \supset \mathbf{A}_{xy}(z^+).$$

Then by generalization and *modus ponens*

$$\vdash \forall z\mathbf{A}_{xy}(z)$$

which is essentially (3). Do (4) and (5) by similar inductions and derive (6) from (4) and (5) (with 23.17).

2. Let $\boldsymbol{\pi}$ be the two place function constant given by

$$\boldsymbol{\pi} \rightsquigarrow \mathrm{RZC}\boldsymbol{\sigma}\mathrm{I}_1{}^3\,\mathrm{I}_3{}^3$$

(where $\boldsymbol{\sigma}$ was defined in Exercise 1) and for terms **t** and **s** let $(\mathbf{t}\cdot\mathbf{s})$ be the term given by

$$(\mathbf{t}\cdot\mathbf{s}) \rightsquigarrow \boldsymbol{\pi}(\mathbf{t}, \mathbf{s}).$$

Prove

(1) $\vdash (x \cdot 0) = 0$

(2) $\vdash (x \cdot y^+) = ((x \cdot y) + x)$

(3) $\vdash ((x \cdot y) \cdot z) = (x \cdot (y \cdot z))$

(4) $\vdash (0 \cdot x) = 0$

(5) $\vdash (x^+ \cdot y) = ((x \cdot y) + y)$

(6) $\vdash (x \cdot y) = (y \cdot x)$

(7) $\vdash x \cdot \mathbf{k}_1 = x$

(8) $\vdash (x \cdot (y + z)) = ((x \cdot y) + (x \cdot z))$

*3. For terms **t** and **s** let **t** ⩽ **s** be the wff given by

$$\mathbf{t} \leqslant \mathbf{s} \rightsquigarrow \exists \mathbf{x} \,\centerdot\, \mathbf{t} + \mathbf{x} = \mathbf{s}$$

where **x** is a variable not in **t** or **s**. State some of the simple properties of ⩽ and prove them as theorems of RA. (For example, prove $\vdash \forall x \,\centerdot\, 0 \leqslant x$.) Also prove the following schema:

$$\vdash x \leqslant \mathbf{k}_n \equiv \centerdot\, x = \mathbf{k}_0 \vee x = \mathbf{k}_1 \vee x = \mathbf{k}_2 \vee \ldots \vee x = \mathbf{k}_n$$

(for each $n = 0, 1, 2, \ldots$). *Hint:* Prove $x \leqslant y^+ \equiv \centerdot\, x \leqslant y \vee x = y^+$.

*4. Let X be a set. The formal language RA(X) has as its primitive symbols those of RA and, in addition, the elements of X. The definitions of function constant, term, and wff are the same for RA(X) as for RA except that the definition of term is modified by adding the rule that if $a \in X$, then a is a term. The rules of inference of RA(X) are those of RA and the axiom schemas of RA(X) are 23.1–23.9.

A **model of type** RA is a triple $\mathfrak{N} = (X, e, V)$ where X is a set, $e \in X$, and V is a function which assigns to every n-place function constant **f** of RA an n-place function $V(\mathbf{f})$ from X to X. (An n-place function f from X to X is a function which assigns to every n-tuple $(a_1, a_2, \ldots, a_n)$ of elements of X an element $f(a_1, a_2, \ldots, a_n)$ in X.) Given such a model $\mathfrak{N}$ we extend V to the set of all (variable free) terms of RA(X) by the rules:

(1) $V(\mathbf{0}) = e$;

(2) $V(a) = a$ for $a \in X$;

(3) $V(\mathbf{f}(\mathbf{t}_1, \mathbf{t}_2, \ldots, \mathbf{t}_n)) = V(\mathbf{f})(V(\mathbf{t}_1), V(\mathbf{t}_2), \ldots, V(\mathbf{t}_n))$ where **f** is an n-place function constant and $\mathbf{t}_1, \mathbf{t}_2, \ldots, \mathbf{t}_n$ are terms of RA(X).

Then for each sentence **A** of RA(X) the relation $\mathfrak{N} \models \mathbf{A}$ is defined by the rules:

(i) $\mathfrak{N} \models \mathbf{t} = \mathbf{s}$ iff $V(\mathbf{t}) = V(\mathbf{s})$

(ii) $\mathfrak{N} \not\models \mathfrak{f}$

(iii) $\mathfrak{N} \models \mathbf{A} \supset \mathbf{B}$ iff $\mathfrak{N} \not\models \mathbf{A}$ or $\mathfrak{N} \models \mathbf{B}$

(iv) $\mathfrak{N} \models \forall \mathbf{x} \mathbf{A}$ iff $\mathfrak{N} \models \mathbf{S}_a^{\mathbf{x}} \mathbf{A}|$ for all $a \in X$.

Show that if $\mathbf{\Gamma}$ is a consistent set of sentences in RA(X), then there is a model $\mathfrak{N} = (Y, e, V)$ such that $X \subseteq Y$ and $\mathfrak{N} \models \mathbf{\Gamma}$. (See §§16 and 17.)

*5. Let the set X consist of one element: ω (namely, $X = \{\omega\}$). Let **T** be the set of all sentences **A** of RA such that $\mathbf{N} \models \mathbf{A}$ and let $\mathbf{\Gamma}$ be the set of sentences of RA(X) consisting of all the sentences of **T** and, in addition, all the sentences $\mathbf{k}_n \leqslant \omega$ ($n = 0, 1, 2, \ldots$; the abbreviation $\mathbf{t} \leqslant \mathbf{s}$ was defined in Exercise 3 preceding). Show that $\mathbf{\Gamma}$ is consistent in RA(X).

*6. By Exercise 4 preceding there is a model $\mathfrak{N} = (Y, e, V)$ of type RA such that $\mathfrak{N} \models \mathbf{\Gamma}$ where $\mathbf{\Gamma}$ is the set of sentences of Exercise 5.

(1) Show that $\mathfrak{N}$ is equivalent to **N** in the following sense: If **A** is any sentence of RA, then $\mathfrak{N} \models \mathbf{A}$ if and only if $\mathbf{N} \models \mathbf{A}$.

(2) Show that $\mathfrak{N}$ is not isomorphic to **N** in the sense that there is **no** one-to-one correspondence φ between the elements of **N** and those of Y such that for every wff $\mathbf{A}(\mathbf{x}_1, \mathbf{x}_2, \ldots, \mathbf{x}_n)$ of RA (with free variables $\mathbf{x}_1, \mathbf{x}_2, \ldots, \mathbf{x}_n$) the condition

$$\mathbf{N} \models \mathbf{A}(\mathbf{k}_{a_1}, \mathbf{k}_{a_2}, \ldots, \mathbf{k}_{a_n}) \qquad \text{if and only if} \quad \mathfrak{N} \models \mathbf{A}(\varphi(a_1), \varphi(a_2), \ldots, \varphi(a_n))$$

holds for all $a_1, a_2, \ldots, a_n \in \mathbf{N}$. (If $\mathbf{t}_1, \mathbf{t}_2, \ldots, \mathbf{t}_n$ are terms, then $\mathbf{A}(\mathbf{t}_1, \mathbf{t}_2, \ldots, \mathbf{t}_n)$ denotes the result of simultaneously replacing all free occurrences of $\mathbf{x}_1, \mathbf{x}_2, \ldots, \mathbf{x}_n$ in $\mathbf{A}(\mathbf{x}_1, \mathbf{x}_2, \ldots, \mathbf{x}_n)$ by $\mathbf{t}_1, \mathbf{t}_2, \ldots, \mathbf{t}_n$ respectively.)

*7. The formal language $\mathrm{RA_i}$, **intuitionistic first-order arithmetic** is obtained from RA by replacing first-order logic by intuitionistic first order logic (Exercise 8 of §18) as the underlying logic of RA. More specifically, the symbols $\vee$, $\wedge$, and $\exists$ are added as primitive symbols in RA, the formation rules are modified accordingly, and the axion schemas 23.1–23.5 are replaced by the axiom schemas for intuitionistic propositional calculus (Exercise 9 of §6) and the following four schemas:

(i) $\forall \mathbf{x} \mathbf{A} \supset \mathbf{S}_{\mathbf{t}}^{\mathbf{x}} \mathbf{A}|$

(ii) $\forall \mathbf{x}[\mathbf{A} \supset \mathbf{B}] \,\blacksquare\!\supset\! \blacksquare\, \mathbf{A} \supset \forall \mathbf{x} \mathbf{B}$

(iii) $\mathbf{S}_{\mathbf{t}}^{\mathbf{x}} \mathbf{A}| \supset \exists \mathbf{x} \mathbf{A}$

(iv) $\forall \mathbf{x}[\mathbf{B} \supset \mathbf{A}] \supset \blacksquare\, \exists \mathbf{x} \mathbf{B} \supset \mathbf{A}$

[In (i) and (iii) the term **t** is free for **x** in **A** and in (ii) and (iv) the variable **x** is not free in **A**.) The notation $\models_{\mathrm{i}} \mathbf{A}$ means **A** is a theorem of $\mathrm{RA_i}$. Prove the following:

(1) $\vdash_{\mathrm{i}} \mathrm{x} = 0 \vee \exists \mathrm{y} \,\blacksquare\, \mathrm{x} = \mathrm{S}(\mathrm{y})$

(2) $\vdash_{\mathrm{i}} \sim\sim \mathrm{x} = 0 \supset \mathrm{x} = 0$

(3) $\vdash_{\mathrm{i}} \sim\sim \mathrm{y} = \mathrm{x} \supset \mathrm{y} = \mathrm{x}$

Hint: You will need to use 23.17 for each proof. Thus (1) and (2) are proved by induction on x (in the object language). To prove (3) prove instead $\vdash_{\mathrm{i}} \forall \mathrm{y} \,\blacksquare \sim\sim \mathrm{y} = \mathrm{x} \supset \mathrm{y} = \mathrm{x}$; this will require 23.17 (induction on x) and (1) and (2).

*8. Show that if **B** is a wff of RA (not RA_i!) then $\vdash_i \sim\sim \mathbf{B} \supset \mathbf{B}$. Conclude that if $\vdash \mathbf{B}$, then $\vdash_i \mathbf{B}$ (that is, if **B** is a theorem of RA, it is a theorem of RA_i). Hence if RA_i is consistent, then so is RA. *Hint:* See Exercise 12, §18.

REMARKS. This is the Kolmogorov–Gödel proof of the consistency of classical arithmetic relative to intuitionistic arithmetic. Of course, RA *is* consistent by 24.2, however the proof of 24.2 is not constructive for it uses the semantic notion of truth. The relative consistency proof of Exercise 8 is constructive because the proof gives a procedure whereby we can convert a proof of $\mathfrak{f}$ in RA into a proof of $\mathfrak{f}$ in RA_i.

The reader is cautioned that the fact that every theorem of RA is a theorem of RA_i does not mean that these two languages are equivalent for it relies heavily on the fact that $\vee$, $\wedge$, and $\exists$ are not primitive symbols of RA. Indeed we shall see (Exercise 3, §43) that there is a sentence **J** of RA such that $\mathbf{J} \vee \sim \mathbf{J}$ is not a theorem of RA_i (although it is a theorem of RA when considered as an abbreviation).

*9. This exercise follows closely Exercise 19 of §18. The only difference is that in our present context the formal languages have function constants. This difference is inessential and the proof of this exercise is mutatis mutandis the same as the proof of Exercise 19, §18.

Let X be a set. The formal language $RA_i(X)$ is obtained from RA_i by adding the elements of X as individual constants (that is, the definition of term is modified by adding the rule that if $a \in X$, then a is a term). The axiom schemas for $RA_i(X)$ are those of RA_i and $\vdash_i \mathbf{A}$ means **A** is a theorem of $RA_i(X)$. (Clearly if **A** is a theorem of $RA_i(X)$ for some X, then **A** is a theorem of $RA_i(X)$ for every X such that **A** is a sentence of $RA_i(X)$.)

A set of sentences $\mathbf{\Gamma}$ is **inconsistent** iff $\mathbf{\Gamma} \vdash_i \mathfrak{f}$; otherwise $\mathbf{\Gamma}$ is **consistent**. The set $\mathbf{\Gamma}$ is **closed** in $RA_i(X)$ iff $\mathbf{B} \in \mathbf{\Gamma}$ whenever **B** is a sentence of $RA_i(X)$ such that $\mathbf{\Gamma} \vdash_i \mathbf{B}$. The set $\mathbf{\Gamma}$ is **disjunctive** iff either $\mathbf{A} \in \mathbf{\Gamma}$ or $\mathbf{B} \in \mathbf{\Gamma}$ whenever $\mathbf{A} \vee \mathbf{B} \in \mathbf{\Gamma}$. The set $\mathbf{\Gamma}$ is **existential** in $RA_i(X)$ iff there is a term **t** of $RA_i(X)$ such that $\mathbf{S_t^x A}| \in \mathbf{\Gamma}$ whenever $\exists \mathbf{xA} \in \mathbf{\Gamma}$. The set $\mathbf{\Gamma}$ is **regular** in $RA_i(X)$ iff $\mathbf{\Gamma}$ is consistent, closed, disjunctive, and existential in $RA_i(X)$. If $\mathbf{\Gamma}$ is any set of sentences, then $\mathbf{\Gamma}$ is **regular** iff $\mathbf{\Gamma}$ is regular in $RA_i(X)$ for some X.

Prove the following:

(1) If not $\mathbf{\Gamma} \vdash \mathbf{A}$, then there is a regular $\mathbf{\Delta}$ such that $\mathbf{\Gamma} \subseteq \mathbf{\Delta}$ and $\mathbf{A} \notin \mathbf{\Delta}$.

(2) If $\mathbf{\Gamma}$ is regular, then

(2a) $\mathbf{A} \wedge \mathbf{B} \in \mathbf{\Gamma}$ if and only if $\mathbf{A} \in \mathbf{\Gamma}$ and $\mathbf{B} \in \mathbf{\Gamma}$;

(2b) $\mathbf{A} \vee \mathbf{B} \in \mathbf{\Gamma}$ if and only if $\mathbf{A} \in \mathbf{\Gamma}$ or $\mathbf{B} \in \mathbf{\Gamma}$;

(2c) $\mathbf{A} \supset \mathbf{B} \in \mathbf{\Gamma}$ if and only if for every regular $\mathbf{\Delta}$, if $\mathbf{A} \in \mathbf{\Delta}$ and $\mathbf{\Gamma} \subseteq \mathbf{\Delta}$, then $\mathbf{B} \in \mathbf{\Delta}$;

(2d) $\exists \mathbf{xA} \in \mathbf{\Gamma}$ if and only if $\mathbf{S_t^x A}| \in \mathbf{\Gamma}$ for some term **t**;

(2e) $\forall \mathbf{xA} \in \mathbf{\Gamma}$ if and only if for every regular $\mathbf{\Delta}$ such that $\mathbf{\Gamma} \subseteq \mathbf{\Delta}$ and for every term **t** such that $\mathbf{t} = \mathbf{t} \in \mathbf{\Gamma}$, the sentence $\mathbf{S_t^x A}| \in \mathbf{\Delta}$.

*10. In this exercise we construct a Kripke model. Let $\mathbf{T}$ be the set of all sentences which are theorems of RA_i. Let Ω be the class of all sets of sentences $\mathbf{\Gamma}$ such that either $\mathbf{\Gamma} = \mathbf{T}$ or else $\mathbf{\Gamma}$ is regular. For each $\mathbf{\Gamma} \in \Omega$ and each sentence $\mathbf{A}$ (all of whose constants appear in some sentence of $\mathbf{\Gamma}$) we define the relation $\vDash_{\mathbf{\Gamma}} \mathbf{A}$ as follows:

(1) $\vDash_{\mathbf{\Gamma}} \mathbf{t} = \mathbf{s}$ iff $\mathbf{t} = \mathbf{s} \in \mathbf{\Gamma}$;

(2) not $\vDash_{\mathbf{\Gamma}} \mathfrak{f}$;

(3) $\vDash_{\mathbf{\Gamma}} \mathbf{A} \wedge \mathbf{B}$ iff $\vDash_{\mathbf{\Gamma}} \mathbf{A}$ and $\vDash_{\mathbf{\Gamma}} \mathbf{B}$;

(4) $\vDash_{\mathbf{\Gamma}} \mathbf{A} \vee \mathbf{B}$ iff $\vDash_{\mathbf{\Gamma}} \mathbf{A}$ or $\vDash_{\mathbf{\Gamma}} \mathbf{B}$;

(5) $\vDash_{\mathbf{\Gamma}} \mathbf{A} \supset \mathbf{B}$ iff for every $\mathbf{\Delta} \in \Omega$ if $\mathbf{\Gamma} \subseteq \mathbf{\Delta}$ and $\vDash_{\mathbf{\Delta}} \mathbf{A}$, then $\vDash_{\mathbf{\Delta}} \mathbf{B}$;

(6) $\vDash_{\mathbf{\Gamma}} \exists \mathbf{x} \mathbf{A}$ iff $\vDash_{\mathbf{\Gamma}} \mathbf{S}_{\mathbf{t}}^{\mathbf{x}} \mathbf{A}|$ for some term $\mathbf{t}$;

(7) $\vDash_{\mathbf{\Gamma}} \forall \mathbf{x} \mathbf{A}$ iff $\vDash_{\mathbf{\Delta}} \mathbf{S}_{\mathbf{t}}^{\mathbf{x}} \mathbf{A}|$ for every $\mathbf{\Delta} \in \Omega$ such that $\mathbf{\Gamma} \subseteq \mathbf{\Delta}$ and every term $\mathbf{t}$ such that $\mathbf{t} = \mathbf{t} \in \mathbf{\Delta}$.

Clearly $\mathbf{T}$ is a minimal element of Ω; namely, $\mathbf{T} \subseteq \mathbf{\Gamma}$ for every $\mathbf{\Gamma} \in \Omega$. Show that for every $\mathbf{\Gamma} \in \Omega$ and every sentence $\mathbf{A}$ (all of whose constants appear in some sentence of $\mathbf{\Gamma}$) $\vDash_{\mathbf{\Gamma}} \mathbf{A}$ if and only if $\mathbf{A} \in \mathbf{\Gamma}$. *Hint:* This differs from Exercise 20, §18 in that we must show that if $\mathbf{A} \in \mathbf{T}$, then $\vDash_{\mathbf{T}} \mathbf{A}$ (for we do not know yet that $\mathbf{T}$ is regular). For this it suffices to show that $\vDash_{\mathbf{T}} \mathbf{A}$, if $\mathbf{A}$ is an axiom of RA_i (i.e. an instance of 23.6–23.17). For 23.17, show that if $\vDash_{\mathbf{T}} \mathbf{S}_{\mathbf{0}}^{\mathbf{x}} \mathbf{A}|$ and $\vDash_{\mathbf{T}} \forall \mathbf{x}[\mathbf{A} \supset \mathbf{S}_{\mathbf{S(x)}}^{\mathbf{x}} \mathbf{A}|]$ then $\vDash_{\mathbf{T}} \mathbf{S}_{\mathbf{k}_n}^{\mathbf{x}} \mathbf{A}|$ for each $n = 0, 1, 2, \ldots$ and hence $\vDash_{\mathbf{T}} \mathbf{S}_{\mathbf{t}}^{\mathbf{x}} \mathbf{A}|$ for each variable free term $\mathbf{t}$ of RA_i. Note that in proving $\vDash_{\mathbf{\Gamma}} \mathbf{B}$ there are always two cases: the case $\mathbf{\Gamma} = \mathbf{T}$ and the case $\mathbf{\Gamma} \neq \mathbf{T}$.

*11. (1) Show that if $\mathbf{A}$ and $\mathbf{B}$ are sentences of RA_i and $\vdash_i \mathbf{A} \vee \mathbf{B}$ then either $\vDash_i \mathbf{A}$ or $\vdash_i \mathbf{B}$.

(2) Show that if $\exists \mathbf{x} \mathbf{A}$ is a sentence of RA_i and $\vdash_i \exists \mathbf{x} \mathbf{A}$, then $\vDash_i \mathbf{S}_{\mathbf{k}_n}^{\mathbf{x}} \mathbf{A}|$ for some $n = 0, 1, 2, \ldots$.

Hint: Let $\mathbf{T}'$ be the set of sentences $\mathbf{A}$ such that $\vDash_{\mathbf{T}} \mathbf{A}$. Show that $\mathbf{T}'$ is regular. By the preceding exercise $\mathbf{T} = \mathbf{T}'$.

REMARK. Both the results of this exercise fail for RA (see Exercises 3 and 4 of §43).

Chapter 4 ARITHMETIZATION OF SYNTAX

In this chapter we show that RA may serve as a syntactical metalanguage for itself. Since RA has no names for its own formulas but has only names for natural numbers and primitive recursive functions, we must first specify a way of "encoding" the formulas as natural numbers; in other words, a way of using natural numbers as names of formulas. This encoding is called *Gödel numbering*. Our main task is to show that under this encoding the various syntactical functions become primitive recursive.

§26 Finite Sums and Products

We now return to the construction of some primitive recursive functions. In this section we give two methods for constructing new primitive recursive functions from old.

If $a_0, a_1, a_2, \ldots$ is a sequence of natural numbers, then the finite sum $\sum_{k=0}^{n} a_k$ is defined by the equation

$$\sum_{k=0}^{n} a_k = a_0 + a_1 + a_2 + \ldots + a_n.$$

26.1 Proposition. If f is an $(n+1)$-place primitive recursive function $(n \geqslant 0)$, then

$$\sum_{k=0}^{y} f(k, x_1, \ldots, x_n)$$

is a primitive recursive function of $y, x_1, \ldots, x_n$.

PROOF. To simplify the notation, take $n=1$. Then

$$\sum_{k=0}^{0} f(k, x) = f(0, x)$$

$$\sum_{k=0}^{y+1} f(k, x) = f(y+1, x) + \sum_{k=0}^{y} f(k, x). \quad \blacksquare$$

If $a_0, a_1, a_2, \ldots$ is a sequence of natural numbers, then the finite product $\prod_{k=0}^{n} a_k$ is defined by

$$\prod_{k=0}^{n} a_k = a_0 a_1 a_2 \ldots a_n.$$

26.2 Proposition. If f is an $(n+1)$-place primitive recursive function ($n \geqslant 0$), then

$$\prod_{k=0}^{y} f(k, x_1, \ldots, x_n)$$

is a primitive recursive function of $y, x_1, \ldots, x_n$.

PROOF. Take $n=1$ to simplify the notation.

$$\prod_{k=0}^{0} f(k, x) = f(0, x)$$

$$\prod_{k=0}^{y+1} f(k, x) = f(y+1, x) \prod_{k=0}^{y} f(k, x). \quad \blacksquare$$

§27 Primitive Recursive Relations

Recall from §9 that $\mathbf{N}^n$ is the set of n-tuples of natural numbers. An ***n*-place numerical relation** is an n-place relation on $\mathbf{N}$; namely, a subset of $\mathbf{N}^n$. If R is an n-place numerical relation and $a_1, a_2, \ldots, a_n \in \mathbf{N}$ are natural numbers, we shall often write $R(a_1, a_2, \ldots, a_n)$ instead of $(a_1, a_2, \ldots, a_n) \in R$ and not-$R(a_1, a_2, \ldots, a_n)$ instead of $(a_1, a_2, \ldots, a_n) \notin R$.

Let-R be an n-place numerical relation. The **characteristic function of R** is the n-place numerical function K_R defined by

$$\begin{aligned} K_R(a_1, a_2, \ldots, a_n) &= 1 \quad \text{if} \quad R(a_1, a_2, \ldots, a_n) \\ &= 0 \quad \text{otherwise} \end{aligned}$$

for $a_1, a_2, \ldots, a_n \in \mathbf{N}$. The relation R is a **primitive recursive relation** iff K_R is a primitive recursive function. A one-place primitive recursive relation is also called a *primitive recursive set* or a *primitive recursive predicate*.

As in §20 we shall resort to certain abuses of language to simplify the exposition. For example we shall say,

"$x < y$ is a primitive recursive relation in x and y"

rather than

"$\{(x, y) \in \mathbf{N}^2 | x < y\}$ is a primitive recursive relation."

27.1 Proposition. The following are primitive recursive relations in x and y:

1. $x = y$
2. $x \neq y$
3. $x < y$
4. $x \leqslant y$

PROOF. We have $x = y$ if and only if $(x \dot{-} y) + (y \dot{-} x) = 0$, where $x \dot{-} y$ was defined in §20. Hence if K_1 is defined by

$$K_1(x, y) = 1 \dot{-} ((x \dot{-} y) + (y \dot{-} x))$$

then $K_1(x, y)$ is the characteristic function of $x = y$; $K_2(x, y) = 1 \dot{-} K_1(x, y)$ is the characteristic function of $x \neq y$; $K_3(x, y) = 1 \dot{-} (x \dot{-} y)$ is the characteristic function of $x \leqslant y$; and $K_4(x, y) = K_2(x, y) \cdot K_3(x, y)$ is the characteristic function of $x < y$. ∎

The following proposition says that the primitive recursive functions are closed under the operations of the propositional calculus.

27.2 Proposition. If R and S are primitive recursive relations, then so are the following:

1. not-R;
2. R and S;
3. R or S;
4. R implies S;
5. R if and only if S.

PROOF. If $K_{\sim R}$ denotes the characteristic function of not R then

$$K_{\sim R}(a_1, \ldots, a_n) = 1 \dot{-} K_R(a_1, \ldots, a_n)$$

(for $a_1, \ldots, a_n \in N$) and hence $K_{\sim R}$ is primitive recursive. If $K_{R \wedge S}$ denotes the characteristic function of "R and S," then

$$K_{R \wedge S}(a_1, \ldots, a_n) = K_R(a_1, \ldots, a_n) \cdot K_S(a_1, \ldots, a_n)$$

so $K_{R \wedge S}$ is primitive recursive. The remaining propositional connectives can be defined from "not" and "and". Hence $K_{R \vee S} = K_{\sim(\sim R \wedge \sim S)}$ is the characteristic function of "R or S"; $K_{R \supset S} = K_{\sim R \vee S}$ is the characteristic function of "R implies S"; and $K_{R \equiv S} = K_{(R \supset S) \wedge (S \supset R)}$ is the characteristic function of "R if and only if S." ∎

The primitive recursive relations are not closed under quantification; that is, just because $R(x, y)$ is a primitive recursive relation of x and y, it does not necessarily follow that $\forall y R(x, y)$ or $\exists \mathbf{y} R(x, y)$ are primitive recursive relations of x. The primitive recursive relations are closed under **bounded quantification**. We now explain this.

If R is an $(n+1)$-place numerical relation, we define an $(n+1)$-place numerical relation

$$\forall z \leqslant y R(z, x_1, \ldots, x_n)$$

on $y, x_1, \ldots, x_n$; it is true if $R(z, x_1, \ldots, x_n)$ for every $z = 0, 1, \ldots, y$ and false otherwise. Similarly

$$\exists z \leqslant y R(z, x_1, \ldots, x_n)$$

is true if there is a $z = 0, 1, \ldots, y$ such that $R(z, x_1, \ldots, x_n)$ and false otherwise.

27.3 Proposition. If R is an $(n+1)$-place primitive recursive relation, then the relations

$$\forall z \leqslant y R(z, x_1, \ldots, x_n)$$

and

$$\exists z \leqslant y R(z, x_1, \ldots, x_n)$$

are primitive recursive in $y, z_1, \ldots, x_n$.

PROOF. Let K_R be the characteristic function of R and $K_\forall$ the characteristic function of $\forall z \leqslant y R(z, x_1, \ldots, x_n)$. Then

$$K_\forall(y, x_1, \ldots, x_n) = \prod_{z=0}^{y} K_R(z, x_1, \ldots, x_n).$$

Hence $K_\forall$ is primitive recursive by 26.2. This proves that $\forall z \leqslant y R(z, x_1, \ldots, x_n)$ is a primitive recursive relation in $y, x_1, \ldots, x_n$. Now clearly $\exists z \leqslant y R(z, x_1, \ldots, x_n)$ if and only if not-$\forall z \leqslant y$ not-$R(z, x_1, \ldots, x_n)$. Hence, by 27.2 and what we have just proved, $\exists z \leqslant y R(z, x_1, \ldots, x_n)$ is primitive recursive in $y, x_1, \ldots, x_n$. ∎

§28 Definition by Cases and the Least Number Operator

In this section we describe two methods for constructing primitive recursive functions from primitive recursive relations.

28.1 Proposition. Let g and h be n-place primitive recursive functions and R an n-place primitive recursive relation. Then the function f defined by

$$\begin{aligned} f(x_1, \ldots, x_n) &= g(x_1, \ldots, x_n) \quad &&\text{if } R(x_1, \ldots, x_n) \\ &= h(x_1, \ldots, x_n) &&\text{otherwise} \end{aligned}$$

is primitive recursive.

PROOF. Take $n = 1$ to simplify the notation. Then

$$f(x) = K_R(x) \cdot g(x) + (1 \dot{-} K_R(x)) \cdot h(x). \quad \blacksquare$$

Proposition 28.1 admits a simple generalization. The n-place relations $R_1, R_2, \ldots, R_k$ are called *pairwise disjoint* iff no two (distinct) R_i and R_j $(i, j = 1, \ldots, k)$ intersect; that is, if $i \neq j$ and $a_1, a_2, \ldots, a_n \in \mathbf{N}$, then either not-$R_i(a_1, \ldots, a_n)$ or not-$R_j(a_1, \ldots, a_n)$.

28.2 Proposition. Let $R_1, \ldots, R_k$ be pairwise disjoint n-place primitive recursive relations, $g_1, \ldots, g_k, h$ be n-place primitive recursive functions, and f the function defined by

$$\begin{aligned} f(x_1, \ldots, x_n) &= g_1(x_1, \ldots, x_n) \quad &&\text{if } R_1(x_1, \ldots, x_n) \\ &= g_2(x_1, \ldots, x_n) &&\text{if } R_2(x_1, \ldots, x_n) \\ &\ \ \vdots \\ &= g_k(x_1, \ldots, x_n) &&\text{if } R_k(x_1, \ldots, x_n) \\ &= h(x_1, \ldots, x_n) &&\text{otherwise.} \end{aligned}$$

Then f is primitive recursive.

PROOF. Take $n = 1$ for simplicity. Then

$$\begin{aligned} f(x) = K_{R_1}(x) \cdot g_1(x) + \ldots + K_{R_k}(x) \cdot g_k(x) + (1 \dot{-} (K_{R_1}(x) + \ldots \\ + K_{R_k}(x))) \cdot h(x). \quad \blacksquare \end{aligned}$$

If R is an $(n+1)$-place numerical relation, then the $(n+1)$-place numerical function $\mu z \leqslant y R(z, x_1, \ldots, x_n)$ (a function of $y, x_1, \ldots, x_n$) is defined by

$$\begin{aligned} \mu z \leqslant y R(z, x_1, \ldots, x_n) &= \text{the smallest } z \leqslant y \text{ such that } R(z, x_1, \ldots, x_n) \\ &\qquad \text{if } \exists z \leqslant y R(z, x_1, \ldots, x_n); \\ &= 0 \qquad \text{otherwise.} \end{aligned}$$

28.3 Proposition. If R is an $(n+1)$-place primitive recursive relation, then $\mu z \leqslant yR(z, x_1, \ldots, x_n)$ is a primitive recursive function of $y, x_1, \ldots, x_n$.

PROOF.

$$\mu z \leqslant 0R(z, x_1, \ldots, x_n) = 0$$

$$\begin{aligned} \mu z \leqslant y+1R(z, x_1, \ldots, x_n) &= \mu z \leqslant yR(z, x_1, \ldots, x_n) \\ &\quad \text{if } \exists z \leqslant yR(z, x_1, \ldots, x_n); \\ &= y+1 \quad \text{if } R(y+1, x_1, \ldots, x_n) \\ &\quad \text{and not-}\exists z \leqslant yR(z, x_1, \ldots, x_n); \\ &= 0 \quad \text{otherwise.} \end{aligned}$$ ∎

EXERCISES

1. The notation $x|y$ means "x divides y" and holds exactly when there is a natural number z such that $xz = y$. Show that $x|y$ is a primitive recursive two-place relation in x and y.

2. The greatest integer in α is denoted by $[\alpha]$ and is defined in §20 Exercise 4. Define a function p by

$$\begin{aligned} p(x, y) &= [x/y] \quad \text{if } y \neq 0 \\ &= 0 \quad \text{if } y = 0. \end{aligned}$$

Show that p is primitive recursive.

3. For each pair of natural numbers x and y with $y \neq 0$ there exist unique natural numbers $q = q(x, y)$ and $r = r(x, y)$ such that

$$x = q \cdot y + r \quad \text{and} \quad 0 \leqslant r < y.$$

For $y = 0$ define $q(x, 0) = r(x, 0) = 0$. Show that $q(x, y)$ and $r(x, y)$ are primitive recursive functions of x and y.

REMARK. The existence of q and r is called *Euclid's algorithm*. You learned it in grade school when you studied long division; the q stands for "quotient" and the r for "remainder".

4. The *greatest common divisor of x and y* is denoted by (x, y) and is defined to be the largest number z such that $z|x$ and $z|y$. Show that (x, y) is a primitive recursive function of x and y.

5. If α is a real number, then $|\alpha|$, the absolute value of α, is defined by

$$|\alpha| = \alpha \quad \text{if} \quad \alpha \geqslant 0$$
$$= -\alpha \quad \text{if} \quad \alpha < 0.$$

Show that $|x - y|$ is a primitive recursive function of x and y.

6. The notation $x \equiv y \pmod z$ is read "x is congruent to y modulo z" and means $z \mid |x - y|$. Show that it is a primitive recursive relation in x, y, and z.

§29 Prime Numbers

A natural number p is **prime** iff $p \neq 0$, $p \neq 1$ and p is not the product of two smaller numbers. Thus 2, 3, 5, 7, 11, 13, 17, 19, 23, . . . are primes; $4 = 2 \cdot 2$, $6 = 2 \cdot 3$, $8 = 2 \cdot 4$, $9 = 3 \cdot 3$, $12 = 3 \cdot 4$, . . . are not primes. There are infinitely many primes and infinitely many nonprimes.

Every number may be written as the product of its prime factors; this factorization is called the **prime decomposition** of the number. For example

$$420 = 2 \cdot 2 \cdot 3 \cdot 5 \cdot 7 = 2^2 \cdot 3^1 \cdot 5^1 \cdot 7^1$$
$$540 = 2 \cdot 2 \cdot 3 \cdot 3 \cdot 3 \cdot 5 = 2^2 \cdot 3^3 \cdot 5^1$$
$$29{,}106 = 2 \cdot 3 \cdot 3 \cdot 3 \cdot 7 \cdot 7 \cdot 11 = 2^1 \cdot 3^3 \cdot 5^0 \cdot 7^2 \cdot 11^1.$$

The prime decomposition enables us to interpret finite sequences (of natural numbers) as natural numbers and vice versa. This we now explain.

Let $p_1, p_2, p_3, \ldots$ be the sequence of prime numbers; namely $p_1 = 2$, $p_2 = 3$, $p_3 = 5$, $p_4 = 7$, $p_5 = 11$, $p_6 = 13$, $p_7 = 17 \ldots$ and so on. If $a_1, a_2, \ldots, a_n$ is a finite sequence of natural numbers, we define a natural number $\langle a_1, a_2, \ldots, a_n \rangle$ by the equation

$$\langle a_1, a_2, \ldots, a_n \rangle = p_1^{a_1} \cdot p_2^{a_2} \cdot \ldots \cdot p_n^{a_n}.$$

Conversely, given a natural number $x \geqslant 1$ we may define a sequence $(x)_1, (x)_2, (x)_3, \ldots$ by setting $(x)_i$ = exponent of p_i in the prime decomposition of x. In other words, $(x)_i$ is the highest power of p_i which evenly divides x. Of course, if p_i doesn't divide x at all, then $(x)_i = 0$. We see by the definition that

$$(\langle a_1, a_2, \ldots, a_n \rangle)_i = a_i \quad \text{for} \quad i = 1, 2, \ldots, n$$
$$= 0 \quad \text{for} \quad i > n.$$

In the above examples,

$$420 = \langle 2, 1, 1, 1\rangle$$
$$540 = \langle 2, 3, 1\rangle$$
$$29{,}106 = \langle 1, 3, 0, 2, 1\rangle.$$

Note that $\langle a_1, \ldots, a_n\rangle = \langle a_1, \ldots, a_n, 0, 0, \ldots, 0\rangle$ so that

$$540 = \langle 2, 3, 1, 0\rangle = \langle 2, 3, 1, 0, 0, 0\rangle.$$

We also have

$$(29{,}106)_1 = 1$$
$$(29{,}106)_2 = 3$$
$$(29{,}106)_3 = 0$$
$$(29{,}106)_4 = 2$$
$$(29{,}106)_5 = 1$$
$$(29{,}106)_n = 0 \qquad \text{for} \quad n = 6, 7, 8, \ldots$$

In order that p_n and $(x)_n$ be defined for all values of n and x we arbitrarily define[1]

$$p_0 = 1 \qquad (0)_n = 0 \qquad (x)_0 = 0.$$

For the most part, we shall be concerned with finite sequences of positive natural numbers. When such sequences are encoded in a natural number x via the prime decomposition, the length of the sequence may be computed from x; it is denoted by $L(x)$. The number $L(x)$ is the largest n such that p_n evenly divides x. We arbitrarily set $L(0) = 0$ so that L is everywhere defined. Clearly

$$L(\langle a_1, a_2, \ldots, a_n\rangle) = n$$

if and only if $a_n \neq 0$. In the above examples, $L(420) = 4$, $L(540) = 3$, and $L(29{,}106) = 5$.

Now if $a_1, a_2, \ldots, a_n$ and $b_1, b_2, \ldots, b_m$ are finite sequences of positive natural numbers, then the sequence $a_1, a_2, \ldots, a_n, b_1, b_2, \ldots, b_m$ is encoded by the number $\langle a_1, a_2, \ldots, a_n, b_1, b_2, \ldots, b_m\rangle$ which is also denoted by

$$\langle a_1, a_2, \ldots, a_n\rangle * \langle b_1, b_2, \ldots, b_m\rangle.$$

---

[1] The reader is cautioned that some authors start counting with 0 so that 2 is the "zeroth" prime rather than the first prime. Such authors set $p_0 = 2$, $p_1 = 3, \ldots$ and so on. For our purposes it is more convenient to start counting with 1.

In order that $x * y$ be defined for all natural numbers x and y (and not just those representing sequences of positive natural numbers) we define it by the equation

$$x * y = x \cdot \prod_{k=0}^{L(y)} p_{L(x)+k}^{(y)_k}.$$

(Note that the factor corresponding to $k = 0$ in the product is 1.) We see that $x * 0 = x$ if $x > 0$ and $0 * y = 0$ for each y. Of course, it is not generally true that $x * y = y * x$, but $*$ is associative; that is,

$$x * (y * z) = (x * y) * z.$$

For example,

$$\begin{aligned} 63 * 10 &= (3^2 \cdot 7) * (2 \cdot 5) \\ &= \langle 0, 2, 0, 1 \rangle * \langle 1, 0, 1 \rangle \\ &= \langle 0, 2, 0, 1, 1, 0, 1 \rangle \\ &= 2^0 \cdot 3^2 \cdot 5^0 \cdot 7^1 \cdot 11^1 \cdot 13^0 \cdot 17^1 \\ &= 9 \cdot 7 \cdot 11 \cdot 17 \\ &= 11{,}832. \end{aligned}$$

EXERCISES

1. Calculate $p_1, p_2, p_3, \ldots, p_{20}$.

2. Calculate the prime decompositions of 90, 210, 600, 900, 200.

3. Calculate $(90)_1, (90)_2, (90)_3, (90)_4$.

4. Calculate $(x)_i$ for x = 210, 600, 900, 200 and $i = 1, 2, 3, 4$.

5. Calculate $\langle 2, 1, 1 \rangle, \langle 2, 1, 0, 1 \rangle, \langle 2, 1, 1, 0 \rangle, \langle 4, 1 \rangle, \langle 2, 3 \rangle$.

6. Calculate $2 * 3, 3 * 2, 10 * 5, 6 * 10, 10 * 6, 30 * 4, 4 * 30$.

7. Calculate $x * y$ when $x, y = 90, 210, 600, 200, 900$.

EXAMPLE.

$90 = \langle 1, 2, 1 \rangle$ so $90 * 90 = \langle 1, 2, 1, 1, 2, 1 \rangle = 2 \cdot 3^2 \cdot 5 \cdot 7 \cdot 11 \cdot 13^2 \cdot 17.$

§30 Primitive Recursiveness of the Prime Decomposition

In this section we show that the various functions and relations defined in §29 are primitive recursive.

30.1 Proposition. The one-place relation $x|y$, which holds exactly when x (evenly) divides y is primitive recursive.

PROOF.[2] We see that $x|y \Leftrightarrow \exists z \leqslant y[y = x \cdot z]$. ∎

30.2 Proposition. The one place relation *prime* (x), which holds exactly when x is prime, is primitive recursive.

PROOF. Write

$$\textit{prime}\,(x) \Leftrightarrow x \neq 0 \text{ and } x \neq 1 \quad \text{and} \quad \forall y \leqslant x[y = 1 \quad \text{or} \quad y = x \quad \text{or} \quad \text{not } y|x]. \quad ∎$$

30.3 Proposition p_n, the nth prime (with $p_0 = 1$), is primitive recursive in n.

PROOF.

$$p_0 = 1$$
$$p_{n+1} = \mu x \leqslant (p_n)^n + 1\ [\textit{prime}\,(x) \text{ and } p_n < x].$$

To see that the bound $(p_n)^n + 1$ is indeed $\geqslant p_{n+1}$ note that $p_{n+1} \leqslant p_1 \cdot p_2 \cdot p_3 \cdot \ldots \cdot p_n + 1$ since the number on the right is not evenly divisible by any of the primes $p_1, p_2, \ldots, p_n$ and must therefore be divisible by some prime larger than these (or else be itself a prime). Clearly $p_1 \cdot p_2 \cdot \ldots \cdot p_n + 1 \leqslant p_n \cdot p_n \cdot \ldots \cdot p_n + 1 = (p_n)^n + 1$. ∎

30.4 Proposition. $(x)_n$ is a primitive recursive function of x and n.

PROOF.

$$(x)_n = 0 \qquad \text{if} \quad x = 0 \quad \text{or} \quad n = 0;$$
$$= \mu k \leqslant x[p_n{}^k | x \text{ and not } p_n^{k+1} | x] \qquad \text{otherwise.} \quad ∎$$

30.5 Proposition. $L(x)$ is a primitive recursive function of x.

---

[2] The notation $\Leftrightarrow$ is a standard mathematical abbreviation for "if and only if". The boldface brackets are used for punctuation.

PROOF.

$$L(x) = \mu n \leqslant x[p_n | x \text{ and } \forall k \leqslant x \text{ [either } k \leqslant n \text{ or not } p_k | x]]. \blacksquare$$

30.6 Proposition. $x * y$ is a primitive recursive function of x and y.

PROOF. The formula given in §29 to define $x * y$ shows that $x * y$ is primitive recursive. ▮

30.7 Proposition. $\langle x_1, x_2, \ldots, x_n \rangle$ is an n-place primitive recursive function of $x_1, x_2, \ldots, x_n$ (for each $n = 1, 2, \ldots$).

PROOF. The formula given in §29 to define $\langle x_1, x_2, \ldots, x_n \rangle$ shows that it is a recursive function. ▮

§31 Gödel Numbers

In this section we begin our program of arithmetizing RA. We shall assign **Gödel numbers** first to the sixteen primitive symbols of RA, then to the formulas of RA (namely, finite sequences of primitive symbols of RA) and finally to the finite sequences of formulas of RA. Our aim is to show that the syntactic properties (for instance, "being a wff" or "being a proof") are primitive recursive in this interpretation; more precisely, the set of all Gödel numbers of wffs of RA is a primitive recursive set.

Gödel numbers are assigned to the sixteen primitive symbols of RA via the following table:

Z	S	I	|
1	2	3	4
R	C	**0**	v
5	6	7	8
=	⊃	f	∀
9	10	11	12
(	)	[	]
13	14	15	16

If $\mathbf{e}_1\ \mathbf{e}_2 \ldots \mathbf{e}_n$ is a formula of RA (so that each $\mathbf{e}_i$ ($i = 1, \ldots, n$) is a primitive symbol), then the Gödel number of $\mathbf{e}_1\ \mathbf{e}_2 \ldots \mathbf{e}_n$ is denoted by $''\mathbf{e}_1\ \mathbf{e}_2 \ldots \mathbf{e}_n''$ and is defined by the equation

$$''\mathbf{e}_1\ \mathbf{e}_2 \ldots \mathbf{e}_n'' = \langle e_1, e_2, \ldots, e_n \rangle$$

where e_i ($i = 1, 2, \ldots, n$) is the Gödel number of the primitive symbol $\mathbf{e}_i$ as determined by the above table. For example,

$$\begin{aligned} ''\mathrm{RSZ}'' &= \langle 5, 2, 1 \rangle \\ &= 2^5 \cdot 3^2 \cdot 5 = 1440 \end{aligned}$$

and

$$\begin{aligned} ''\supset = \mathrm{ZZ}'' &= \langle 10, 9, 1, 1 \rangle \\ &= 2^{10} \cdot 3^9 \cdot 5^1 \cdot 7^1 \\ &= 712{,}306{,}720 \end{aligned}$$

Finally if $\mathbf{A}_1, \mathbf{A}_2, \ldots, \mathbf{A}_k$ is a sequence of formulas, then the Gödel number of $\mathbf{A}_1, \mathbf{A}_2, \ldots, \mathbf{A}_k$ is

$$\langle ''\mathbf{A}_1'', ''\mathbf{A}_2'', \ldots, ''\mathbf{A}_k'' \rangle.$$

Thus the Gödel number of the sequence ZS, SZ is

$$\begin{aligned} \langle ''\mathrm{ZS}'', ''\mathrm{SZ}'' \rangle &= \langle 2^1\, 3^2, 3^2\, 3^1 \rangle \\ &= \langle 18, 12 \rangle \\ &= 2^{18} \cdot 3^{12}. \end{aligned}$$

Notice that an individual primitive symbol has three Gödel numbers; one when viewed as a primitive symbol, another when viewed as a formula consisting of the one primitive symbol, and a third when viewed as a one-element sequence of formulas. For example, the Gödel number of Z as a primitive symbol is 1; as a formula it is $''\mathrm{Z}'' = 2^1 = 2$; and as a sequence of formulas it is $2^2 = 4$. Similarly SZ has Gödel number $''\mathrm{SZ}'' = 2^2\, 3^1 = 12$ when viewed as a formula and $2^{12} = 4096$ when viewed as a sequence of formulas consisting of one element. We shall always reserve the double primes $''\quad''$ for the Gödel number of a formula; thus $''\mathrm{Z}'' = 2^1 = 2$ and not 1 or 4.

Note also that certain numbers are Gödel numbers of both formulas and sequences of formulas. Thus $2^2\, 3^6$ is the Gödel number of the formula CC and also the sequence of formulas ZZ, ZZ. This will cause no confusion.

The following propositions illustrate the kind of thing we shall be doing in the next few sections.

31.1 Proposition. $''\mathrm{x}_n''$ is a primitive recursive function of n.

PROOF. By (D6) the formula x_n is (v||. . .|). Hence

$$"x_n" = "(v " * \prod_{i=0}^{n} p_i^4 * ")". \quad \blacksquare$$

31.2 Proposition. The one place relation *var* (a), which holds exactly when a is the Gödel number of a variable, is primitive recursive (in a).

PROOF. We have $var(a) \Leftrightarrow \exists n \leqslant a["x_n" = a]$. ∎

31.3 Proposition. $"I_i^n"$ is a primitive recursive function of n and i.

PROOF. Let $\alpha(n)$ be the Gödel number of the index consisting of n strokes. The function α is primitive recursive since

$$\alpha(n) = \prod_{i=0}^{n} p_i^4.$$

Now by (D7)

$$"I_i^n" = "(" * \alpha(n) * "I" * \alpha(i) * ")". \quad \blacksquare$$

EXERCISES

1. Calculate the Gödel numbers of the following formulas:

(1) (|I|)
(2) I_1^1
(3) $S(x_0)$
(4) 0 = 0
(5) [[S
(6) ⊃⊃
(7) [0 = 0 ⊃ 0 = 0]

EXAMPLE. (1) "(|I|)" = ⟨13, 4, 3, 4, 14⟩.
(2) "I_1^1" = "(|I|)" since I_1^1 is an abbreviation for (|I|).

2. Calculate the Gödel numbers of the following sequences of formulas.

(1) 0 = 0
(2) I_1^1, 0 = 0
(3) ⊃⊃, 0, 0
(4) 00, ||, ZS
(5) =, =, = k_1
(6) ⊃⊃

EXAMPLE. (1) "0 = 0" = ⟨7, 9, 7⟩ so that the Gödel number of 0 = 0 (considered as a sequence consisting of one formula) is $\langle\langle 7, 9, 7\rangle\rangle = 2^{\langle 7,9,7\rangle}$.
(2) It is $\langle a, b\rangle = 2^a 3^b$ where $a = \langle 13, 4, 3, 4, 14\rangle$ and $b = \langle 7, 9, 7\rangle$.

3. Is there any number which is both a Gödel number of a primitive symbol, a Gödel number of a formula, and a Gödel number of a sequence of formulas?

4. Give some examples of natural numbers which are not Gödel numbers of formulas. Can two different formulas have the same Gödel number?

§32 Primitive Recursiveness of the Notion of Function Constant

In this section we show that the two-place relation *function* (f, n) which holds exactly when f is the Gödel number of an n-place function constant, is primitive recursive.

A *formation sequence for function constants* is a finite sequence of pairs

$$(\mathbf{f}_1, n_1), (\mathbf{f}_2, n_2), \ldots, (\mathbf{f}_k, n_k)$$

where each $(\mathbf{f}_j, n_j)$ satisfies one of the following conditions:

(1) $(\mathbf{f}_j, n_j)$ is $(\mathrm{Z}, 1)$;

(2) $(\mathbf{f}_j, n_j)$ is $(\mathrm{S}, 1)$;

(3) $(\mathbf{f}_j, n_j)$ is of form (I_i^n, n);

(4) $(\mathbf{f}_j, n_j)$ is of form $(R\mathbf{gh}, n+1)$ where $(\mathbf{g}, n)$ is $(\mathbf{f}_i, n_i)$ for some $i<j$ and $(\mathbf{h}, n+2)$ is $(\mathbf{f}_l, n_l)$ for some $l<j$;

(5) $(\mathbf{f}_j, n_j)$ is of form $(\mathrm{C}\mathbf{h}\mathbf{g}_1 \ldots \mathbf{g}_m, n)$ where $(\mathbf{h}, m)$ is $(\mathbf{f}_i, n_i)$ for some $i<j$ and for each $q=1, 2, \ldots, m$ $(\mathbf{g}_q, n)$ is $(\mathbf{f}_l, n_l)$ for some $l=l(q)<j$.

Compare this definition with the definition of function constant given in §21 (Fcn1)–(Fcn5). A formation sequence for function constants is a kind of proof, according to the rules (Fcn1)–(Fcn5), that a formula is an n-place function constant. Clearly $\mathbf{f}$ is an n-place function constant if and only if there is a formation sequence $(\mathbf{f}_1, n_1), (\mathbf{f}_2, n_2), \ldots, (\mathbf{f}_k, n_k)$ such that $(\mathbf{f}_k, n_k)$ is $(\mathbf{f}, n)$.

We assign the Gödel number

$$\langle\langle ''\mathbf{f}_1'', n_1\rangle, \langle ''\mathbf{f}_2'', n_2\rangle, \ldots, \langle ''\mathbf{f}_k'', n_k\rangle\rangle$$

to the above formation sequence.

32.1 Proposition. *Formfcn* (σ), which holds exactly when σ is the Gödel of a formation sequence for function constants, is primitive recursive in σ.

PROOF. $Formfcn\,(\sigma) \Leftrightarrow \sigma \neq 0$ and $\forall j \leqslant L(\sigma)\,[F_1$ or F_2 or . . . or F_5 or $j=0]$

where F_1 is $(\sigma)_j = \langle "Z", 1\rangle$

F_2 is $(\sigma)_j = \langle "S", 1\rangle$

F_3 is $\exists n \leqslant \sigma\, \exists i \leqslant \sigma [1 \leqslant i$ and $i \leqslant n$ and $(\sigma)_j = \langle "I_i{}^{n}", n\rangle]$

F_4 is $\exists i \leqslant \sigma\, \exists l \leqslant \sigma\, \exists g \leqslant \sigma\, \exists h \leqslant \sigma\, \exists n \leqslant \sigma\;\; [i < j$ and $l < j$ and $(\sigma)_i = \langle g, n\rangle$ and $(\sigma)_l = \langle h, n+2\rangle$ and $(\sigma)_j = \langle "(R" * g * h * ")", n+1\rangle]$.

F_5 is $\exists h \leqslant \sigma\, \exists g \leqslant \sigma\, \exists n \leqslant \sigma\;\; [(\sigma)_j = \langle "(C" * h * g * ")", n\rangle$ *and* $\exists i < j$ $[(\sigma)_i = \langle h, L(g)\rangle]$ *and* $\forall q \leqslant L(g)\, \exists l < j\, [1 \leqslant q$ implies $(\sigma)_l = \langle (g)_q, n\rangle]]$. ∎

32.2 Proposition. The two place relation *function* (f, n), which holds exactly when f is the Gödel number of an n-place function constant, is primitive recursive in f and n.

PROOF. Let $B(f)$ be the primitive recursive function of f defined by

$$B(f) = \prod_{i=0}^{L(f)} p_i^{\langle f, f\rangle}.$$

Then

$$function\,(f, n) \Leftrightarrow \exists \sigma \leqslant B(f)\; [Formfcn\,(\sigma) \text{ and } (\sigma)_{L(\sigma)} = \langle f, n\rangle].$$

We must show that the bound $B(f)$ is sufficiently large; that is, if f is in fact the Gödel number of an n-place function constant, then there is a formation sequence whose last element is (f, n) and whose Gödel number σ is $\leqslant B(f)$. This we now prove.

If $f = \alpha * "I_i{}^{m}" * \beta$, then $m \leqslant f$. But if an m-place function constant $(m > 1)$ occurs somewhere in the definition of a function constant **f**, then a function constant of form $I_i{}^m$ must occur earlier in the definition of **f**, because all other clauses in the definition of function constant do *not* increase the number of places. Thus the number of steps in the definition of **f** is $\leqslant L("\mathbf{f}")$; at each step a function constant of $\leqslant "\mathbf{f}"$ places is being defined; and that function constant, being shorter than **f**, has a Gödel number $\leqslant "\mathbf{f}"$. Hence $B("\mathbf{f}")$ is an upper bound on the Gödel numbers of possible formation sequences for **f**; that is, any formation sequence of function constants whose last element is $(\mathbf{f}, n)$ has Gödel number $\leqslant B("\mathbf{f}")$.

EXERCISE

1. Give formation sequences of function constants for (i.e. whose last member is) each of the following function constants.

   (1) CZS

   (2) $RI_1{}^1CSI_3{}^3$

(3) $(C(RI_1^1(CSI_3^3))I_1^3 I_3^3)$

(4) $RZ(C(RI_1^1(CSI_3^3))I_1^3 I_3^3)$

EXAMPLE. (2) $I_1^1, I_3^3, S, CSI_3^3, RI_1^1 CSI_3^3$.

§33 Primitive Recursiveness of the Notion of Term

In this section we show that the one-place relation term (t), which holds exactly when t is the Gödel number of a term, is primitive recursive. The argument is parallel to that of §14.

A sequence $\mathbf{t}_1, \mathbf{t}_2, \ldots, \mathbf{t}_k$ of terms is called a *formation sequence of terms* iff for every $i = 1, 2, \ldots, k$ one of the following holds:

(1) $\mathbf{t}_i$ is 0;

(2) $\mathbf{t}_i$ is a variable;

(3) $\mathbf{t}_i$ is $\mathbf{f}(\mathbf{s}_1, \mathbf{s}_2, \ldots, \mathbf{s}_n)$ where $\mathbf{f}$ is an n-place function constant and for each $l = 1, 2, \ldots, n$ there is a $j < i$ such that $\mathbf{s}_l$ is $\mathbf{t}_j$.

This should be compared with the definition of the class of terms in §21 (Term 1)–(Term 3). Clearly, a formula is a term if and only if it is the last element of a formation sequence of terms.

33.1 Proposition. *Formterm* (σ), the one-place predicate which holds exactly when σ is the Gödel number of a formation sequence of terms, is primitive recursive.

PROOF. *Formterm* $(\sigma) \Leftrightarrow \sigma \neq 0$ and $\forall i \leqslant L(\sigma)$ $[T_1$ or T_2 or T_3 or $i = 0]$,

where T_1 is $(\sigma)_i = "0"$;

T_2 is *var* $((\sigma)_i)$;

T_3 is $\exists f \leqslant \sigma\, \exists s \leqslant \sigma$ $[$*function* $(f, L(s))$ and $\forall l \leqslant L(s)\, \exists j < i$ $[l = 0$ or $(s)_l = (\sigma)_j]$ and $(\sigma)_i = f * "(" * s * ")"]$.

Recall that the one-place relation *var* (x) was defined in 31.2. ∎

33.2 Proposition. *term* (t), the one-place relation which holds exactly when t is the Gödel number of a term, is primitive recursive.

PROOF.

$$\textit{term}\ (t) \Leftrightarrow \exists \sigma \leqslant \prod_{i=0}^{L(t)} p_i^{\,t}\ [(\sigma)_{L(\sigma)} = t \text{ and } \textit{formterm}\ (\sigma)].$$

We leave as an exercise for the reader the proof that the bound is sufficiently large. ∎

EXERCISE

1. Give formation sequences for each of the following terms.

   (1) CZS(**0**).
   (2) $\mathrm{RI}_1^{\,1}\,\mathrm{CSI}_3^{\,3}$(S(**0**), S(S(**0**))).
   (3) $\mathrm{RI}_1^{\,1}\,\mathrm{CSI}_3^{\,3}(\mathrm{x}_0, \mathrm{x}_1)$.
   (4) $\mathrm{RI}_1^{\,1}\,\mathrm{CSI}_3^{\,3}(\mathrm{x}_1$, S(**0**)).
   (5) $\mathrm{RI}_1^{\,1}\,\mathrm{CSI}_3^{\,3}(\mathrm{S}(\mathrm{x}_1)$, S(S(**0**))).

   EXAMPLE. (4) x_1, **0**, S(**0**), $\mathrm{RI}_1^{\,1}\,\mathrm{CSI}_3^{\,3}(\mathrm{x}_1$, S(**0**)).

§34 Primitive Recursiveness of the Notion of Wff

In this section we show that the one-place relation *wff* (*a*), which holds exactly when *a* is the Gödel number of a wff, is primitive recursive.

A sequence $\mathbf{A}_1, \mathbf{A}_2, \ldots, \mathbf{A}_n$ of wffs is called a *formation sequence of wffs* iff each $\mathbf{A}_i$ ($i = 1, 2, \ldots, n$) satisfies one of the following:

(1) $\mathbf{A}_i$ is $\mathbf{t} = \mathbf{s}$ where **t** and **s** are terms;

(2) $\mathbf{A}_i$ is $\mathfrak{f}$;

(3) $\mathbf{A}_i$ is $[\mathbf{A}_j \supset \mathbf{A}_k]$ where $j, k < i$;

(4) $\mathbf{A}_i$ is $\forall \mathbf{x} \mathbf{A}_j$ where $j < i$.

Compare this definition to the definition of wff given in §21. A formula is a wff if and only if it is the last element in a formation sequence of wffs.

34.1 Proposition. The one-place relation *Formwff* (σ), which holds exactly when σ is the Gödel number of a formation sequence of wffs, is primitive recursive.

PROOF. $\mathit{Formwff}(\sigma) \Leftrightarrow \sigma \neq 0$ and $\forall i \leqslant L(\sigma)$ $[W_1$ or W_2 or W_3 or W_4 or $i = 0]$,

where W_1 is $\exists t \leqslant \sigma\, \exists s \leqslant \sigma$ [*term* (t) and *term* (s) and $(\sigma)_i = t * {''{=}''} * s$];
W_2 is $(\sigma)_i = {''\mathfrak{f}''}$;
W_3 is $\exists j < i\, \exists k < i\, [(\sigma)_i = {''[''} * (\sigma)_j * {''\supset''} * (\sigma)_k * {'']''}]$;
W_4 is $\exists j < i\, \exists x \leqslant \sigma$ [*var* (x) and $(\sigma)_i = {''\forall''} * x * (\sigma)_j$]. ∎

34.2 Proposition. The one-place relation *wff* (a), which holds exactly when a is the Gödel number of a wff, is primitive recursive.

PROOF.

$$wff(a) \Leftrightarrow \exists \sigma \leqslant \prod_{i=0}^{L(a)} p_i^{\,a} \, [Formwff(\sigma) \text{ and } (\sigma)_{L(\sigma)} = a].$$

We leave to the reader the proof that the bound on the quantifier is sufficient. ▮

EXERCISE

1. Give formation sequences for each of the following wffs:

(1) $[\mathfrak{f} \supset \mathbf{0} = \mathbf{0}]$

(2) $[[\mathbf{0} = \mathbf{0} \supset \mathrm{S}(\mathbf{0}) = \mathbf{0}] \supset \mathfrak{f}]$

(3) $\forall \mathrm{x}_0 [\mathbf{0} = \mathbf{0} \supset \mathfrak{f}]$

(4) $[\mathbf{0} = \mathbf{0} \supset \forall \mathrm{x}_0\, \mathrm{S}(\mathrm{x}_0) = \mathbf{0}]$

(5) $[\mathbf{0} = \mathbf{0} \supset [\mathfrak{f} \supset \mathbf{0} = \mathbf{0}]]$

EXAMPLE. (1) $\mathfrak{f}, \mathbf{0} = \mathbf{0}, [\mathfrak{f} \supset \mathbf{0} = \mathbf{0}]$.

§35 Substitution

Define the numerical function *Sub* (x, t, a) by the equations

$$Sub(x, t, a) = "\mathbf{S}_{\mathbf{t}}^{\mathbf{x}} \mathbf{A}|" \quad \text{if } x = "\mathbf{x}", \; t = "\mathbf{t}", \text{ and } a = "\mathbf{A}"$$

where $\mathbf{x}$ is an individual variable, $\mathbf{t}$ a term, and $\mathbf{A}$ a wff

$$= a \quad \text{otherwise.}$$

The main aim of this section is to prove the following proposition.

35.1 Proposition. *Sub* (x, t, a) is a primitive recursive function of x, t, a.

PROOF. This will require several steps. First define the four-place primitive recursive relation

$$occur(a_1, x, a_2, a) \Leftrightarrow wff(a), \; var(x), \text{ and } a = a_1 * x * a_2.$$

The relation holds when a_1 is the Gödel number of that part of a formula to the left of an occurrence of a variable with Gödel number x in a wff with Gödel number a; and a_2 is the Gödel number of that part to the right.

$$\begin{aligned} bound(a_1, x, a_2, a) \Leftrightarrow\ & occur(a_1, x, a_2, a) \text{ and } \exists c_1 \leqslant a\, \exists c_2 \leqslant a \\ & \exists c \leqslant a[a = c_1 * \text{"}\forall\text{"} * x * c * c_2 \text{ and} \\ & wff(c) \text{ and } L(c_1) \leqslant L(a_1) \text{ and } L(c_2) \leqslant L(a_2)]. \end{aligned}$$

This relation holds when the above mentioned occurrence is bound.

$$free(a_1, x, a_2, a) \Leftrightarrow occur(a_1, x, a_2, a) \text{ and } not\text{-}bound(a_1, x, a_2, a).$$

This relation holds when the above mentioned occurrence is free.

$$\begin{aligned} S(x, t, a) = \ & \mu b \leqslant t * a * t[\exists a_1 \leqslant a\, \exists a_2 \leqslant a[free(a_1, x, a_2, a) \\ & \text{and } b = a_1 * t * a_2]] \quad (\text{if } \exists a_1 \leqslant a\, \exists a_2 \leqslant a\, free(a_1, x, a_2, a)); \\ = \ & a \text{ (otherwise)}. \end{aligned}$$

Thus (speaking very loosely) $S(x, t, a)$ replaces one free occurrence of x in a by t when this is possible and leaves a untouched otherwise. Now let

$$S^0(x, t, a) = a$$
$$S^{n+1}(x, t, a) = S(x, t, S^n(x, t, a)).$$

Thus $S^n(x, t, a)$ iterates $S(x, t, a)$. We might think that $S^n(x, t, a) = Sub(x, t, a)$ if n is large enough. This is not quite correct for the term t may itself have occurrences of x which will eventually be replaced by t and so on so that the process does not stop. To overcome this difficulty, we first replace x by a variable which occurs nowhere in a or t and then replace that variable by t.

$$M(x, t, a) = S^{L(a)}(x, \text{"}x_{L(a)+L(t)}\text{"}, a)$$
$$Sub(x, t, a) = S^{L(a)}(\text{"}x_{L(a)+L(t)}\text{"}, t, M(x, t, a)). \quad \blacksquare$$

35.2 Proposition. The three-place relation *freefor* (t, x, a); which holds exactly when t is the Gödel number of a term **t**, x is the Gödel number of a variable **x**, a is the Gödel number of a wff **A**, and **t** is free for **x** in **A**, is a primitive recursive relation of t, x, and a.

PROOF.
$$\begin{aligned} freefor(t, x, a) \Leftrightarrow\ & term(t) \text{ and } var(x) \text{ and } wff(a) \text{ and} \\ & \forall a_1 \leqslant a\, \forall a_2 \leqslant a\, [free(a_1, x, a_2, a) \text{ implies} \\ & \text{not } \exists c_1 \leqslant a\, \exists c_2 \leqslant a\, \exists c \leqslant a\, \exists y \leqslant a \\ & \exists t_1 \leqslant t\, t_2 \leqslant t[wff(c) \text{ and } var(y) \text{ and} \\ & L(c_1) \leqslant L(a_1) \text{ and } L(c_2) \leqslant L(a_2) \text{ and} \\ & a = c_1 * \text{"}\forall\text{"} * y * c * c_2 \text{ and } t = t_1 * y * t_2]]. \quad \blacksquare \end{aligned}$$

35.3 Proposition. The two-place relation *nofree* (x, a), which holds exactly when x is the Gödel number of an individual variable **x**, a is the Gödel number of a wff **A**, and x has no free occurrence in **A**, is primitive recursive in x and a.

PROOF. $nofree\ (x, a) \Leftrightarrow \text{not}\ \exists a_1 \leqslant a\ \exists a_2 \leqslant a\ free\ (a_1, x, a_2, a)$. ∎

The following function will be used in proving the second Gödel theorem.

35.4 Proposition. Let *sub* (x, n, a) be the function whose value is

$$"\mathbf{S}^{\mathbf{x}}_{\mathbf{k}_n}\mathbf{A}|"$$

if a is the Gödel number of a wff **A** (that is, $a = "\mathbf{A}"$), and x is the Gödel number of an individual variable **x** (that is, $x = "\mathbf{x}"$) and whose value is a otherwise. Then *sub* is primitive recursive.

PROOF. First note that $"\mathbf{k}_n"$ is a primitive recursive function of n:

$$"\mathbf{k}_0" = "0" \quad \text{and} \quad "\mathbf{k}_{n+1}" = "S(" * \mathbf{k}_n * ")".$$

Then

$$sub\ (x, n, a) = Sub\ (x, "\mathbf{k}_n", a). \ ∎$$

§36 Deductions

In this section we show that the one place relation *ded* (σ), which holds exactly when σ is the Gödel number of a deduction, is primitive recursive.

36.1 Proposition. The one-place relations $ax_n(w)$ $(n = 1, 2, \ldots, 17)$, which hold exactly when w is the Gödel number of an instance of axion schema 23.n, all are primitive recursive.

PROOF. We shall do the cases $n = 1, 3, 4, 5$, and 11 and leave the remaining cases as exercises for the reader.

$$ax_1(w) \Leftrightarrow \exists a \leqslant w\ \exists b \leqslant w[wff\ (a) \text{ and } wff\ (b) \text{ and } w = "[" * a * " \supset [" * b * " \supset " * a * "]]"]$$

$$ax_3(w) \Leftrightarrow \exists a \leqslant w[wff\ (a) \text{ and } w = "[[[" * a * " \supset \mathfrak{f}] \supset \mathfrak{f}] \supset " * a * "]"]$$

$$ax_4(w) \Leftrightarrow \exists a \leqslant w\ \exists x \leqslant w\ \exists t \leqslant w[wff\ (a) \text{ and } var\ (x) \text{ and } term\ (t) \text{ and } freefor\ (t, x, a) \text{ and } w = "[\forall " * x * a * " \supset " * Sub\ (x, t, a) * "]"]$$

$ax_5(w) \Leftrightarrow \exists a \leqslant w\ \exists b \leqslant w\ \exists x \leqslant w[\mathit{wff}(a)$ and $\mathit{wff}(b)$ and
$\mathit{var}(x)$ and $\mathit{nofree}(x, a)$ and
$w = "[\forall\ " * x * "[" * a * "\supset" * b * "] \subset [" * a * "\supset \forall" * x * b * "]]"]$

$ax_{11}(w) \Leftrightarrow w = "S(x_0) \neq 0".$ ▮

36.2 Proposition. The one-place relation *ded* (σ), which holds exactly when σ is the Gödel number of a deduction, is primitive recursive.

PROOF. $\mathit{ded}(\sigma) \Leftrightarrow \forall i \leqslant L(\sigma)[i = 0$ or $ax_1((\sigma)_i)$ or $ax_2((\sigma)_i)$ or . . . or $ax_{17}((\sigma)_i)]$ or $\exists j < i\ \exists k < i$
$(\sigma)_k = "[" * (\sigma)_j * "\supset" * (\sigma)_i * "]"]$ or $\exists j < i\ \exists x \leqslant \sigma$
$[\mathit{var}(x)$ and $(\sigma)_i = "\forall" * x * (\sigma_j)].$ ▮

36.3 Proposition. The two-place relation *ded* (σ, *a*), which holds exactly when *a* is a Gödel number of a wff and σ is the Gödel number of a deduction whose last element is the wff with Gödel number *a*, is primitive recursive.

PROOF. $\mathit{ded}(\sigma, a) \Leftrightarrow \mathit{ded}(\sigma)$ and $(\sigma)_{L(\sigma)} = a.$ ▮

If we could construct a primitive recursive function $b(a)$ which would be larger than the Gödel number of a deduction of the wff with Gödel number *a* (provided that wff is a theorem), we could show that the predicate *th* (*a*), which holds exactly when *a* is the Gödel number of a theorem, is primitive recursive; for exactly as in §§32–34

$$\mathit{th}(a) \Leftrightarrow \exists \sigma \leqslant b(a)\ \mathit{ded}(\sigma, a).$$

However, there is no such primitive recursive function $b(a)$; in fact, *th* (*a*) is *not* primitive recursive, as we shall see.

Chapter 5 THE INCOMPLETENESS THEOREMS AND OTHER APPLICATIONS OF THE LIAR PARADOX

A form of the liar paradox appears in the New Testament. In Paul's letter to Titus, he writes, "One of themselves [identified by commentators as Epimenides], even a prophet of their own, said, 'The Cretans are always liars, evil beasts, lazy gluttons.' This testimony is true." Paul apparently fails to see the humor in this for he goes on to say that the Cretans (Epimenides presumably included) should be rebuked.

This form of the liar paradox is known as the Epimenides paradox. Indeed, it is not really a paradox at all: a liar is someone who sometimes (but not necessarily always) speaks other than the truth; the most we may conclude from Epimenides' statement is that Epimenides himself is a liar. (For if his statement is true, then Epimenides, being himself a Cretan, is a liar; and if the statement is false, then Epimenides has told us a lie and is thus a liar.)[1]

A better form of the liar paradox is,

"This sentence is false."

If the sentence is true, it is false, and if it is false, it is true. Thus it can be neither true nor false. In this form the liar paradox is a genuine antinomy. The ancients knew of this paradox and devoted a great deal of thought to it. According to the Encyclopedia Britannica, Chrysippus alone is said to have written 28 books about it and there is an ancient epitaph which says that Philetus of Cos died from spending his nights thinking about it.

The best known example of a paradox of this sort in mathematics is due to

---

[1] Actually, we should not conclude even this. For a liar is someone who sometimes utters falsehoods with the intent to deceive. Since we cannot discover Epimenides' intentions from his assertion, this definition of "liar" vindicates him.

Bertrand Russell. Russell's paradox is as follows: Consider the set R of all sets which are not members of themselves. If R is a member of itself, it is not a member of itself; and if R is not a member of itself, it is a member of itself. In his autobiography Russell says, "It seemed unworthy of a grown man to spend his time on such trivialities, but what was I to do?" What he finally did do was write (with A. N. Whitehead) *Principia Mathematica*, a magnificently complicated tome of three volumes which took ten years to complete. *Principia* was supposed to put mathematics once again on firm ground—to save it from the paradoxes. The effort was not entirely satisfactory but is of great historical importance.

In this chapter we shall see that the paradoxes, when properly interpreted in a consistent formal language, always give incompleteness results; that is, results which say that the formal language is incapable of doing certain things (such as proving all true sentences or formulating its own semantics).

EXERCISES

1. Examine the Epimenides paradox in case the word "liar" is taken to mean "a person who never tells the truth".

2. Could there exist a town in which the town barber shaves all men who don't shave themselves? *Hint:* If such a town exists, who shaves the barber?

3. Is there a book which lists in its bibliography precisely those books which do not list themselves in their bibliographies?

§37 The First Gödel Incompleteness Theorem

In §36 we showed that *ded* (σ, a), the two-place relation which holds exactly when σ is the Gödel number of a deduction of a wff whose Gödel number is a, is primitive recursive. Hence, if K_{ded} denotes the characteristic function of this relation, then K_{ded} is primitive recursive (by the definition of primitive recursive relation) and we may construct a function constant $\mathbf{K}_{ded}$ which denotes K_{ded} ($val\,(\mathbf{K}_{\mathbf{ded}}) = K_{ded}$ in the notation of §22). For terms $\mathbf{t}_1$ and $\mathbf{t}_2$ we define a wff $\mathbf{ded}\,(\mathbf{t}_1, \mathbf{t}_2)$ in RA by the definition schema

$$\mathbf{ded}\,(\mathbf{t}_1, \mathbf{t}_2) \rightsquigarrow \mathbf{K}_{\mathbf{ded}}(\mathbf{t}_1, \mathbf{t}_2) = \mathbf{k}_1 .$$

For each term $\mathbf{t}$ we define the wff $\mathbf{Th}\,(\mathbf{t})$ by the definition schema

$$\mathbf{Th}\,(\mathbf{t}) \rightsquigarrow \exists \mathbf{x}\, \mathbf{ded}\,(\mathbf{x}, \mathbf{t})$$

where **x** is a variable (say the one of shortest length) which does not appear in **t**. The intuitive meaning of **ded** ($\mathbf{t}_1$, $\mathbf{t}_2$) is "$\mathbf{t}_1$ is a deduction of $\mathbf{t}_2$" and the intuitive meaning of **Th** (**t**) is "**t** is a theorem of RA."

We also showed (35.4) that the function *sub* (x, n, a), whose value is the Gödel number of the wff which results from the wff with Gödel number a on substituting the numeral $\mathbf{k}_n$ for the individual variable with Gödel number x at free occurrences (if a and x are the Gödel numbers respectively of a wff and a variable), is primitive recursive. Let **sub** be a function constant denoting this primitive recursive function.

Let **I** be the wff defined by

$$\mathbf{I} \rightsquigarrow \sim \mathbf{Th}\ (\mathbf{sub}\ (\mathbf{k}_{''\mathrm{x}_0''}, \mathrm{x}_0, \mathrm{x}_0))$$

where $\mathbf{k}_{''\mathrm{x}_0''}$ is the numeral corresponding to the number $''\mathrm{x}_0''$ which is the Gödel number of the individual variable x_0. Let i be the Gödel number of **I**; namely,

$$i = ''\mathbf{I}''.$$

Let **J** be the sentence

$$\mathbf{J} \rightsquigarrow \sim \mathbf{Th}\ (\mathbf{sub}\ (\mathbf{k}_{''\mathrm{x}_0''}, \mathbf{k}_i, \mathbf{k}_i))$$

and let j be the Gödel number of **J**; namely,

$$j = ''\mathbf{J}''.$$

Observe that **J** is $\mathrm{S}^{\mathrm{x}_0}_{\mathbf{k}_i}\mathbf{I}|$ so that

$$sub\ (''\mathrm{x}_0'', i, i) = j.$$

37.1 First Gödel Incompleteness Theorem. If RA is consistent, then **J** is not a theorem of RA.

REMARK. The reason for the hypothesis that RA is consistent is explained below.

PROOF. Suppose $\vdash$ **J**; that is,

(1) $\quad \vdash \sim \mathbf{Th}\ (\mathbf{sub}\ (\mathbf{k}_{''\mathrm{x}_0''}, \mathbf{k}_i, \mathbf{k}_i))$.

Then there is a deduction of **J**; and if σ is the Gödel number of this deduction, the numerical relation *ded* (σ, a) holds. Hence by the weak completeness theorem (25.5)

$$\vdash \mathbf{ded}\ (\mathbf{k}_\sigma, \mathbf{k}_j).$$

Now by 14.9 $\vdash \exists \mathrm{x}$ **ded** $(\mathrm{x}, \mathbf{k}_j)$; that is,

(2) $\quad \vdash \mathbf{Th}\,(\mathbf{k}_j)$.

On the other hand $\mathbf{J}$ is $\mathrm{S}^{\mathrm{x}_0}_{\mathbf{k}_i}\mathrm{I}|$ so that *sub* ("x_0", i, i) $= j$. Hence by 25.5 again

(3) $\quad \vdash \mathbf{sub}\,(\mathbf{k}_{''\mathrm{x}_0''}, \mathbf{k}_i, \mathbf{k}_i) = \mathbf{k}_j$

so that by (1), (3), and substitutivity of equality (25.6),

(4) $\quad \vdash \sim \mathbf{Th}\,(\mathbf{k}_j)$.

Hence by (2), (4), and *modus ponens* $\vdash \mathfrak{f}$ contradicting the hypothesis that RA is consistent. ▌

The reader may be puzzled as to why we have made it a hypothesis of 37.1 that RA is consistent when, in fact, we have proved that RA is consistent in §24 (24.2). The answer is that the proof which we gave that RA is consistent involved a "nonconstructive" notion, namely the notion of truth ($\mathbf{N} \models \mathbf{A}$), whereas the proof of 37.1 involves no such notion and is in fact constructive. To be more precise, the proof of 37.1 can be formalized in RA itself and in fact we may prove

$$\vdash \mathbf{cons}_{\mathbf{RA}} \supset \sim \mathbf{Th}\,(\mathbf{k}_j)$$

where $\mathbf{cons}_{\mathbf{RA}}$ stands for $\sim \mathbf{Th}\,(\mathbf{k}_{''\mathfrak{f}''})$. This, of course, is simply the statement of 37.1 translated from the English language into the language RA. On the other hand the proof of 24.2 cannot be so formalized; in fact, as we shall see $\mathbf{cons}_{\mathbf{RA}}$ is not a theorem of RA.

We now shall prove an easy corollary. The formal language RA is called **ω inconsistent** iff there is a wff **A** and individual variable **x** such that for every $n = 0, 1, 2, \ldots$

$$\vdash \sim \mathbf{S}^{\mathbf{x}}_{\mathbf{k}_n}\mathbf{A}| \qquad \text{and, in addition,} \qquad \vdash \exists \mathbf{x}\mathbf{A}.$$

The formal language RA is **ω consistent** iff it is not ω inconsistent.

37.2 Corollary. If RA is ω consistent, then $\sim \mathbf{J}$ is not a theorem of RA.

PROOF. If RA is ω consistent, it is clearly consistent; for if it were inconsistent, every wff would be a theorem of RA (since $\vdash \mathfrak{f} \supset \mathbf{A}$).

Suppose that RA is ω consistent. Then by 37.1, **J** is not a theorem; that is, no natural number is the Gödel number of a proof of RA. Thus for each $\sigma = 0, 1, 2, \ldots$ the relation *ded* (σ, j) is false and hence by weak completeness (25.5)

$$\vdash \sim \mathbf{ded}\,(\mathbf{k}_\sigma, \mathbf{k}_j)$$

for each $\sigma = 0, 1, 2, \ldots$. Now by (3) above, 5.22, and substitutivity of equality (7.6)

(5) $\quad \vdash \sim \mathbf{ded}\,(\mathbf{k}_\sigma, \mathbf{sub}\,(\mathbf{k}_{''\mathrm{x}_0''}, \mathbf{k}_i, \mathbf{k}_i))$

for $\sigma = 0, 1, 2, \ldots$. If $\vdash \sim \mathbf{J}$, then

$$\vdash \sim\sim \exists \mathbf{x}\,\mathbf{ded}\,(\mathbf{x}, \mathbf{sub}\,(\mathbf{k}_{''\mathrm{x}_0''}, \mathbf{k}_i, \mathbf{k}_i))$$

and so by the propositional calculus

(6) $\quad \vdash \exists \mathbf{x}\,\mathbf{ded}\,(\mathbf{x}, \mathbf{sub}\,(\mathbf{k}_{''\mathrm{x}_0''}, \mathbf{k}_i, \mathbf{k}_i))$;

Statements (5) and (6) contradict ω consistency. ▮

Now, of course, RA *is* ω consistent. For if **A** is a sentence such that $\vdash \sim \mathbf{S}^{\mathbf{x}}_{\mathbf{k}_n}\mathbf{A}|$ for $n = 0, 1, 2, \ldots$, then by the soundness theorem (24.1) $\mathbf{N} \models \sim \mathbf{S}^{\mathbf{x}}_{\mathbf{k}_n}\mathbf{A}|$ for $n = 0, 1, 2, \ldots$ and hence $\mathbf{N} \models \forall \mathbf{x} \sim A$. If $\vdash \exists \mathbf{x}\mathbf{A}$, then by the soundness theorem again, $\mathbf{N} \models \exists \mathbf{x}\mathbf{A}$ so that $\mathbf{N} \not\models \forall \mathbf{x} \sim \mathbf{A}$, a contradiction. The reason for making the hypothesis of ω-consistency in 37.2 is the same as the reason for making the hypothesis of consistency in 37.1.

Combining 37.1 and the proof of 37.2 we get

37.3 Corollary. $\mathbf{N} \models \mathbf{J}$ but **J** is not a theorem.

Proof. It was shown in 37.2 that

$$\vdash \sim \mathbf{ded}\,(\mathbf{k}_\sigma, \mathbf{sub}\,(\mathbf{k}_{''\mathrm{x}_0''}, \mathbf{k}_i, \mathbf{k}_i))$$

for each $\sigma = 0, 1, 2, \ldots$ and hence by the soundness theorem (24.1),

$$\mathbf{N} \models \sim \mathbf{ded}\,(\mathbf{k}_\sigma, \mathbf{sub}\,(\mathbf{k}_{''\mathrm{x}_0''}, \mathbf{k}_i, \mathbf{k}_i))$$

for each σ. Hence

$$\mathbf{N} \models \sim \exists \mathbf{x}\,\mathbf{ded}\,(\mathbf{x}, \mathbf{sub}\,(\mathbf{k}_{''\mathrm{x}_0''}, \mathbf{k}_i, \mathbf{k}_i))$$

that is, $\mathbf{N} \models \mathbf{J}$. ▮

The intuitive idea of the first Gödel theorem is the liar paradox. The meaning of **J** is this: "The sentence which results from the wff with Gödel number i (namely, **I**) on substituting the numeral $\mathbf{k}_i$ for the variable x_0 is not a theorem." But this sentence is **J** itself! Thus **J** says, "The sentence **J** is not a theorem." Thus if **J** is a theorem it is false; **J** is not a theorem. But then **J** is true. So we have a true sentence which is not provable.

It is, of course, not particularly surprising that a particular set of axioms is not complete. The full impact of the Gödel theorem comes on realizing that the proof of the Gödel theorem works for any reasonable set of axioms for arithmetic. So long as the set of Gödel numbers of axioms is primitive recursive, the Gödel technique can be applied to yield a true sentence which is not provable. Thus if we form a new formal language RA′ by adding **J** as an axiom to the axioms of RA, we have a new two-place primitive recursive predicate *ded′* (σ, a), which says that σ is the Gödel number of a deduction in RA′ of the wff with Gödel number a, and by exactly the same construction as above, we get a sentence $\mathbf{J}'$ which is true but is not a theorem of RA'. Thus, as long as we demand of a formal language that there be an effective procedure for recognizing which sequences of wffs are deductions (i.e. $ded(\sigma, a)$ is primitive recursive), there is no formal language whose theorems consist of precisely the true sentences of arithmetic.

§38 Proof of the First Gödel Theorem in RA

As already remarked in §37, the proof of 37.1 can be carried out in RA. Actually doing this involves translating much of §§26–37 from English into RA. This is tedious but relatively routine work and we shall include here only a sketch of what needs to be done. The reader is invited to supply more details himself.

Let us consider how Lemma 25.1, the key step in the weak completeness theorem (25.5), might be formalized in RA. Given an n-place function constant $\mathbf{f}$ we defined $num_{\mathbf{f}}(a_1, a_2, \ldots, a_n, b)$ (for $a_1, a_2, \ldots, a_n, b \in \mathbf{N}$) by

$$num_{\mathbf{f}}(a_1, a_2, \ldots, a_n, b) = {}''\mathbf{f}(\mathbf{k}_{a_1}, \mathbf{k}_{a_2}, \ldots, \mathbf{k}_{a_n}) = \mathbf{k}_b''.$$

Thus $num_{\mathbf{f}}(a_1, a_2, \ldots, a_n, b)$ is the Gödel number of a certain sentence of RA. One easily sees that for each $\mathbf{f}$ the $num_{\mathbf{f}}$ is an $(n+1)$-place primitive recursive function. Let $\mathbf{num_f}$ be a function constant denoting $num_{\mathbf{f}}$. Then 25.1 becomes 38.1.

38.1 Proposition. For each function constant **f**,

$$\vdash \mathbf{f}(\mathrm{x}_1, \mathrm{x}_2, \ldots, \mathrm{x}_n) = \mathrm{y} \supset \mathbf{Th}\,(\mathbf{num_f}(\mathrm{x}_1, \mathrm{x}_2, \ldots, \mathrm{x}_n, \mathrm{y})).$$

The proof of 38.1 would proceed by induction (in the metalanguage) on the length of **f**. In case **f** is **Rgh** an induction in the object language (that is, an application of axiom schema 23.17) would be used as well. The proof would parallel very closely the proof of 25.1.

The general theorems on primitive recursive functions have analogs in RA. To cite an example, consider the following theorem schema which is an analog of Proposition 28.1 where definition by cases is shown to be primitive recursive.

38.2 Proposition. Let **g**, **h**, and **r** be n-place function constants. Then there is an n-place function constant **f** such that

$$\vdash \mathbf{r}(\mathrm{x}_1, \ldots, \mathrm{x}_n) = \mathbf{k}_1 \supset \mathbf{f}(\mathrm{x}_1, \ldots, \mathrm{x}_n) = \mathbf{g}(\mathrm{x}_1, \ldots, \mathrm{x}_n)$$

and

$$\vdash \mathbf{r}(\mathrm{x}_1, \ldots, \mathrm{x}_n) \neq \mathbf{k}_1 \supset \mathbf{f}(\mathrm{x}_1, \ldots, \mathrm{x}_n) = \mathbf{h}(\mathrm{x}_1, \ldots, \mathrm{x}_n).$$

The other theorems on primitive recursive functions have similar "translations" into RA and the resulting theorem schemas would shorten the work of anyone who would try to supply all the details of a proof of Gödel's first theorem in RA.

Using schemas such as 38.1 and 38.2 one can prove some of the general properties of the predicate **Th** (**x**) in RA. Of course, this necessitates settling on a particular definition of the wff **Th** (**x**); that is, a particular function constant $\mathbf{K}_{\mathbf{ded}}$ denoting the characteristic function of *ded* (σ, a). For example it should be the case that

$$\vdash \mathbf{Th}\,(\mathbf{k}_a) \supset \centerdot\ \mathbf{Th}\,(\mathbf{k}_c) \supset \mathbf{Th}\,(\mathbf{k}_b)$$

whenever a is the Gödel number of a wff **A**, b of a wff **B**, and c of the wff $\mathbf{A} \supset \mathbf{B}$.

Now using these general properties of the predicate **Th** (**x**) one should be able to prove

$$\vdash \mathbf{Th}\,(\mathbf{k}_j) \supset \mathbf{Th}\,(\mathbf{k}_k)$$
$$\vdash \mathbf{Th}\,(\mathbf{k}_j) \supset \mathbf{Th}\,(\mathbf{k}_{k'})$$
$$\vdash \mathbf{Th}\,(\mathbf{k}_k) \supset \centerdot\ \mathbf{Th}\,(\mathbf{k}_{k'}) \supset \mathbf{Th}\,(\mathbf{k}_{''\mathfrak{f}''})$$

where k is the Gödel number of $\mathbf{Th}\,(\mathbf{k}_j)$ and k' is the Gödel number of $\sim \mathbf{Th}\,(\mathbf{k}_j)$. The proofs will parallel the arguments of 37.1. Then by the propositional calculus

$$\vdash \sim \mathbf{Th}\,(\mathbf{k}_{''\mathfrak{f}''}) \supset \sim \mathbf{Th}\,(\mathbf{k}_j)$$

which is the first Gödel theorem expressed in RA.

The arguments in this section are not by any means intended to be rigorous. A careful proof would require much time and space. The details of such a proof would not be quite so oppressive in RA as in some other formulations of arithmetic, but would still be rather complicated.

It is hoped that the reader has gathered some experience in proving theorems in RA and has gained some confidence in the strength of RA as a formal language. He may then be willing to accept on faith that the proof sketched above can actually be carried out. Of course, all this is handwaving, and the only really convincing argument that the proof can be carried out is actually to do it.

§39 The Second Gödel Incompleteness Theorem

We define the sentence $\mathbf{cons}_{\mathrm{RA}}$ by:

$$\mathbf{cons}_{\mathrm{RA}} \rightsquigarrow \sim \mathbf{Th}\,(\mathbf{k}_{''\mathfrak{f}''}).$$

The intuitive meaning of the sentence $\mathbf{cons}_{\mathrm{RA}}$ is "$\mathfrak{f}$ is not a theorem of RA"; in other words, "RA is consistent".

The first Gödel theorem says that there are true sentences which are not theorems. The second Gödel theorem says that $\mathbf{cons}_{RA}$ is such a sentence.

39.1 Second Gödel Incompleteness Theorem. If RA is consistent, then $\mathbf{cons}_{RA}$ is not a theorem of RA.

PROOF. We shall assume (see §38) that the first Gödel theorem can be proved in RA; that is

$$\vdash \mathbf{cons}_{RA} \supset \sim \mathbf{Th}\,(\mathbf{k}_j).$$

Suppose $\vdash \mathbf{cons}_{RA}$. Then by *modus ponens* $\vdash \sim \mathbf{Th}\,(\mathbf{k}_j)$. Now, as in the proof of 37.1,

$$\vdash \mathbf{sub}\,(\mathbf{k}_{''x_0''}, \mathbf{k}_i, \mathbf{k}_i) = \mathbf{k}_j$$

and so by substitutivity of equality

$$\vdash \sim \mathbf{Th}\,(\mathbf{sub}\,(\mathbf{k}_{''x_0''}, \mathbf{k}_i, \mathbf{k}_i))$$

that is, $\vdash \mathbf{J}$. But, if RA is consistent, this is impossible by the first Gödel theorem. Hence the assumption that $\vdash \mathbf{cons}_{RA}$ leads to a contradiction; hence $\mathbf{cons}_{RA}$ is not a theorem of RA (if RA is consistent). ▮

Analogous to 37.2 we have 39.2.

39.2 Corollary. If RA is ω consistent, then $\sim \mathbf{cons}_{RA}$ is not a theorem of RA.

PROOF. Suppose RA is ω consistent. Then RA is consistent and $\mathfrak{f}$ is not a theorem of RA. Hence for each $\sigma = 0, 1, 2, \ldots, \sigma$ is not the Gödel number of a proof of $\mathfrak{f}$; that is, *ded* $(\sigma, ''\mathfrak{f}'')$ is false. By weak completeness

$$\vdash \sim \mathbf{ded}\,(\mathbf{k}_\sigma, \mathbf{k}_{''\mathfrak{f}''})$$

for each $\sigma = 0, 1, 2, \ldots$. If $\vdash \sim \mathbf{cons}_{RA}$, then by propositional calculus,

$$\vdash \exists \mathbf{x}\, \mathbf{ded}\,(\mathbf{x}, \mathbf{k}_{''\mathfrak{f}''})$$

contradicting ω consistency. ▮

The following corollary should be compared with 37.3.

39.3 Corollary. $\mathbf{N} \models \mathbf{cons}_{RA}$ but $\mathbf{cons}_{RA}$ is not a theorem of RA.

The proof of 39.3 is not constructive; indeed the notion of $\mathbf{N} \models \mathbf{A}$ cannot be expressed by a formula of RA, as we shall see.

As was the case with the first Gödel theorem, the force of the second Gödel theorem is that it holds for any reasonable formulation of arithmetic. Indeed, the argument works for any formal language which is powerful enough to do very simple arithmetic. Thus no consistent formal language (adequate for arithmetic) is strong enough to prove its own consistency. Any consistency proof must use principles which are too strong to be expressed in the language being proved consistent.

Therefore, if someone has doubts about the consistency of some formal language (say RA), then those doubts, in a sense, can never be resolved (unless of course they are correct), for any proof that RA is consistent would use principles more open to doubt than the axioms of RA themselves.

§40 Tarski's Theorem

According to the *correspondence theory of truth*, first advanced by Aristotle, a sentence is true if and only if it "corresponds" to the facts. For example, the sentence "it is snowing" is true if and only if it is snowing. A theory of truth may have a lot more to it than this, but certainly this property should hold for any definition of truth. Tarski's theorem, which we state and prove below, can be interpreted as saying that no consistent formal language can be used to adequately formulate a theory of truth which applies to itself; more simply, no consistent formal language is adequate for its own semantics.

In place of the substitution operator, $\mathbf{S}_{\mathbf{t}}^{\mathbf{x}}\mathbf{A}|$, we shall use a simpler notation in this section. The notations $\mathbf{A}(\mathbf{x})$, $\mathbf{B}(\mathbf{x})$, . . . shall be used for wffs with a free variable $\mathbf{x}$. Then, if $\mathbf{t}$ is a term, $\mathbf{A}(\mathbf{t})$ shall denote the result of replacing each free occurrence of $\mathbf{x}$ in $\mathbf{A}(\mathbf{x})$ by $\mathbf{t}$; that is, $\mathbf{A}(\mathbf{t})$ is $\mathbf{S}_{\mathbf{t}}^{\mathbf{x}}\mathbf{A}(\mathbf{x})|$.

40.1 Tarski's Theorem. If RA is consistent, then there is no wff $\mathbf{T}(\mathbf{x})$ of RA having $\mathbf{x}$ as its only free variable such that

$$\vdash \mathbf{T}(\mathbf{k}_{''\mathbf{A}''}) \equiv \mathbf{A}$$

for every sentence $\mathbf{A}$ of RA.

REMARK. If $\mathbf{A}$ is the sentence $2 + 2 = 4$, then the meaning of the sentence $\mathbf{T}(\mathbf{k}_{''\mathbf{A}''}) \equiv \mathbf{A}$ would be, "The sentence "$2+2=4$" is true if and only if $2+2=4$." Thus the wff $\mathbf{T}(\mathbf{x})$, if it existed, would exhibit the minimal property for a definition of truth discussed above.

PROOF. The proof is another application of the liar paradox and is exactly like the proof of the first Gödel incompleteness theorem (37.1).

Suppose such a formula $\mathbf{T}(\mathbf{x})$ does exist. We shall show that RA is inconsistent. Let **sub** be the function constant of §37. Let i be the Gödel number of the wff

$$\sim \mathbf{T}(\mathbf{sub}\,(\mathbf{k}_{''\mathrm{x}_0''}, \mathrm{x}_0, \mathrm{x}_0))$$

Let **J** be the sentence

$$\sim \mathbf{T}(\mathbf{sub}\,(\mathbf{k}_{''x_0''}, \mathbf{k}_i, \mathbf{k}_i))$$

and let j be the Gödel number of **J** (namely, $j = ''\mathbf{J}''$). According to our assumption

$$\vdash \mathbf{T}(\mathbf{k}_j) \equiv \mathbf{J}.$$

But since $j = sub\,(''x_0'', i, i)$ we have (as in §37)

$$\vdash \mathbf{k}_j = \mathbf{sub}\,(\mathbf{k}_{''x_0''}, \mathbf{k}_i, \mathbf{k}_i).$$

Hence by substitutivity of equality

$$\vdash \mathbf{T}(\mathbf{sub}\,(\mathbf{k}_{''x_0''}, \mathbf{k}_i, \mathbf{k}_i)) \equiv \mathbf{J}$$

that is,

$$\vdash \mathbf{T}(\mathbf{sub}\,(\mathbf{k}_{''x_0''}, \mathbf{k}_i, \mathbf{k}_i)) \equiv \sim \mathbf{T}(\mathbf{sub}\,(\mathbf{k}_{''x_0''}, \mathbf{k}_i, \mathbf{k}_i)).$$

Whence by the propositional calculus $\vdash \mathfrak{f}$; in other words, RA is inconsistent. ∎

As was the case with the incompleteness theorems, the argument in Tarski's theorem works for any formal language adequate for arithmetic.

We remark here that "limited" truth definitions are possible. In fact for each $n = 0, 1, 2, \ldots$ there is a wff $\mathbf{T}_n(\mathbf{x})$ of RA such that

$$\vdash \mathbf{T}_n(\mathbf{k}_{''\mathbf{A}''}) \equiv \mathbf{A}$$

for every wff **A** of RA having at most n quantifiers (n occurrences of $\forall$). See Exercise 9, §43.

We also remark that if RA is enlarged to a language RA_2 (second-order recursive arithmetic; see Exercise 10, §43) by adding variables ranging over sets of natural numbers, quantifiers over these variables, and suitable new axioms, then there is a wff $\mathbf{T}(\mathbf{x})$ of RA_2 such that for each sentence **A** of RA

$$RA_2 \vdash \mathbf{T}(\mathbf{k}_{''\mathbf{A}''}) \equiv \mathbf{A}.$$

(This will, of course, fail in general if **A** is a sentence of RA_2 by Tarski's Theorem for RA_2.) In RA_2 the soundness theorem (24.1) for RA may be formalized and proved:

$$RA_2 \vdash \mathbf{Th}\,(\mathbf{x}) \supset \mathbf{T}(\mathbf{x}).$$

Then since

$$RA_2 \vdash \mathbf{T}(\mathbf{k}_{''\mathfrak{f}''}) \equiv \mathfrak{f}$$

we have

$$RA_2 \vdash \sim \mathbf{T}(\mathbf{k}_{''\mathfrak{f}''})$$

and hence

$$\mathrm{RA}_2 \vdash \sim \mathbf{Th}\,(\mathbf{k}_{''\mathbf{f}''})$$

that is,

$$\mathrm{RA}_2 \vdash \mathbf{cons}_{\mathrm{RA}}.$$

Thus the consistency of RA can be proved in RA_2, but not in RA (see §39). The formal language RA_2 is a language strong enough for the semantics of RA; but we have not circumvented the liar paradox: RA_2 is not strong enough to discuss its own semantics. See Exercise 11, §43 for the definition of $\mathbf{T}(\mathbf{x})$.

§41 Arithmetical Sets

A set X of natural numbers is **arithmetical** iff there is a wff $\mathbf{A}(\mathbf{x})$ of RA with a single free variable $\mathbf{x}$ such that

$$X = \{n \in \mathbf{N} \mid \mathbf{N} \models \mathbf{A}(\mathbf{k}_n)\};$$

in other words, X is arithmetical iff there is a wff $\mathbf{A}(\mathbf{x})$ such that X is the set of all natural numbers n such that the sentence $\mathbf{A}(\mathbf{k}_n)$ is true. If this is the case, the wff $\mathbf{A}(\mathbf{x})$ is said to *define* the set X. We are using the notation of the previous section: $\mathbf{A}(\mathbf{k}_n)$ is $\mathbf{S}^{\mathbf{x}}_{\mathbf{k}_n}\mathbf{A}(\mathbf{x})|$.

The set $\mathbf{N}$ of all natural numbers is arithmetical since

$$\mathbf{N} = \{n \in \mathbf{N} \mid \mathbf{N} \models \mathbf{k}_n = \mathbf{k}_n\}.$$

The empty set $\emptyset$ is arithmetical since

$$\emptyset = \{n \in \mathbf{N} \mid \mathbf{N} \models \mathbf{k}_n \neq \mathbf{k}_n\}.$$

The set E of even natural numbers is arithmetical since

$$E = \{n \in \mathbf{N} \mid \mathbf{N} \models \exists \mathrm{x} \,\centerdot\, \mathbf{k}_n = \mathrm{x} + \mathrm{x}\}.$$

More generally, any primitive recursive set S of natural numbers is arithmetical since

$$S = \{n \in \mathbf{N} \mid \mathbf{N} \models \mathbf{K}_S(\mathbf{k}_n) = \mathbf{k}_1\}$$

where $\mathbf{K}_S$ is a function constant of RA denoting the characteristic function K_S of S.

Let T be the set of all Gödel numbers of true sentences of RA:

$$T = \{''\mathbf{A}'' \mid \mathbf{N} \models \mathbf{A}\}.$$

Our next application of the liar paradox follows.

41.1 Theorem. The set T is not arithmetical.

PROOF. Suppose T is arithmetical; then there is a wff $\mathbf{T(x)}$ with a single free variable $\mathbf{x}$ such that

(∗) $T = \{n \in \mathbf{N} | \mathbf{N} \models \mathbf{T(k}_n\mathbf{)}\}$.

Let i be the Gödel number of the wff

$$\sim \mathbf{T(sub\,(k}_{"x_0"}, \mathrm{x}_0, \mathrm{x}_0))$$

where **sub** is the function constant of §37. Let **J** be the sentence

$$\sim \mathbf{T(sub\,(k}_{"x_0"}, \mathbf{k}_i, \mathbf{k}_i))$$

and let j be the Gödel number of $\mathbf{J}$ ($j = "\mathbf{J}"$). Then $j = sub\,("x_0", i, i)$ so that

$$\mathbf{N} \models \mathbf{k}_j = \mathbf{sub\,(k}_{"x_0"}, \mathbf{k}_i, \mathbf{k}_i).$$

Suppose $j \in T$. Then by (∗) we obtain $\mathbf{N} \models \mathbf{T(k}_j)$. Hence

$\mathbf{N} \models \mathbf{T(sub\,(k}_{"x_0"}, \mathbf{k}_i, \mathbf{k}_i))$; namely $\mathbf{N} \not\models \mathbf{J}$; namely $j \notin T$.

Suppose, on the other hand, $j \notin T$. Then $\mathbf{N} \not\models \mathbf{J}$; that is

$\mathbf{N} \models \mathbf{T(sub\,(k}_{"x_0"}, \mathbf{k}_i, \mathbf{k}_i))$. Hence $\mathbf{N} \models \mathbf{T(k}_j)$. Hence by (∗) we obtain $j \in T$.

Thus the assumptions $j \in T$ and $j \notin T$ both lead to contradiction. Hence the original assumption that T is arithmetical is incorrect. ▮

This result should be compared with Tarski's theorem (40.1); it differs from 40.1 in that it asserts the nonexistence of a formula having a particular semantic property (namely the property of defining a certain set of natural numbers) whereas 40.1 asserts the nonexistence of a formula having certain syntactic properties (namely the property that a particular schema of sentences of RA be a theorem schema). Nonetheless the idea behind both theorems is the same: the property of being a true sentence of RA is not expressible in the formal language RA.

EXERCISE

1. Prove 40.1 directly from 41.1. *Hint:* If $\vdash \mathbf{T(k}_{"A"}) \equiv \mathbf{A}$ for each sentence $\mathbf{A}$ show that $T = \{n \in \mathbf{N} | \mathbf{N} \models \mathbf{T(k}_n)\} \cap W$ where W is the set of Gödel numbers of sentences of RA.

§42 Recursive Sets and Decision Procedures

If X is a set of natural numbers, then the *complement* of X is denoted by $\mathbf{N}\backslash X$ and is the set of natural numbers which are not elements of X:

$$\mathbf{N}\backslash X = \{n \in \mathbf{N} | n \notin X\}.$$

A set X of natural numbers is **recursively enumerable** iff either X is empty or there is a primitive recursive function f such that the numbers $f(0), f(1), f(2), \ldots$ are precisely the elements of X:

$$(*) \qquad X = \{f(n) | n \in \mathbf{N}\}.$$

When Eq. (*) holds we say the function f **enumerates** the set X; note that we allow repetitions in the enumeration. The same set may be enumerated by different functions. For example if X is the set of perfect squares and f is the square function $[f(n) = n^2]$ then clearly f enumerates X. On the other hand the function f_1 defined by the equations

$$\begin{aligned} f_1(n) &= n && \text{if } n \text{ is a square} \\ &= 16 && \text{otherwise} \end{aligned}$$

also enumerates X (but with the perfect square 16 repeated infinitely many times in the enumeration).

A set X is **recursive** iff both X and $\mathbf{N} \backslash X$ are recursively enumerable.

If X is a recursive set then there is an *algorithm* or *decision procedure* for deciding whether or not $n \in X$ for a natural number n; more precisely, there is a procedure which, when applied to a natural number n, answers the question, "Is n a member of X?" The procedure is this: let f and g be primitive recursive functions enumerating X and $\mathbf{N} \backslash X$ respectively. Compute the sequence of numbers

$$f(0), g(0), f(1), g(1), f(2), g(2), \ldots$$

Every number appears in this sequence and, in particular, the number n appears. When n appears, stop. If $n = f(k)$, then $n \in X$; and if $n = g(k)$, then $n \notin X$ $(n \in \mathbf{N} \backslash X)$. Of course, if $X = \mathbf{N}$ or $X = \emptyset$, then the algorithm is trivial: in the first case the algorithm for answering the question "is $n \in X$?" is to say "yes"; in the second case, to say "no."

For example, the set X of perfect squares is recursive. To see this let f be the square function $(f(n) = n^2)$ and let g be the function defined by

$$\begin{aligned} g(n) &= 2 && \text{if } \exists x \leqslant n\, [x^2 = n] \\ &= n && \text{otherwise.} \end{aligned}$$

Then f enumerates X and g enumerates $\mathbf{N} \backslash X$ (notice that $2 \notin X$ since 2 is not a perfect square). Clearly both f and g are primitive recursive; thus X is a recursive set.

Now let us decide if $25 \in X$. According to the procedure outlined above we compute:

$$\begin{array}{llll} f(0) = 0 & g(0) = 2 & f(1) = 1 & g(1) = 2 \\ f(2) = 4 & g(2) = 2 & f(3) = 9 & g(3) = 3 \\ f(4) = 16 & g(4) = 2 & f(5) = 25 & \end{array}$$

The number 25 has appeared in the sequence, so we stop. Then since $25 = f(5)$, we conclude that $25 \in X$.

Now let us decide whether $6 \in X$. We compute

$$\begin{array}{llll} f(0)=0 & g(0)=2 & f(1)=1 & g(1)=2 \\ f(2)=4 & g(2)=2 & f(3)=9 & g(3)=3 \\ f(4)=16 & g(4)=2 & f(5)=25 & g(5)=5 \\ f(6)=36 & g(6)=6 & & \end{array}$$

The number 6 has appeared in the sequence, so we stop. Since $g(6) = 6$, we conclude that $6 \notin X$.

Of course, this is a very clumsy and inefficient algorithm; a more efficient algorithm would be to calculate the numbers $0^2, 1^2, 2^2, 3^2, 4^2, \ldots, n^2$ and see if n appears in the list. But clumsy or no, it is an algorithm and it always yields an answer after a finite number of steps.

Now, the above definition of the notion of recursive set is only one of several equivalent definitions. Some of the other definitions are much closer to our intuitive idea of what an algorithm is (for example, definitions via *Turing machines* or the *equational calculus*). We shall not consider these other definitions here, but shall merely remark that they all determine the same class of sets (the class of recursive sets).[2]

Since the various attempts to make precise the notion of an algorithm or "decidable set" all lead to the class of recursive sets, mathematicians generally accept the notion of recursive set as the precise definition of a decidable problem. Of course, in order to apply this definition to a problem not directly concerned with numbers, one must first encode the problem in the form "given a natural number n, is $n \in X$?". This is done via the technique of Gödel numbering. The thesis that the mathematical notion of recursiveness makes precise the intuitive notion of effective decidability is known as *Church's thesis*.

We illustrate this with the following theorem.

42.1 Theorem. Let T_0 be the set of Gödel numbers of those sentences of RA which (1) contain no variables and (2) are theorems of RA. Then T_0 is recursive.

PROOF. Let $R(\sigma)$ be the one place relation which holds exactly when σ is the Gödel number of a deduction in RA whose last element is a sentence

---

[2] The interested reader should consult the excellent book by Hans Hermes: *Enumerability, Decidability, and Computability* (Springer-Verlag, New York, 1965).

without variables. Via the techniques developed in Chapter 4, R is a primitive recursive relation. We define a primitive recursive function f by

$$f(\sigma) = (\sigma)_{L(\sigma)} \quad \text{if} \quad R(\sigma)$$
$$= "0 = 0" \quad \text{otherwise.}$$

Clearly f enumerates T_0.

Now let $Q(a)$ be the one place relation which holds exactly when a is the Gödel number of a sentence without variables. The relation Q is primitive recursive and if the function h is defined by

$$h(n) = 0 \quad \text{if} \quad Q(a)$$
$$= n \quad \text{otherwise}$$

then $h(0), h(1), h(2), \ldots$ are precisely those numbers which are not Gödel numbers of sentences without variables. (Note that 0 is not a Gödel number.)

Define a function q by

$$q(b) = "\mathbf{A}" \quad \text{if} \quad b = "{\sim}\mathbf{A}"$$
$$= 0 \quad \text{otherwise.}$$

Then the reader may show that q is primitive recursive. Finally define g by

$$g(2n) = h(n)$$
$$g(2n+1) = q((n)_{L(n)}) \quad \text{if} \quad R(n)$$
$$g(2n+1) = 0 \quad \text{otherwise.}$$

The reader may show that g is primitive recursive. Then the numbers $g(0)$, $g(1)$, $g(2), \ldots$ are those numbers a such that either (1) a is not the Gödel number of a sentence without variables or (2) a is the Gödel number of a sentence without variables whose negation is a theorem. In view of the weak completeness theorem (25.5) every sentence without variables is either a theorem or the negation of a theorem; hence g enumerates $\mathbf{N} \backslash T_0$. ▌

According to Church's thesis we have shown that the problem of deciding whether a given number is the Gödel number of a theorem of RA without variables is effectively decidable; that is, there is an algorithm for settling the problem. Speaking more loosely, we may say that there is an algorithm for deciding if a sentence without variables is a theorem of RA; indeed given such a sentence $\mathbf{A}$ we compute its Gödel number $"\mathbf{A}"$ and then decide if $"\mathbf{A}" \in T_0$.

An algorithm for settling this last question may be described simply as follows: given a sentence $\mathbf{A}$ without variables, enumerate the deductions of RA in some order (for instance, by order of increasing Gödel number). Since either $\vdash$ **A** or $\vdash \sim$**A**, a deduction of **A** of $\sim$**A** eventually occurs in the enumeration. When this happens, stop. If the deduction is of **A**, then $\vdash$ **A**; if the deduction is of $\sim$**A**, then **A** is not a theorem. Indeed this is the idea behind the proof of 42.1.

We remark here that every primitive recursive set (i.e., a set whose characteristic function is primitive recursive) is recursive, but the converse is not true. In fact, the set T_0 of 42.1 is not primitive recursive (see Exercise 5, §43).

EXERCISE

1. Show that every recursive set is recursively enumerable and every recursively enumerable set is arithmetical.

§43 Church's Theorem for RA

The importance of making the notion of effective decidability precise (§42) lies not so much in positive results like 42.1 but in negative results like 43.1 that follows. To show that a problem is effectively solvable an intuitive algorithm is as convincing and frequently more useful than a proof that a certain set is recursive. However, showing that a problem is not effectively solvable (i.e., showing the nonexistence of an algorithm) requires a precise definition of the notion of algorithm. As our first unsolvability result (and next application of the liar paradox) we prove 43.1.

43.1 Church's Theorem for RA. Let *Th* be the set of Gödel numbers of theorems of RA:

$$Th = \{''\mathbf{A}'' \mid \vdash \mathbf{A}\}.$$

Then *Th* is recursively enumerable but (if RA is ω consistent) not recursive.

PROOF. In 36.2 it is shown that the one-place relation *ded* (σ) which holds exactly when σ is the number of a deduction in RA is primitive recursive. Define a primitive recursive function *f* by

$$\begin{aligned} f(\sigma) &= (\sigma)_{L(\sigma)} && \text{if } \; ded(\sigma) \\ &= ''0 = 0'' && \text{otherwise.} \end{aligned}$$

The function *f* clearly enumerates *Th*. Thus *Th* is recursively enumerable.

Now suppose *Th* is recursive; that is, $\mathbf{N}\backslash Th$ is recursively enumerable. Then there is a primitive recursive function *g* which enumerates $\mathbf{N}\backslash Th$. Let **g** be a function constant denoting *g*. Let *i* be the Gödel number of the wff

$$\exists \mathrm{x}_1 \centerdot \mathbf{g}(\mathrm{x}_1) = \mathbf{sub}\,(\mathbf{k}_{''\mathrm{x}_0''}, \mathrm{x}_0, \mathrm{x}_0).$$

(Here **sub** is the function constant introduced in §37.) Let **J** be the sentence

$$\exists x_1 \centerdot \mathbf{g}(x_1) = \mathbf{sub}\,(\mathbf{k}_{''x_0''}, \mathbf{k}_i, \mathbf{k}_i)$$

and j be the Gödel number of **J** ($j = ''\mathbf{J}''$).

Suppose **J** is not a theorem; that is, $j \in \mathrm{N}\backslash Th$. Then for some integer n, $g(n) = j$. Hence by weak completeness (25.5)

$$\vdash \mathbf{g}(\mathbf{k}_n) = \mathbf{k}_j.$$

As in §37

$$\vdash \mathbf{sub}\,(\mathbf{k}_{''x_0''}, \mathbf{k}_i, \mathbf{k}_i) = \mathbf{k}_j$$

so by substitutivity of equality (28.6),

$$\vdash \mathbf{g}(\mathbf{k}_n) = \mathbf{sub}\,(\mathbf{k}_{''x_0''}, \mathbf{k}_i, \mathbf{k}_i)$$

and hence by 14.9

$$\vdash \exists x_1 \centerdot \mathbf{g}(x_1) = \mathbf{sub}\,(\mathbf{k}_{''x_0''}, \mathbf{k}_i, \mathbf{k}_i)$$

or $\vdash$ **J**. The assumption that **J** is not a theorem leads to a contradiction.

Very well then, assume $\vdash$ **J**. Then $j \in Th$ so $j \notin \mathrm{N}\backslash Th$ and for each n, $g(n) \neq j$. By weak completeness (25.5)

$$\vdash \mathbf{g}(\mathbf{k}_n) \neq \mathbf{k}_j$$

and hence

$$\vdash \mathbf{g}(\mathbf{k}_n) \neq \mathbf{sub}\,(\mathbf{k}_{''x_0''}, \mathbf{k}_i, \mathbf{k}_i)$$

for $n = 0, 1, 2, \ldots$. This contradicts ω consistency. Thus the assumption that Th is recursive is incorrect. ▌

Church's Theorem means that there is no effective procedure or algorithm for deciding if a wff of RA is a theorem. This also holds for most of the languages L($\mathfrak{S}$, X) of Chapter 2 (see Exercises 11–15 of §56).

EXERCISES

*1. (Rosser's Extension of the Gödel Incompleteness Theorem).

The abbreviation $\mathbf{t} \leqslant \mathbf{s}$ was introduced in Exercise 3 of §24. Let *neg* be a primitive recursive function such that *neg* ($''\mathbf{A}''$) = $''{\sim}\mathbf{A}''$ for each wff **A** and let **neg** be a function constant denoting *neg*. Let **I** be the wff given by

$$\mathbf{I} \rightsquigarrow \forall x_1 \centerdot \mathbf{ded}\,(x_1, \mathbf{sub}\,(\mathbf{k}_{''x_0''}, x_0, x_0)) \supset \exists x_2 \centerdot x_2 \leqslant x_1 \wedge \mathbf{ded}\,(x_2, \mathbf{neg}\,(\mathbf{sub}\,(\mathbf{k}_{''x_0''}, x_0, x_0)))$$

and let i be the Gödel number of $\mathbf{I}$ ($i = {}''\mathbf{I}''$). Define $\mathbf{J}$ by

$$\mathbf{J} \rightsquigarrow \mathbf{S}^{\mathbf{x}_0}_{\mathbf{k}_i}\mathbf{I}|.$$

Show that if RA is consistent, then neither $\mathbf{J}$ not $\sim\mathbf{J}$ is a theorem of RA. *Hint:* You will need to prove some properties of $\leqslant$ in RA. See Exercise 3, §24.

REMARK. This theorem slightly strengthens 37.1 and 37.2 in that the hypothesis of ω consistency in 37.2 is weakened to consistency. The proof is constructive in the sense explained in §37.

★2. Show that the hypothesis of ω consistency in Church's theorem for RA (43.1) may be weakened to consistency (without destroying the "constructiveness" of the proof). *Hint:* Use Rosser's construction described in Exercise 1 above.

★3. Show that if $\mathbf{J}$ is the Gödel sentence of §37 (or the sentence of Exercise 1 above), then $\mathbf{J} \vee \sim\mathbf{J}$ is not a theorem of $\mathrm{RA_i}$ ($\mathrm{RA_i}$ is intuitionistic arithmetic; see Exercise 7, §25). *Hint:* Use Exercise 11, §25.

★4. Let $\mathbf{A}$ be the wff of RA (with free variable $\mathbf{x}$) defined by

$$\mathbf{A} \rightsquigarrow \exists\mathbf{y}\ \mathbf{ded}\,(\mathbf{y}, \mathbf{k}_{''\mathfrak{f}''}) \supset \exists\mathbf{z} \centerdot \mathbf{z} \leqslant \mathbf{x} \wedge \mathbf{ded}\,(\mathbf{z}, \mathbf{k}_{''\mathfrak{f}''})$$

(see §37 for the definition of **ded** and Exercise 3, §25, for the definition of $\mathbf{z} \leqslant \mathbf{x}$). Show that $\exists\mathbf{x}\mathbf{A}$ is a theorem of RA but for each $n = 0, 1, 2, \ldots$ $\mathbf{S}^{\mathbf{x}}_{\mathbf{k}_n}\mathbf{A}|$ is not a theorem of RA. *Hint:* Show that if $\vdash \mathbf{S}^{\mathbf{x}}_{\mathbf{k}_n}\mathbf{A}$ for some n then $\vdash \mathbf{cons}_{\mathrm{RA}}$ contradicting 39.1. You will need the theorem schema

$$\vdash \mathbf{x} \leqslant \mathbf{k}_n \centerdot\equiv\centerdot \mathbf{x} = \mathbf{k}_0 \vee \mathbf{x} = \mathbf{k}_1 \vee \ldots \vee \mathbf{x} = \mathbf{k}_n.$$

Contrast this result with Exercise 11, §25. What principle is used in the proof of $\vdash \exists\mathbf{x}\mathbf{A}$ which is not intuitionistically valid?

★5. Show that the set T_0 which was shown to be recursive in 42.1 is not primitive recursive. *Hint:* If T_0 is primitive recursive, then there is a wff $\mathbf{T}_0(\mathbf{x})$ with no quantifiers such that $\vdash \mathbf{T}_0(\mathbf{k}_n)$ if $n \in T_0$ and $\vdash \sim\mathbf{T}_0(\mathbf{k}_n)$ otherwise. Use the liar paradox.

★6. The formal language RA_0 has as wffs all the sentences of RA of form $\mathbf{t} = \mathbf{k}_n$ where $\mathbf{t}$ is a variable free term of RA and $\mathbf{k}_n$ is a numeral of RA. The axiom schemas for RA_0 are the three following:

1. $\mathrm{Z}(\mathbf{k}_n) = 0$
2. $\mathbf{k}_n = \mathbf{k}_n$
3. $\mathrm{I}_i^n(\mathbf{k}_{a_1}, \mathbf{k}_{a_2}, \ldots, \mathbf{k}_{a_n}) = \mathbf{k}_{a_i}$ for $n = 1, 2, \ldots, i = 1, 2, \ldots, n.$

The rules of inference of RA_0 are the four following:

4. From $\mathbf{g}(\mathbf{k}_{a_1}, \mathbf{k}_{a_2}, \ldots, \mathbf{k}_{a_n}) = \mathbf{k}_c$ to infer $\mathbf{Rgh}(\mathbf{k}_{a_1}, \mathbf{k}_{a_2}, \ldots, \mathbf{k}_{a_n}, 0) = \mathbf{k}_c$.

5. From $\mathbf{Rgh}(\mathbf{k}_{a_1}, \mathbf{k}_{a_2}, \ldots, \mathbf{k}_{a_n}, \mathbf{k}_b) = \mathbf{k}_c$ and $\mathbf{h}(\mathbf{k}_{a_1}, \mathbf{k}_{a_2}, \ldots, \mathbf{k}_{a_n}, \mathbf{k}_b, \mathbf{k}_c) = \mathbf{k}_d$ to infer $\mathbf{Rgh}(\mathbf{k}_{a_1}, \mathbf{k}_{a_2}, \ldots, \mathbf{k}_{a_n}, \mathbf{k}_{b+1}) = \mathbf{k}_d$.

6. From $\mathbf{g}_1(\mathbf{k}_{a_1}, \mathbf{k}_{a_2}, \ldots, \mathbf{k}_{a_n}) = \mathbf{k}_{b_1}, \mathbf{g}_2(\mathbf{k}_{a_1}, \mathbf{k}_{a_2}, \ldots, \mathbf{k}_{a_n}) = \mathbf{k}_{b_2}, \ldots,$ $\mathbf{g}_m(\mathbf{k}_{a_1}, \mathbf{k}_{a_2}, \ldots, \mathbf{k}_{a_n}) = \mathbf{k}_{b_m}$, and $\mathbf{h}(\mathbf{k}_{b_1}, \mathbf{k}_{b_2}, \ldots, \mathbf{k}_{b_m}) = \mathbf{k}_c$ to infer $\mathbf{Chg}_1\, \mathbf{g}_2 \ldots \mathbf{g}_m(\mathbf{k}_{a_1}, \mathbf{k}_{a_2}, \ldots, \mathbf{k}_{a_n}) = \mathbf{k}_c$.

7. From $\mathbf{t}_1 = \mathbf{k}_{a_1}, \mathbf{t}_2 = \mathbf{k}_{a_2}, \ldots, \mathbf{t}_n = \mathbf{k}_{a_n}$, and $\mathbf{f}(\mathbf{k}_{a_1}, \mathbf{k}_{a_2}, \ldots, \mathbf{k}_{a_n}) = \mathbf{k}_b$ to infer $\mathbf{f}(\mathbf{t}_1, \mathbf{t}_2, \ldots, \mathbf{t}_n) = \mathbf{k}_b$.

Show that if $\mathbf{t}$ is any variable-free term and a is its value [that is, $\mathrm{v}(\mathbf{t}) = a$], then $\mathbf{t} = \mathbf{k}_a$ is a theorem of RA_0.

*7. Let $V(t, a)$ be the two-place numerical relation which holds exactly when t is the Gödel number of a term $\mathbf{t}$ such that $\mathbf{t} = \mathbf{k}_a$ is a theorem of the language RA_0 of the previous exercise. Construct a wff $\mathbf{V}(\mathbf{x}, \mathbf{y})$ of RA (with free variables $\mathbf{x}$ and $\mathbf{y}$ and one existential quantifier) which expresses the two place relation V. Let $\mathbf{E}(\mathbf{x}, \mathbf{y})$ be the wff given by

$$\mathbf{E}(\mathbf{x}, \mathbf{y}) \rightsquigarrow \exists \mathbf{z} \,\blacksquare\, \mathbf{V}(\mathbf{x}, \mathbf{z}) \wedge \mathbf{V}(\mathbf{y}, \mathbf{z}).$$

Prove the following:

(1) $RA \vdash \mathbf{V}(\mathbf{k}_t, \mathbf{k}_a)$ if and only if $V(t, a)$ $(t, a = 0, 1, 2, \ldots)$;

(2) $RA \vdash \mathbf{V}(\mathbf{x}_1, \mathbf{x}_2) \wedge \mathbf{V}(\mathbf{x}_1, \mathbf{x}_3) \supset \mathbf{x}_2 = \mathbf{x}_3$;

(3) For variable free terms $\mathbf{t}$ and $\mathbf{s}$ with Gödel numbers t and s respectively (i.e. $t = {''}\mathbf{t}{''}$ and $s = {''}\mathbf{s}{''}$) we have

$$RA \vdash \mathbf{E}(\mathbf{k}_t, \mathbf{k}_s) \equiv \mathbf{t} = \mathbf{s}.$$

Hint: Part (2) will require proving some theorems on the prime decomposition in RA. The proof of (2) is by induction on $\mathbf{x}_1$ (in RA). Use an induction schema of the form

$$\forall \mathbf{x}[(\forall \mathbf{y} < \mathbf{x})\, \mathbf{A}(\mathbf{y}) \supset \mathbf{A}(\mathbf{x})] \supset \forall \mathbf{x} \mathbf{A}(\mathbf{x})$$

(here $(\forall \mathbf{y} < \mathbf{x})\mathbf{A}(\mathbf{y})$ stands for $\forall \mathbf{y}[\mathbf{y} < \mathbf{x} \supset \mathbf{A}(\mathbf{y})]$; this schema may be proved from 23.17). To prove (3) note that if a is the value of $\mathbf{t}$ then $RA \vdash \mathbf{V}(\mathbf{t}, \mathbf{k}_a)$ by (1) and hence by (2) $RA \vdash \mathbf{V}(\mathbf{k}_t, \mathbf{x}) \supset \mathbf{k}_a = \mathbf{x}$. Since $RA \vdash \mathbf{t} = \mathbf{k}_a$, we have $RA \vdash \mathbf{V}(\mathbf{k}_t, \mathbf{x}) \supset \mathbf{t} = \mathbf{x}$. Taking the analogous result for $\mathbf{s}$ we obtain $RA \vdash \mathbf{E}(\mathbf{k}_t, \mathbf{k}_s) \supset \mathbf{t} = \mathbf{s}$. To prove $RA \vdash \mathbf{t} = \mathbf{s} \supset \mathbf{E}(\mathbf{k}_t, \mathbf{k}_s)$ note that there are two cases: the case $RA \vdash \mathbf{t} = \mathbf{s}$ and the case $RA \vdash \mathbf{t} \neq \mathbf{s}$.

*8. Construct a wff $\mathbf{T}_0(\mathbf{x})$ with one free variable $\mathbf{x}$ such that for every sentence $\mathbf{A}$ of RA without variables

$$RA \vdash \mathbf{T}_0(\mathbf{k}_{''\mathbf{A}''}) \equiv \mathbf{A}.$$

Hint: Every sentence without variables is equivalent to a sentence of form $\mathbf{t} = 0$. For example,

$$\mathfrak{f} \equiv \mathbf{k}_1 = \mathbf{k}_0$$
$$\mathbf{t} = \mathbf{s} \equiv (\mathbf{t} \dot{-} \mathbf{s}) + (\mathbf{s} \dot{-} \mathbf{t}) = 0$$
$$\mathbf{t} = \mathbf{k}_0 \supset \mathbf{s} = \mathbf{k}_0 \;.\!\equiv (\mathbf{k}_1 \dot{-} \mathbf{t})\mathbf{s} = \mathbf{k}_0$$

(where $\mathbf{t} \dot{-} \mathbf{s}$ is suitably defined). Construct a primitive recursive function e such that for every sentence $\mathbf{A}$ without variables $e(''\mathbf{A}'') = ''\mathbf{t}''$ where $\vdash \mathbf{A} \equiv \mathbf{t} = 0$. We may define $T_0(\mathbf{x})$ by

$$\mathbf{T}_0(\mathbf{x}) \rightsquigarrow \mathbf{E}(\mathbf{e}(\mathbf{x}), \mathbf{k}_0)$$

where $\mathbf{E}$ is the wff of the previous exercise and $\mathbf{e}$ is a function constant denoting e.

*9. For each $n = 0, 1, 2, \ldots$ construct a wff $\mathbf{T}_n(\mathbf{x})$ such that for every sentence $\mathbf{A}$ of RA having n or less quantifiers:

$$\mathrm{RA} \vdash T_n(\mathbf{k}_{''\mathbf{A}''}) \equiv \mathbf{A}.$$

Show that such a wff $T_n(\mathbf{x})$ must have more than n quantifiers.

Warning: Exercises 7, 8, and 9 will require a good deal of tedious work (theorem proving in RA). If the reader wishes to forego this tedium, he may be satisfied to construct formulas $T_n(\mathbf{x})$ such that for each $n = 0, 1, 2, \ldots$ the set

$$\{a \in \mathbf{N} \mid \mathbf{N} \models \mathbf{T}_n(\mathbf{k}_a)\}$$

is precisely the set of Gödel numbers of true sentences having n or less quantifiers.

*10. The formal language RA_2, **second-order recursive arithmetic**, has as primitive symbols the primitive symbols of RA and in addition the following infinite list

$$\alpha_1, \alpha_2, \alpha_3, \ldots$$

of symbols called **set variables**. The definitions of index, individual variable, function constant, and term are the same as for RA (§21), but the definition of wff is modified by adding the following rules:

(i) If $\boldsymbol{\alpha}$ is a set variable and $\mathbf{t}$ is a term, then $\boldsymbol{\alpha}(\mathbf{t})$ is a wff.

(ii) If $\boldsymbol{\alpha}$ is a set variable and A is a wff, then $\forall\boldsymbol{\alpha}\mathrm{A}$ is a wff.

The notion "free (and bound) occurrence of a set variable $\boldsymbol{\alpha}$ in A" and "the set variable $\boldsymbol{\alpha}$ is free for the set variable $\boldsymbol{\beta}$ in A" are the *mutatis mutandis* the same as for first-order logic (§8) and definition schema (D5) applies for set variables as well (namely, $\exists\boldsymbol{\alpha}\mathbf{A}$ stands for $\sim\forall\boldsymbol{\alpha} \sim \mathbf{A}$). The rules of inference are *modus ponens* and generalization, but now generalization is allowed on set variables as well as individual variables. The axiom schemas are those of RA except that 23.17 is omitted (it will be a theorem schema) and in addition the following are axiom schemas of RA_2 (in the following $\boldsymbol{\alpha}$ and $\boldsymbol{\beta}$ are set variables, α is α_1, x is x_0, y is x_1, $\mathbf{x}$ is an individual variable, and $\mathbf{A}$ and $\mathbf{B}$ are wffs; in (1)

$\boldsymbol{\beta}$ is free for $\boldsymbol{\alpha}$ in A and in (2) and (4) $\boldsymbol{\alpha}$ has no free occurrence in **A**; as before, $\mathbf{S}_{\beta}{}^{\alpha}\mathbf{A}|$ is the result of replacing $\boldsymbol{\alpha}$ by $\boldsymbol{\beta}$ in **A** at free occurrences of $\boldsymbol{\alpha}$):

(1) $\forall\alpha\mathbf{A} \supset \mathbf{S}_{\beta}{}^{\alpha}\mathbf{A}|$

(2) $\forall\alpha[\mathbf{A} \supset \mathbf{B}] \supset \centerdot\, \mathbf{A} \supset \forall\alpha\mathbf{B}$

(3) $\mathrm{x} = \mathrm{y} \supset \alpha(\mathrm{x}) \equiv \alpha(\mathrm{y})$

(4) $\exists\alpha\forall\mathbf{x} \centerdot \alpha(\mathbf{x}) \equiv \mathbf{A}$

(5) $\alpha(0) \supset \centerdot\, \forall\mathrm{x}[\alpha(\mathrm{x}) \supset \alpha(S(\mathrm{x}))] \supset \forall\mathrm{x}\alpha(\mathrm{x})$

Schema (4) is the **comprehension axiom**, and (5) is the **axiom of induction**. Show that 23.17 is a theorem schema of RA_2 and hence that every theorem of RA is a theorem of RA_2.

★11. Show that there is a wff **T(x)** of RA_2 having a single free variable **x** such that for every sentence **A** of RA

$$RA_2 \vdash T(\mathbf{k}_a) \equiv \mathbf{A}$$

where $a = ''\mathbf{A}''$. *Hint:* Let $\Phi(\alpha)$ be a wff of RA_2 which says that the set α has the following three properties:

(1) If a is the Gödel number of a true variable free sentence, then $a \in \alpha$ (Exercise 8 above);

(2) If $a \notin \alpha$ or $b \in \alpha$, then $''['' * a * ''\supset'' * b * '']'' \in \alpha$;

(3) If $sub\,(x, n, a) \in \alpha$ for every n, then $''\forall'' * x * a \in \alpha$ (*sub* is the primitive recursive function defined in 35.4).

Then define **T(x)** by

$$\mathbf{T(x)} \rightsquigarrow \forall\alpha \centerdot \Phi(\alpha) \supset \alpha(\mathbf{x}).$$

REMARK. As was the case in Exercise 9, proving the theorem schema $T(\mathbf{k}_a) \equiv \mathbf{A}$ in RA_2 will require a good deal of preliminary theorem proving in RA_2. The reader who wishes to forego this tedious work may content himself with constructing the formula **T(x)** and verifying that it defines the set of Gödel numbers of true sentences of RA.

★12. Show that there is no algorithm which decides, for each sentence **A** of RA, whether or not $\mathbf{N} \vDash \mathbf{A}$. Is this assertion the same as 43.1? Why not? *Hint:* You must show that the set $\{''\mathbf{A}'' | \mathbf{N} \vDash \mathbf{A}\}$ is not recursive. Show that every recursive set is arithmetical and use 41.1.

Chapter 6 SECOND-ORDER LOGIC

In this chapter we study a family of languages known as second-order languages. They differ from the first-order languages in that quantification over relations among individuals (and in particular over sets of individuals) is allowed.

A second-order logic is determined by a set of relation constants $\mathfrak{S}$ and a set of individual constants X and the second-order logic having these constants will be denoted by $L_2(\mathfrak{S}, X)$. What we here call an n-place relation constant we called in Chapter 2 an n-place predicate letter. We have here changed away from the more conventional terminology to emphasize a point of view: an individual constant is the name of an individual; an n-place relation constant is the name of an n-place relation.

One nice feature of second-order logic is that in this logic we can give a finite set of axioms adequate for arithmetic. This results in the formal language PA_2 introduced in §49. The formal language PA_2 has no names for the natural numbers and no names for primitive recursive functions. This proves to be no handicap however. Even though PA_2 has no name for the natural number 4, it does have a formula $Z_4(x)$ whose meaning is that $x = 4$, and even though PA_2 has no name for the primitive recursive function $+$, it does have a formula $\mathbf{A}_+(x, y, z)$ whose meaning is that $x + y = z$. This is explained in §§50 and 51.

The fact that the primitive recursive functions can be represented in PA_2 allows us to apply the techniques of Chapter 5 to PA_2. In particular, there is a Gödel incompleteness theorem for PA_2 (§52) and a Church's theorem for PA_2 (§53). These metatheorems on PA_2 give us insight also into second-order logic in general; the transition is possible largely because PA_2 has only finitely many nonlogical axioms.

§44 Formation Rules for $L_2(\mathfrak{S}, X)$

A **system of relation constants for second-order logic** is a doubly-infinite sequence of symbols

$$\begin{array}{l} P_1{}^1, P_2{}^1, P_3{}^1, \ldots \\ P_1{}^2, P_2{}^2, P_3{}^2, \ldots \\ \quad\vdots \\ P_1{}^n, P_2{}^n, P_3{}^n, \ldots \\ \quad\vdots \end{array}$$

where each row may be empty, finite, or infinite. (We do not exclude the possibility that every row is empty.) We denote such a system by $\mathfrak{S}$ and call the elements of the sequence **relation constants** of $\mathfrak{S}$. More precisely, a relation constant with superscript k (namely, one of form $P_i{}^k$) is called a k-**place relation constant**. The subscripts serve merely to distinguish various relation constants.

Any set X, whether empty, finite, or infinite may serve as a **set of individual constants for a second order logic**.

Let $\mathfrak{S}$ be a system of relation constants and X a set of individual constants. We shall define $L_2(\mathfrak{S}, X)$, the **second-order language determined by** $\mathfrak{S}$ and X:

The **primitive symbols** of $L_2(\mathfrak{S}, X)$ are the elements of $\mathfrak{S}$ and X and in addition:

1. the infinite list of symbols

$$x, y, z, x_1, y_1, z_1, x_2, y_2, z_2, \ldots$$

called **individual variables**;

2. for each $n = 1, 2, 3, \ldots$ an infinite sequence of symbols

$$\alpha^n, \beta^n, \gamma^n, \alpha_1{}^n, \beta_1{}^n, \gamma_1{}^n, \alpha_2{}^n, \beta_2{}^n, \gamma_2{}^n, \ldots$$

called n-**place relation variables**;

3. and the eight symbols

$$\supset \quad \mathfrak{f} \quad \forall \quad [\quad] \quad (\quad) \quad ,$$

whose names are by now familiar.

A **variable** is a symbol which is either an individual variable or an n-place relation for some $n = 1, 2, 3, \ldots$. Any finite sequence of primitive symbols of $L_2(\mathfrak{S}, X)$ is a **formula** of $L_2(\mathfrak{S}, X)$. The class of **well formed formulas** or **wffs** of $L_2(\mathfrak{S}, X)$ is defined inductively by the following rules:

(W1) If $\boldsymbol{\varphi}$ is an n-place relation variable or an n-place relation constant and $\mathbf{a}_1, \mathbf{a}_2, \ldots, \mathbf{a}_n$ is a sequence of (not necessarily distinct) symbols each of which is either an individual variable or an individual constant, then $\boldsymbol{\varphi}(\mathbf{a}_1, \mathbf{a}_2, \ldots, \mathbf{a}_n)$ is a wff of $L_2(\mathfrak{S}, X)$;

(W2) The symbol $\mathfrak{f}$ is a wff of $L_2(\mathfrak{S}, X)$;

(W3) If **A** and **B** are wffs of $L_2(\mathfrak{S}, X)$, then so is $[\mathbf{A} \supset \mathbf{B}]$;

(W4) If **A** is a wff of $L_2(\mathfrak{S}, X)$ and **v** is any variable, then $\forall \mathbf{v} \mathbf{A}$ is a wff of $L_2(\mathfrak{S}, X)$;

(W5) A formula is a wff only as required by (W1)–(W4).

Clearly the main difference between the notion of a wff of a first-order language and of a wff of a second-order language lies in (W4): in a second-order language we are allowed to quantify on a relation variable.

We use all the abbreviations introduced in Chapters 1 and 2 including the conventions about the omission of brackets and the definition schemas (D1)–(D5). The definition schema (D5) is here extended to relation variables as well:

If **A** is a wff and **v** a variable, then

(D5) $\exists \mathbf{v} \mathbf{A} \rightsquigarrow \sim \forall \mathbf{v} \sim \mathbf{A}$.

(We shall always omit superscripts from the relation variables and constants since they can be recognized from the context.)

The notions of free and bound occurrences of variables and of a variable or constant being free for another variable in a wff extend *mutatis mutandis* to relation variables (see §8). Thus if $\boldsymbol{\alpha}$ is an n-place relation variable, then each occurrence of $\boldsymbol{\alpha}$ in a wff of form $\forall \boldsymbol{\alpha} \mathbf{A}$ is bound. As usual, a **sentence** is a wff with no free variables.

We extend the substitution notation of §8 to our present context as well. Thus if $\boldsymbol{\alpha}$ is an n-place relation variable and $\boldsymbol{\varphi}$ is an n-place relation variable or relation constant and if A is a wff, then the notation

$$\mathbf{S}_{\boldsymbol{\varphi}}{}^{\boldsymbol{\alpha}} \mathbf{A}|$$

denotes the wff which results on replacing each free occurrence of $\boldsymbol{\alpha}$ in **A** by $\boldsymbol{\varphi}$. Thus $\boldsymbol{\varphi}$ is free for $\boldsymbol{\alpha}$ in **A** if and only if **A** and $\mathbf{S}_{\boldsymbol{\varphi}}{}^{\boldsymbol{\alpha}} \mathbf{A}|$ have exactly the same number of bound (occurrences of) variables.

§45 Axiomatics for $L_2(\mathfrak{S}, X)$

The axiom schemas for $L_2(\mathfrak{S}, X)$ are the six following:

45.1 $\mathbf{A} \supset . \mathbf{B} \supset \mathbf{A}$

45.2 $\mathbf{A} \supset [\mathbf{B} \supset \mathbf{C}] . \supset . [\mathbf{A} \supset \mathbf{B}] \supset [\mathbf{A} \supset \mathbf{C}]$

45.3 $\sim \sim \mathbf{A} \supset \mathbf{A}$

45.4 $\forall \mathbf{v}\mathbf{A} \supset \mathbf{S}_{\mathbf{a}}^{\mathbf{v}}\mathbf{A}|$ where **v** is any variable and **a** is a variable or constant of the same type (that is, an individual variable or constant if **v** is an individual variable and an n-place relation variable or constant if **v** is an n-place relation variable) and **a** is free for **v** in **A**.

45.5 $\forall \mathbf{v}[\mathbf{A} \supset \mathbf{B}] \supset . \mathbf{A} \supset \forall \mathbf{v}\mathbf{B}$ where **v** has no free occurrence in **A**.

45.6 $\exists \boldsymbol{\alpha}\, \forall \mathbf{x}_1\, \forall \mathbf{x}_2 \ldots \forall \mathbf{x}_n\, .\, \boldsymbol{\alpha}(\mathbf{x}_1, \mathbf{x}_2, \ldots, \mathbf{x}_n) \equiv \mathbf{A}$ where $\boldsymbol{\alpha}$ is any n-place relation variable not occurring free in **A** and $\mathbf{x}_1, \mathbf{x}_2, \ldots, \mathbf{x}_n$ are individual variables.

(Schema 45.6 is called the **comprehension axiom schema**. It says roughly that every wff defines a relation.)

The rules of inference of $L_2(\mathfrak{S}, X)$ are

45.7 (*modus ponens*) From **A** and $\mathbf{A} \supset \mathbf{B}$ to infer **B**.

45.8 (generalization) From **A**, if **v** is any variable, to infer $\forall \mathbf{v}\mathbf{A}$.

Let $\mathbf{A}_1, \mathbf{A}_2, \ldots, \mathbf{A}_n$ be wffs of $L_2(\mathfrak{S}, X)$. A sequence $\mathbf{B}_1, \mathbf{B}_2, \ldots, \mathbf{B}_m$ of wffs of $L_2(\mathfrak{S}, X)$ is called a **deduction (of $\mathbf{B}_m$) from the hypotheses $\mathbf{A}_1, \mathbf{A}_2, \ldots, \mathbf{A}_n$** iff each $\mathbf{B}_k$ ($k = 1, 2, \ldots, m$) satisfies either

(DH1) $\mathbf{B}_k$ is some $\mathbf{A}_j$ ($j = 1, 2, \ldots, n$); *or*

(DH2) $\mathbf{B}_k$ is an axiom of $L_2(\mathfrak{S}, X)$ (that is it has one of the forms 45.1–45.6); *or*

(DH3) $\mathbf{B}_k$ results from some $\mathbf{B}_i$ and $\mathbf{B}_j$ with $i, j < k$ by *modus ponens* (namely for some $i, j < k$, $\mathbf{B}_i$ is $\mathbf{B}_j \supset \mathbf{B}_k$); *or*

(DH4) $\mathbf{B}_k$ results from some $\mathbf{B}_i$ ($i < k$) by generalization on a variable **v** which is not free in $\mathbf{A}_1, \mathbf{A}_2, \ldots, \mathbf{A}_n$ (that is, $\mathbf{B}_k$ is $\forall \mathbf{v}\mathbf{B}_i$ for some $i < k$ where **v** is any variable not free in $\mathbf{A}_1, \mathbf{A}_2, \ldots, \mathbf{A}_n$); *or*

(DH5) $\mathbf{B}_k$ is of the form

$$\forall \mathbf{u}\mathbf{S}_{\mathbf{v}}^{\mathbf{u}}\mathbf{C}| \supset \forall \mathbf{v}\mathbf{C}$$

where **u** and **v** are variables of the same type and **v** has at least one free occurrence in some hypothesis $\mathbf{A}_1, \mathbf{A}_2, \ldots, \mathbf{A}_n$ and **u** has no occurrence in **C**.

(The reason for (DH5) is explained below. Notice, however, that the clause (DH5) is never satisfied when $\mathbf{A}_1, \mathbf{A}_2, \ldots, \mathbf{A}_n$ are sentences. In particular the definition of a deduction from no hypotheses would not be affected if clause (DH5) were omitted.)

As usual, the notation

$$\mathbf{A}_1, \mathbf{A}_2, \ldots, \mathbf{A}_n, \vdash \mathbf{B}$$

means there is a deduction of B from the hypotheses $\mathbf{A}_1, \mathbf{A}_2, \ldots, \mathbf{A}_n$. The A wff $\mathbf{B}$ is called a **theorem** iff $\vdash \mathbf{B}$.

As expected, we have the

45.9 Deduction Theorem. If $\mathbf{A}_1, \mathbf{A}_2, \ldots, \mathbf{A}_n \vdash \mathbf{B}$, then $\mathbf{A}_1, \mathbf{A}_2, \ldots, \mathbf{A}_{n-1} \vdash \mathbf{A}_n \supset \mathbf{B}$.

PROOF. The proof is almost word for word the same as the proof for first order logic (13.2). Let $\mathbf{B}_1, \mathbf{B}_2, \ldots, \mathbf{B}_m$ be a deduction of $\mathbf{B}$ from $\mathbf{A}_1, \mathbf{A}_2, \ldots, \mathbf{A}_n$ ($\mathbf{B}_m$ is $\mathbf{B}$) and show by induction on k ($k = 1, 2, \ldots, m$) that $\mathbf{A}_1, \mathbf{A}_2, \ldots, \mathbf{A}_{n-1} \vdash \mathbf{A}_n \supset \mathbf{B}_k$. The only difference in the proofs occurs when $\mathbf{B}_k$ is obtained from (DH5). Then $\mathbf{B}_k$ is $\forall \mathbf{u} \mathbf{S}_{\mathbf{v}}^{\mathbf{u}} \mathbf{C}| \supset \forall \mathbf{v} \mathbf{C}$ where $\mathbf{v}$ has a free occurrence in $\mathbf{A}_1, \mathbf{A}_2, \ldots, \mathbf{A}_n$. If $\mathbf{v}$ occurs free in $\mathbf{A}_1, \mathbf{A}_2, \ldots, \mathbf{A}_{n-1}$, then by (DH5) $\mathbf{A}_1, \mathbf{A}_2, \ldots, \mathbf{A}_{n-1} \vdash \mathbf{B}_k$. If $\mathbf{v}$ has no free occurrence in $\mathbf{A}_1, \mathbf{A}_2, \ldots, \mathbf{A}_{n-1}$, then $\mathbf{A}_1, \mathbf{A}_2, \ldots, \mathbf{A}_{n-1} \vdash \mathbf{B}_k$ by 45.4, by generalization on $\mathbf{v}$, by 45.5, and by *modus ponens*. In either case, $\mathbf{A}_1, \mathbf{A}_2, \ldots, \mathbf{A}_{n-1} \vdash \mathbf{A}_n \supset \mathbf{B}_k$ by 45.1 and by *modus ponens*. We leave further details to the reader.

Recall from §13 that the definition of deduction from hypotheses given there had the undesirable feature that a wff provable from a set of hypotheses may not be provable from a larger set of hypotheses (because free variables in the new hypotheses could invalidate a generalization). The addition of the clause (DH5) is designed to circumvent this difficulty.

45.10 Extra Hypotheses Theorem. If $\mathbf{A}_1, \mathbf{A}_2, \ldots, \mathbf{A}_n \vdash \mathbf{B}$ and $\mathbf{C}_1, \mathbf{C}_2, \ldots, \mathbf{C}_p$ are wffs, then $\mathbf{A}_1, \mathbf{A}_2, \ldots, \mathbf{A}_n, \mathbf{C}_1, \mathbf{C}_2, \ldots, \mathbf{C}_p \vdash \mathbf{B}$.

PROOF. Let $\mathbf{B}_1, \mathbf{B}_2, \ldots, \mathbf{B}_m$ ($\mathbf{B}_m$ is $\mathbf{B}$) be a deduction of $\mathbf{B}$ from $\mathbf{A}_1, \mathbf{A}_2, \ldots, \mathbf{A}_n$. This sequence might fail to be a deduction of $\mathbf{B}$ from $\mathbf{A}_1, \mathbf{A}_2, \ldots, \mathbf{A}_n, \mathbf{C}_1, \mathbf{C}_2, \ldots, \mathbf{C}_p$ because of generalization on a variable $\mathbf{v}$ which appears free in some one of $\mathbf{C}_1, \mathbf{C}_2, \ldots, \mathbf{C}_p$. Let $\mathbf{B}_k$ be the first point at which this happens. Then $\mathbf{B}_1, \mathbf{B}_2, \ldots, \mathbf{B}_{k-1}$ is a (correct) deduction from $\mathbf{A}_1, \mathbf{A}_2, \ldots, \mathbf{A}_n, \mathbf{C}_1, \mathbf{C}_2, \ldots, \mathbf{C}_p$ and $\mathbf{B}_k$ is $\forall \mathbf{v} \mathbf{B}_i$ for some $i < k$ where $\mathbf{v}$ occurs free in one of $\mathbf{C}_1, \mathbf{C}_2, \ldots, \mathbf{C}_p$, but not in $\mathbf{A}_1, \mathbf{A}_2, \ldots, \mathbf{A}_n$. Let $\mathbf{u}$ be a variable of the same type as $\mathbf{v}$ which occurs nowhere in $\mathbf{A}_1, \ldots, \mathbf{A}_n, \mathbf{C}_1, \ldots, \mathbf{C}_p, \mathbf{B}_1, \ldots, \mathbf{B}_k$. Then the sequence

$$\mathbf{S}_{\mathbf{v}}^{\mathbf{u}} \mathbf{B}_1|, \mathbf{S}_{\mathbf{v}}^{\mathbf{u}} \mathbf{B}_2|, \ldots, \mathbf{S}_{\mathbf{v}}^{\mathbf{u}} \mathbf{B}_{k-1}|, \qquad \forall \mathbf{u} \mathbf{S}_{\mathbf{v}}^{\mathbf{u}} \mathbf{B}_i| \qquad \forall \mathbf{u} \mathbf{S}_{\mathbf{v}}^{\mathbf{u}} \mathbf{B}_i| \supset \mathbf{B}_k \qquad \mathbf{B}_k$$

is a (correct) deduction of $\mathbf{B}_k$ from $\mathbf{A}_1, \mathbf{A}_2, \ldots, \mathbf{A}_n, \mathbf{C}_1, \mathbf{C}_2, \ldots, \mathbf{C}_p$ [the next to the last element of the sequence satisfies (DH5)]. Repeating this argument a finite number of times gives a deduction of $\mathbf{B}_m$ from $\mathbf{A}_1, \mathbf{A}_2, \ldots, \mathbf{A}_n, \mathbf{C}_1, \mathbf{C}_2, \ldots, \mathbf{C}_p$. ∎

Clearly $L_2(\mathfrak{S}, X)$ has all the power of first-order logic and of the propositional calculus. Note, for example, that all the theorem schemas of §14 are theorem schemas of $L_2(\mathfrak{S}, X)$ even when the symbols $\mathbf{x}$ and $\mathbf{y}$ (used in §14 to denote arbitrary individual variables) are interpreted as denoting arbitrary variables of $L_2(\mathfrak{S}, X)$ (individual or relation). It is also amusing to note that none of these proofs requires the comprehension axiom (45.6).

§46 Semantics of Second-Order Logic

Let $\mathfrak{S}$ be a set of relational constants for second-order logic and X a set of individual constants. A **second-order structure of type** $(\mathfrak{S}, X)$ is an infinite sequence

$$\mathfrak{M} = \langle V, D, \mathfrak{D}_1, \mathfrak{D}_2, \mathfrak{D}_3, \ldots \rangle \qquad \text{where}$$

(1) D is a nonempty set called the **domain of individuals** of $\mathfrak{M}$;

(2) Each $\mathfrak{D}_n$ ($n = 1, 2, \ldots$) is a nonempty set of n-place relations on D called the *set of n-place relations* of $\mathfrak{M}$ (that is, each element of $\mathfrak{D}_n$ is a subset of D^n);

(3) V is a function which assigns to each individual constant $a \in X$ an individual $V(a) \in D$ and to each n-place relations constant $\mathbf{P}$ of $\mathfrak{S}$ an n-place relation $V(\mathbf{P}) \in \mathfrak{D}_n$ ($n = 1, 2, 3, \ldots$).

Now let $\mathfrak{M} = \langle V, D, \mathfrak{D}_1, \mathfrak{D}_2, \ldots \rangle$ be a second-order structure of type $(\mathfrak{S}, X)$. An **evaluation of variables in** $\mathfrak{M}$ is a function E which assigns to each individual variable $\mathbf{x}$ of $L_2(\mathfrak{S}, X)$ and element $E(\mathbf{x}) \in D$ of the domain of individuals of $\mathfrak{M}$ and to each n-place relation variable $\boldsymbol{\alpha}$ an element $E(\boldsymbol{\alpha}) \in \mathfrak{D}_n$ of the set of n-place relations of $\mathfrak{M}$.

If $\mathfrak{M} = \langle V, D, \mathfrak{D}_1, \mathfrak{D}_2, \ldots \rangle$ is a second-order structure of type $(\mathfrak{S}, X)$, E is an evaluation of variables in $\mathfrak{M}$, and $\mathbf{A}$ is a wff of $L_2(\mathfrak{S}, X)$ we will define what it means for $\mathbf{A}$ to **hold in** $\mathfrak{M}$ **for the evaluation** E. This is written

$$\mathfrak{M}, E \models \mathbf{A}$$

and is defined inductively by the following rules ($\mathfrak{M}, E \not\models \mathbf{A}$ means not $\mathfrak{M}, E \models \mathbf{A}$):

(M1) If $\boldsymbol{\varphi}$ is an n-place relation constant or variable and $\mathbf{a}_1, \mathbf{a}_2, \ldots, \mathbf{a}_n$ are individual constants or variables, define φ by

$$\begin{aligned} \varphi &= V(\boldsymbol{\varphi}) \text{ if } \boldsymbol{\varphi} \text{ is an } n\text{-place relation constant;} \\ &= E(\boldsymbol{\varphi}) \text{ if } \boldsymbol{\varphi} \text{ is an } n\text{-place relation variable;} \end{aligned}$$

and for each $i = 1, 2, \ldots, n$ define a_i by

$$\begin{aligned} a_i &= V(\mathbf{a}_i) \quad \text{if } \mathbf{a}_i \text{ is an individual constant} \\ &= E(\mathbf{a}_i) \quad \text{if } \mathbf{a}_i \text{ is an individual variable.} \end{aligned}$$

Then

$$\mathfrak{M}, E \models \boldsymbol{\varphi}(\mathbf{a}_1, \mathbf{a}_2, \ldots, \mathbf{a}_n)$$

iff $(a_1, a_2, \ldots, a_n)$ satisfies φ [that is, $(a_1, a_2, \ldots, a_n) \in \varphi$].

(M2) $\mathfrak{M}, E \not\models \mathfrak{f}$.

(M3) $\mathfrak{M}, E \not\models \mathbf{A} \supset \mathbf{B}$ if $\mathfrak{M}, E \models \mathbf{A}$ and $\mathfrak{M}, E \not\models \mathbf{B}$;

$\mathfrak{M}, E \models \mathbf{A} \supset \mathbf{B}$ otherwise.

(M4) $\mathfrak{M}, E \models \forall \mathbf{v} \mathbf{A}$ if $\mathfrak{M}, E' \models \mathbf{A}$ for every evaluation of variables E' having the property that $E'(\mathbf{u}) = E(\mathbf{u})$ for all variables $\mathbf{u}$ of $L_2(\mathfrak{S}, X)$ except possibly $\mathbf{v}$;

$\mathfrak{M}, E \not\models \forall \mathbf{v} \mathbf{A}$ otherwise.

46.1 Lemma. Let $\mathfrak{M}$ be a second-order structure of type $(\mathfrak{S}, X)$, E_1 and E_2 evaluations of variables in $\mathfrak{M}$, and $\mathbf{A}$ a wff of $L_2(\mathfrak{S}, X)$. Suppose $E_1(\mathbf{v}) = E_2(\mathbf{v})$ for each variable $\mathbf{v}$ which has a free occurrence in $\mathbf{A}$. Then, $\mathfrak{M}$ $E_1 \models \mathbf{A}$ if and only if $\mathfrak{M}, E_2 \models \mathbf{A}$. In particular, if $\mathbf{A}$ is a sentence, then the notion $\mathfrak{M}, E \models \mathbf{A}$ is independent of E; more precisely, $\mathfrak{M}, E \models \mathbf{A}$ for some evaluation E if and only if $\mathfrak{M}, E \models \mathbf{A}$ for every evaluation E.

Lemma 46.1 says that the truth or falsity of a wff $\mathbf{A}$ in a model $\mathfrak{M}$ depends only on the values of the variables which appear in $\mathbf{A}$. This is intuitively obvious. A rigorous proof may be constructed by induction on the length of $\mathbf{A}$. We leave the details of such a proof to the reader.

According to 46.1 we make the following definition: if $\mathbf{A}$ is a sentence of $L_2(\mathfrak{S}, X)$, then **A holds in** $\mathfrak{M}$, in symbols,

$$\mathfrak{M} \models \mathbf{A}$$

iff $\mathfrak{M}, E \models \mathbf{A}$ for some (and hence every) evaluation E of variables in $\mathfrak{M}$.

A wff $\mathbf{A}$ of $L_2(\mathfrak{S}, X)$ is **valid in a second-order structure** $\mathfrak{M}$ iff $\mathfrak{M}, E \models \mathbf{A}$ for every evaluation of variables E in $\mathfrak{M}$. Clearly, this is equivalent to demanding that $\mathfrak{M} \models \mathbf{A}'$ where $\mathbf{A}'$ is the universal closure of $\mathbf{A}$. (As usual, the **universal closure** of $\mathbf{A}$ is the wff

$$\forall \mathbf{v}_1 \forall \mathbf{v}_2 \ldots \forall \mathbf{v}_k \mathbf{A}$$

where $\mathbf{v}_1, \mathbf{v}_2, \ldots, \mathbf{v}_k$ are the variables which appear free in $\mathbf{A}$.)

46.2 Proposition. Let $\mathfrak{M}$ be a second-order structure. Then each axiom of one of the forms 45.1–45.5 is valid in $\mathfrak{M}$ and the rules of inference 4.7 (*modus ponens*) and 4.8 (generalization) yield wffs valid in $\mathfrak{M}$ when applied to wffs valid in $\mathfrak{M}$.

46.3 Corollary. If **A** is a theorem of $L_2(\mathfrak{S}, X)$ which can be proved without using 45.6 (the comprehension axiom), then **A** is valid in every second order structure $\mathfrak{M}$.

The proofs of 46.2 and 46.3 are straightforward and are left to the reader. To see why the comprehension axiom (45.6) may fail to hold in a second-order structure $\mathfrak{M} = \langle V, D, \mathfrak{D}_1, \mathfrak{D}_2, \ldots \rangle$ consider the following instance of 45.6:

$$\exists \gamma \, \forall x \, . \, \gamma(x) \equiv \alpha(x) \wedge \beta(x).$$

This wff is valid in $\mathfrak{M}$ if and only if $\mathfrak{D}_1$ contains the intersection of each two of its elements. This clearly does not follow from the definition of second-order structure. To remedy this we make the following definition.

DEFINITION. Let $\mathfrak{M}$ be a second-order structure of type $(\mathfrak{S}, X)$. Then $\mathfrak{M}$ is a **second-order model of type** $(\mathfrak{S}, X)$ iff every instance of the comprehension axiom schema (45.6); namely iff

$$\mathfrak{M}, E \models \exists \boldsymbol{\alpha} \, \forall \mathbf{x}_1 \ldots \forall \mathbf{x}_n \, . \, \boldsymbol{\alpha}(\mathbf{x}_1, \ldots, \mathbf{x}_n) \equiv \mathbf{A}$$

for every wff **A** and every evaluation E of variables in $\mathfrak{M}$ (where $\boldsymbol{\alpha}$ is an n-place function variable not occurring free in **A**).

We shall say that a wff **A** of $L_2(\mathfrak{S}, X)$ is **valid** iff **A** is valid in every second-order model $\mathfrak{M}$ of type $(\mathfrak{S}, X)$. Then as an immediate consequence of 46.2 we have

46.4 Soundness Theorem. If $\vdash$ **A**, then **A** is valid.

The completeness theorem (47.4) is the converse of this.

Roughly speaking, a second-order model is a second-order structure $\mathfrak{M}$ which contains every relation "definable" in $\mathfrak{M}$ via a wff of second-order logic. We shall express this idea precisely:

If E is an evaluation of variables in a second order structure $\mathfrak{M} = \langle V, D, \mathfrak{D}_1, \mathfrak{D}_2, \mathfrak{D}_3, \ldots \rangle$, $\mathbf{x}_1, \mathbf{x}_2, \ldots, \mathbf{x}_n$ are distinct individual variables, and $a_1, a_2, \ldots, a_n$ are elements of D (the domain of individuals of $\mathfrak{M}$), then

$$E^{\mathbf{x}_1 \, \mathbf{x}_2 \, \ldots \, \mathbf{x}_n}_{a_1 \, a_2 \, \ldots \, a_n}$$

denotes the evaluation which agrees with E on all variables other than $\mathbf{x}_1, \mathbf{x}_2, \ldots, \mathbf{x}_n$ and whose value on $\mathbf{x}_i$ $(i = 1, 2, \ldots, n)$ is a_i. An n-place relation R on D (namely $R \subseteq D^n$) is said to be **definable in** $\mathfrak{M}$ iff there is a wff **A** of

$L_2(\mathfrak{S}, X)$, an evaluation of variables E in $\mathfrak{M}$, and distinct individual variables $\mathbf{x}_1, \mathbf{x}_2, \ldots, \mathbf{x}_n$ such that

$$R = \{(a_1, a_2, \ldots, a_n) \in D^n | \mathfrak{M}, E^{\mathbf{x}_1\,\mathbf{x}_2\,\ldots\,\mathbf{x}_n}_{a_1\,a_2\,\ldots\,a_n} \models \mathbf{A}\}.$$

46.5 Proposition. Let $\mathfrak{M} = \langle V, D, \mathfrak{D}_1, \mathfrak{D}_2, \ldots \rangle$ be a second-order structure. Then $\mathfrak{M}$ is a second-order model if and only if $\mathfrak{M}$ contains every n-place relation definable in $\mathfrak{M}$; that is, if and only if for every n-place relation $R \subseteq D^n$ which is definable in $\mathfrak{M}$ we have that $R \in \mathfrak{D}_n$ $(n = 1, 2, \ldots)$.

Proposition 46.5 is intuitively obvious. It is nothing more than a long winded way of saying that the comprehension axiom says that that every wff defines an n-place relation.

It should be clear that there is one kind of second-order structure which is always a second-order model; namely those second-order structures $\mathfrak{M} = \langle V, D, \mathfrak{D}_1, \mathfrak{D}_2, \ldots \rangle$ such that each $\mathfrak{D}_n$ $(n = 1, 2, \ldots)$ consists of *all* the n-place relations on D. Such models are called **full**. They are the standard models of second-order logic, the "intended interpretations" we have in mind when axiomatizing second-order logic. The other models are in some sense "nonstandard" or "unintended" or "extraneous." We shall see, however, that if we neglect these nonstandard models, our completeness theorem fails: there are wffs which are valid in all full models but are not valid in all models and are thus not theorems of second-order logic. Moreover, this phenomenon cannot be avoided by adding more axiom schemas (see §54).

§47 The Completeness Theorem for Second-Order Logic

The completeness theorem for second-order logic is much the same as that for first-order logic (§17). We shall only sketch the argument here; the reader may fill in the details himself by following closely §§16 and 17. Throughout $\mathfrak{S}$ is a set of relation constants for second-order logic and X is a set of individual constants.

Let $\mathbf{\Gamma}$ be a set of sentences of $L_2(\mathfrak{S}, X)$. If $\mathbf{B}$ is a wff of $L_2(\mathfrak{S}, X)$, then the notation

$$\mathbf{\Gamma} \vdash \mathbf{B}$$

means that there is a finite sequence $\mathbf{A}_1, \mathbf{A}_2, \ldots, \mathbf{A}_n$ of sentences of $\mathbf{\Gamma}$ such that $\mathbf{A}_1, \mathbf{A}_2, \ldots, \mathbf{A}_n \vdash \mathbf{B}$. If $\mathfrak{M}$ is a model of type $(\mathfrak{S}, X)$, then the notation

$$\mathfrak{M} \models \mathbf{\Gamma}$$

means that $\mathfrak{M} \models \mathbf{A}$ for every $\mathbf{A} \in \mathbf{\Gamma}$. The set $\mathbf{\Gamma}$ is **inconsistent** iff $\mathbf{\Gamma} \vdash \mathfrak{f}$; otherwise, $\mathbf{\Gamma}$ is **consistent**. The set $\mathbf{\Gamma}$ is **complete** in $L_2(\mathfrak{S}, X)$ iff for every sentence $\mathbf{A}$ of $L_2(\mathfrak{S}, X)$ either $\mathbf{A} \in \mathbf{\Gamma}$ or $\sim\mathbf{A} \in \mathbf{\Gamma}$. The set $\mathbf{\Gamma}$ is **universal** in $L_2(\mathfrak{S}, X)$ iff $\forall \mathbf{v}\mathbf{B} \in \mathbf{\Gamma}$ whenever $\mathbf{B}$ is a wff of $L_2(\mathfrak{S}, X)$ such that $\mathbf{s}_{\mathbf{a}}{}^{\mathbf{v}}\mathbf{B}| \in \mathbf{\Gamma}$ for every constant $\mathbf{a}$ of $L_2(\mathfrak{S}, X)$ of the same type as $\mathbf{v}$.

47.1 Extension Lemma. Let $\mathbf{\Gamma}$ be a consistent set of sentences of $L_2(\mathfrak{S}, X)$. Then there is a set of relation constants $\mathfrak{S}'$ extending $\mathfrak{S}$ (i.e., $\mathfrak{S} \subseteq \mathfrak{S}'$), a set of individual constants X' extending X, and a set of sentences $\mathbf{\Delta}$ of $L_2(\mathfrak{S}', X')$ such that

(1) $\mathbf{\Gamma} \subseteq \mathbf{\Delta}$;

(2) $\mathbf{\Delta}$ is consistent;

(3) $\mathbf{\Delta}$ is complete in $L_2(\mathfrak{S}', X')$;

(4) $\mathbf{\Delta}$ is universal in $L_2(\mathfrak{S}', X')$.

To prove 47.1 simply define X' by adding an infinite list of new individual constants to X and $\mathfrak{S}'$ by adding, for each $n = 1, 2, 3, \ldots$, an infinite list of new n-place relation constants to $\mathfrak{S}$. Then proceed exactly as in the first-order case (16.1).

Next let $\mathbf{\Delta}$ be any set of sentences of $L_2(\mathfrak{S}', X')$ and define a second-order structure

$$\mathfrak{M}_{\mathbf{\Delta}} = \langle V, D, \mathfrak{D}_1, \mathfrak{D}_2, \mathfrak{D}_3, \ldots \rangle$$

as follows:

(i) $D = X'$;

(ii) $V(a) = a$ for $a \in X'$;

(iii) $V(\mathbf{P}) = \{(a_1, a_2, \ldots, a_n) \in X'^n | \mathbf{P}(a_1, a_2, \ldots, a_n) \in \mathbf{\Delta}\}$ for each n-place relation constant $\mathbf{P}$ of $\mathfrak{S}'$;

(iv) $\mathfrak{D}_n = \{V(\mathbf{P}) | \mathbf{P}$ is an n-place relation constant of $\mathfrak{S}'\}$.

47.2 Lemma. Suppose $\mathbf{\Delta}$ is consistent, complete in $L_2(\mathfrak{S}', X')$, and universal in $L_2(\mathfrak{S}', X')$. Then for each sentence $\mathbf{A}$ of $L_2(\mathfrak{S}', X')$: $\mathfrak{M}_{\mathbf{\Delta}} \models \mathbf{A}$ if and only if $\mathbf{A} \in \mathbf{\Delta}$.

The proof of 47.2 is *mutatis mutandis* the same as the proof of 17.1. Note that $\mathbf{A} \in \mathbf{\Delta}$ if and only if $\mathbf{\Delta} \vdash \mathbf{A}$.

47.3 Completeness Theorem. Let $\mathbf{\Gamma}$ be a set of sentences of $L_2(\mathfrak{S}, X)$. Then $\mathbf{\Gamma}$ is consistent if and only if $\mathbf{\Gamma}$ has a model.

PROOF. "If" is trivial (it is essentially the soundness theorem 46.4) and "only if" follows immediately from 47.1 and 47.2 (as $\mathbf{\Gamma} \subseteq \mathbf{\Delta}$). ▌

As a corollary we obtain the converse to 46.4.

47.4 Corollary. If a wff $\mathbf{A}$ is valid, then $\vdash \mathbf{A}$.

The proof of 47.4 is like the proof of 17.3.

We should remark that the completeness proof really doesn't use the comprehension axiom schema (45.6). The comprehension axiom schema holds in $\mathfrak{M}_\Delta$ as $\mathbf{\Delta}$ contains all theorems of second-order logic. Indeed if we omit the axiom schema 46.5 the above argument proves that a wff $\mathbf{A}$ of $L_2(\mathfrak{S}, X)$ can be proved without using the comprehension axiom (46.5) if and only if $\mathbf{A}$ is valid in every second-order structure of type $(\mathfrak{S}, X)$. (Recall that a second-order structure need not model the comprehension axiom.)

§48 Equality

One of the pleasant features of second-order logic is that equality can be introduced as a definition schema. In first-order logic it was necessary to add additional axioms for equality (see §18), but in second-order logic, if equality is suitably defined, these axioms become theorems. The correct definition schema is

(D11) $\mathbf{a} = \mathbf{b} \rightsquigarrow \forall \alpha \,\blacksquare\, \alpha(\mathbf{a}) \equiv \alpha(\mathbf{b})$.

[In (D11) $\mathbf{a}$ is any individual constant or individual variable and $\mathbf{b}$ is any individual constant or individual variable.] The idea for this definition is due to Leibnitz. If we identify sets (i.e., one-place relations) of individuals with properties of individuals, the definition says that two things are equal if and only if they have the same properties (i.e., belong to the same sets). On an informal level this is obvious, for one of the properties satisfied by an individual $\mathbf{a}$ is the property of being equal to $\mathbf{a}$. On the other hand, in a second-order model a sentence of form $\mathbf{a} = \mathbf{b}$ may hold even though $\mathbf{a}$ and $\mathbf{b}$ are distinct (see Exercise 1 at the end of this section).

A reasonable definition for inequality follows.

(D12) $\mathbf{a} \neq \mathbf{b} \rightsquigarrow \sim \mathbf{a} = \mathbf{b}$

where $\mathbf{a}$ and $\mathbf{b}$ are as in (D11).

Next we prove the analogs of 18.1 and 18.2 in our present context.

48.1 $\vdash x = x$.

PROOF. By the propositional calculus, $\vdash \alpha(x) \equiv \alpha(x)$. Now generalize on α. ∎

48.2 Substitutivity of Equality. Let $\mathbf{a}$ be an individual constant or individual variable, $\mathbf{b}$ be an individual constant or individual variable, and let the wff $\mathbf{B}$ result from a wff $\mathbf{A}$ by replacing some (but not necessarily all) particular free occurrences of $\mathbf{a}$ in $\mathbf{A}$ by $\mathbf{b}$, no one of these occurrences being in a well formed part of $\mathbf{A}$ of form $\forall \mathbf{b} \mathbf{C}$. Then

$$\vdash \mathbf{a} = \mathbf{b} \supset . \mathbf{A} \equiv \mathbf{B}.$$

PROOF. Let $\mathbf{x}$ be an individual variable distinct from both $\mathbf{a}$ and $\mathbf{b}$ and occurring nowhere in $\mathbf{A}$. Let $\mathbf{A}^*$ result from $\mathbf{A}$ by replacing all the occurrences of $\mathbf{a}$ in $\mathbf{A}$ at which $\mathbf{b}$ is substituted in obtaining $\mathbf{B}$ by $\mathbf{x}$. Then $\mathbf{A}$ is $\mathrm{S}_{\mathbf{a}}{}^{\mathbf{x}}\mathbf{A}^*|$ and $\mathbf{B}$ is $\mathrm{S}_{\mathbf{b}}{}^{\mathbf{x}}\mathbf{A}^*|$. Let $\boldsymbol{\alpha}$ be a one-place relation variable not appearing in $\mathbf{A}$. Then by (D11), 45.4, and *modus ponens* (45.7)

$$\mathbf{a} = \mathbf{b} \vdash \boldsymbol{\alpha}(\mathbf{a}) \equiv \boldsymbol{\alpha}(\mathbf{b}).$$

By 45.4 and *modus ponens*

$$\forall \mathbf{x} . \boldsymbol{\alpha}(\mathbf{x}) \equiv \mathbf{A}^* \vdash \boldsymbol{\alpha}(\mathbf{a}) \equiv \mathbf{A}$$

and similarly

$$\forall \mathbf{x} . \boldsymbol{\alpha}(\mathbf{x}) \equiv \mathbf{A}^* \vdash \boldsymbol{\alpha}(\mathbf{b}) \equiv \mathbf{B}.$$

By the last three assertions and the propositional calculus

$$\forall \mathbf{x} . \boldsymbol{\alpha}(\mathbf{x}) \equiv \mathbf{A}^*, \quad \mathbf{a} = \mathbf{b} \vdash \mathbf{A} \equiv \mathbf{B}$$

whence by the deduction theorem

$$\forall \mathbf{x} . \boldsymbol{\alpha}(\mathbf{x}) \equiv \mathbf{A}^* \vdash \mathbf{a} = \mathbf{b} \supset . \mathbf{A} \equiv \mathbf{B}.$$

Now by 14.26

$$\exists \boldsymbol{\alpha} \forall \mathbf{x} . \boldsymbol{\alpha}(\mathbf{x}) \equiv \mathbf{A}^* \vdash \mathbf{a} = \mathbf{b} \supset . \mathbf{A} \equiv \mathbf{B}.$$

The wff to the left of the assertion sign is an instance of the comprehension axiom (45.6). Hence by the deduction theorem, 45.6, and *modus ponens*

$$\vdash \mathbf{a} = \mathbf{b} \supset . \mathbf{A} \equiv \mathbf{B}$$

completing the proof of 48.2. ▮

As corollaries of 48.1 and 48.2 we obtain 48.3 and 48.4.

48.3 $\vdash x = y \supset y = x$

PROOF. By 48.2 $\vdash x = y \supset . x = x \equiv y = x$. Theorem 48.3 follows by the propositional calculus and 48.1. ▮

48.4 $\vdash x = y \supset . y = z \supset x = z$

PROOF. By 48.2 $\vdash x = y \supset . x = z \equiv y = z$. Theorem 48.4 follows by the propositional calculus. ▌

From now on we shall replace the substitution operator $\mathbf{S_a}^{\mathrm{x}}\mathbf{A}|$ by a less cumbersome (and also less precise) notation. A notation

$$\mathbf{A}(\mathbf{x}_1, \mathbf{x}_2, \ldots, \mathbf{x}_n)$$

shall denote a wff and the notation

$$\mathbf{A}(\mathbf{y}_1, \mathbf{y}_2, \ldots, \mathbf{y}_n)$$

denote the result of replacing each free occurrence of $\mathbf{x}_i$ ($i = 1, 2, \ldots, n$) in $\mathbf{A}(\mathbf{x}_1, \mathbf{x}_2, \ldots, \mathbf{x}_n)$ by $\mathbf{y}_i$. The notation $\mathbf{A}(\mathbf{x}_1, \mathbf{x}_2, \ldots, \mathbf{x}_n)$ seems to suggest that each $\mathbf{x}_i$ ($i = 1, 2, \ldots, n$) has at least one free occurrence in $\mathbf{A}(\mathbf{x}_1, \mathbf{x}_2, \ldots, \mathbf{x}_n)$, but it is convenient not to so interpret the notation. Thus, for example, if $\mathbf{A}(x, y, z)$ is the wff $x = y$, then $\mathbf{A}(x_1, x_2, x_3)$ is the wff $x_1 = x_2$, $\mathbf{A}(x, y, y)$ is the wff $x = y$, and $\mathbf{A}(x, x, y)$ is the wff $x = x$. Also by using the notation $\mathbf{A}(\mathbf{x}_1, \mathbf{x}_2, \ldots, \mathbf{x}_n)$ we do not preclude the possibility that $\mathbf{A}(\mathbf{x}_1, \mathbf{x}_2, \ldots, \mathbf{x}_n)$ contains free variables other than $\mathbf{x}_1, \mathbf{x}_2, \ldots, \mathbf{x}_n$. When we wish to express the fact that no free variables other than $\mathbf{x}_1, \mathbf{x}_2, \ldots, \mathbf{x}_n$ appear in $\mathbf{A}(\mathbf{x}_1, \mathbf{x}_2, \ldots, \mathbf{x}_n)$ we shall say something like

"Let $\mathbf{A}(\mathbf{x}_1, \mathbf{x}_2, \ldots, \mathbf{x}_n)$ be a wff with all free variables displayed"

or, more simply,

"$\mathbf{A}(\mathbf{x}_1, \mathbf{x}_2, \ldots, \mathbf{x}_n)$ (all free variables displayed)."

Finally, in using this notation, we shall always assume that no confusion of bound variables occurs (i.e., each $\mathbf{y}_i$ is free for $\mathbf{x}_i$).

With these notational conventions established we introduce the following definition schema:

(D13) $\exists!\mathbf{x}\mathbf{A}(\mathbf{x}) \rightsquigarrow \exists\mathbf{x}\mathbf{A}(\mathbf{x}) \wedge \forall\mathbf{y}\,\forall\mathbf{z} \,.\, \mathbf{A}(\mathbf{y}) \supset . \mathbf{A}(\mathbf{z}) \supset \mathbf{y} = \mathbf{z}.$

(Here $\mathbf{y}$ and $\mathbf{z}$ are distinct individual variables not appearing in $\mathbf{A}(\mathbf{x})$; say, for definiteness the first two in the list of individual variables given in §44.)

The expression $\exists!\mathbf{x}\mathbf{A}(\mathbf{x})$ is read "there exists a unique $\mathbf{x}$ such that $\mathbf{A}(\mathbf{x})$." Clearly we have

48.5 $\vdash \exists!\mathbf{x}\mathbf{A}(\mathbf{x}) \supset \exists\mathbf{x}\mathbf{A}(\mathbf{x})$ and

48.6 $\vdash \exists!\mathbf{x}\mathbf{A}(\mathbf{x}) \supset . \mathbf{A}(\mathbf{y}) \supset . \mathbf{A}(\mathbf{z}) \supset \mathbf{y} = \mathbf{z}.$

EXERCISES

1. Let $\mathfrak{S}$ be the empty set of relation constants and X be the set consisting of two distinct individual constants a and b. Let $\mathfrak{M} = \langle V, D, \mathfrak{D}_1, \mathfrak{D}_2, \ldots\rangle$ be the second-order structure of type $(\mathfrak{S}, X)$ defined by
   (1) D is the set consisting of two distinct elements 1 and 2 (i.e. $D = \{1, 2\}$);
   (2) $V(\mathrm{a}) = 1$, $V(\mathrm{b}) = 2$;

(3) Each $\mathfrak{D}_n$ $(n = 1, 2, \ldots)$ consists of two elements: the empty set and the set of all n-tuples of D.

Show that $\mathfrak{M}$ is a second-order model (i.e. that $\mathfrak{M}$ models the comprehension axiom schema 45.6). Show also that $\mathfrak{M} \models \mathrm{a} = \mathrm{b}$ even though $V(\mathrm{a}) \neq V(\mathrm{b})$ (i.e. $1 \neq 2$).

*2. Modify the notion of a "model respecting equality" to apply to second-order logic (see §18). (The model of Exercise 1 above does not respect equality.) Prove an analog of 18.7 for second-order logic.

3. Prove that $\vdash \forall\alpha[\alpha(\mathrm{x}) \supset \alpha(\mathrm{y})] \supset \mathrm{x} = \mathrm{y}$.

4. Let φ be an n-place relation variable or constant and ψ be an n-place relation variable or constant. Define $\varphi = \psi$ by the definition schema

$$\varphi = \psi \rightsquigarrow \forall \mathrm{x}_1 \forall \mathrm{x}_2 \ldots \forall \mathrm{x}_n \centerdot \varphi(\mathrm{x}_1, \mathrm{x}_2, \ldots, \mathrm{x}_n) \equiv \psi(\mathrm{x}_1, \mathrm{x}_2, \ldots, \mathrm{x}_n).$$

Prove analogs of all the theorems of §48. *Hint:* the proof of the analog of 48.2 is by the induction on the length of A.

§49 Second-Order Peano Arithmetic

In this section we begin our study of the formal language PA_2 called **second-order Peano Arithmetic.**

The wffs of PA_2 are those of $\mathrm{L}_2(\mathfrak{S}_\mathrm{P}, X_\mathrm{P})$ where $\mathfrak{S}_\mathrm{P}$ is the set of relation constants consisting of a single two-place relation constant S and X_P is the empty set of individual constants.

The **standard model for** PA_2 is the model

$$\mathfrak{N} = \langle V, D, \mathfrak{D}_1, \mathfrak{D}_2, \ldots \rangle$$

where

(1) $D = \mathbf{N}$ the set of natural numbers;

(2) $V(\mathrm{S}) = \{(a, b) \in \mathbf{N}^2 | b = a + 1\}$;

(3) For each $n = 1, 2, \ldots$ $\mathfrak{D}_n$ is the set of all n-place relations on $\mathbf{N}$.

Thus $\mathfrak{N}$ is a full model and $\mathrm{S}(\mathrm{x}, \mathrm{y})$ means that y is the successor of x (namely $\mathrm{y} = \mathrm{x} + 1$).

In PA_2 (in addition to all the definition schemas of second-order logic) we also employ the following definition schemas:

(D14) $\mathrm{Z}_0(\mathbf{x}) \rightsquigarrow \forall \mathbf{y} \sim \mathrm{S}(\mathbf{y}, \mathbf{x})$

(D15) $\mathrm{Z}_{n+1}(\mathbf{x}) \rightsquigarrow \exists \mathbf{y} \centerdot \mathrm{S}(\mathbf{y}, \mathbf{x}) \wedge \mathrm{Z}_n(\mathbf{y})$ for $n = 0, 1, 2, \ldots$

Here **x** is any individual variable and **y** is some individual variable distinct from **x**. Note that the definition schema (D15) is inductive; that is, $\mathbf{Z}_{n+1}(\mathbf{x})$ is defined in terms of $\mathbf{Z}_n(\mathbf{x})$. Clearly $\mathbf{Z}_n(\mathbf{x})$ asserts that **x** is the natural number n. These definition schemas make up for the fact that the language PA_2 has no names for the natural numbers (i.e., no individual constants).

The axioms for PA_2 are formalizations of the familiar Peano axioms for arithmetic. They are the following four:

49.1 $\exists ! x Z_0(x)$

49.2 $\exists ! y S(x, y)$

49.3 $S(x, z) \supset . S(y, z) \supset x = y$

49.4 $\forall x[Z_0(x) \supset \alpha(x)] \supset . \forall x \, \forall y[[\alpha(x) \wedge S(x, y)] \supset \alpha(y)] \supset \forall x \alpha(x)$.

Note that these are particular axioms, not axiom schemas. Thus PA_2 has only finitely many (in fact, four) axioms besides those of second-order logic.

The meanings of the axioms are clear. Axiom 49.1 says that there is a unique element with no predecessor; axiom 49.2 says that every element has a unique successor; axiom 49.3 says that predecessors are unique (when they exist); and axiom 49.4 is the **axiom of mathematical induction**: every set which contains 0 and contains the successor of each of its elements contains all the natural numbers. Clearly each of the axioms 49.1–49.4 is valid in the standard model $\mathfrak{N}$.

The notions of deduction, deduction from hypotheses, theorem, etc. are *mutatis mutandis* the same for PA_2 as for the other languages we have studied. We still retain the notation $\vdash$ **A** to mean **A** is a theorem of PA_2. Clearly, all the theorem schemas for second-order logic are theorem schemas for PA_2 as well. Clearly each theorem of PA_2 is valid in the standard model $\mathfrak{N}$.

We now prove some theorem schemas of PA_2.

49.5 $\vdash \exists x Z_n(x)$ for $n = 0, 1, 2, \ldots$

PROOF. By induction on n. For $n = 0$, 49.5 follows from 49.1. Now clearly

$$Z_n(y), S(y, x) \vdash S(y, x) \wedge Z_n(y)$$

so by 14.9

$$Z_n(y), S(y, x) \vdash Z_{n+1}(x).$$

By 14.27

$$Z_n(y), \exists x S(y, x) \vdash \exists x Z_{n+1}(x)$$

and so by 49.2 and the deduction theorem

$$Z_n(y) \vdash \exists x Z_{n+1}(x).$$

Now by 14.26

$$\exists y Z_n(y) \vdash \exists x Z_{n+1}(x).$$

But assuming

$$\vdash \exists y Z_n(y)$$

as induction hypothesis, we obtain

$$\vdash \exists x Z_{n+1}(x)$$

by the deduction theorem and *modus ponens*. ∎

49.6 $\vdash Z_n(x_1) \supset \centerdot\, Z_n(x_2) \supset x_1 = x_2$ for $n = 0, 1, 2, \ldots$

PROOF. Again by induction on n. For $n = 0$, axiom 49.6 follows from 49.1. Assume

$$\vdash Z_n(y_1) \supset \centerdot\, Z_n(y_2) \supset y_1 = y_2$$

as induction hypothesis. Then by propositional calculus

$$S(y_1, x_1) \wedge Z_n(y_1), S(y_2, x_2) \wedge Z_n(y_2) \vdash y_1 = y_2$$

whence by substitutivity of equality $S(y_1, x_2)$ [as well as $S(y_1, x_1)$] can be obtained from these same hypotheses. Then by 49.2

$$S(y_1, x_1) \wedge Z_n(y_1), S(y_2, x_2) \wedge Z_n(y_2) \vdash x_1 = x_2$$

so by 14.26 twice

$$Z_{n+1}(x_1), Z_{n+1}(x_2) \vdash x_1 = x_2$$

and now use the deduction theorem. ∎

49.7 $\vdash \exists! x Z_n(x)$ for $n = 0, 1, 2, \ldots$

PROOF. Proof is immediate from 49.5, 49.6, and (D15). ∎

49.8 $\vdash Z_n(x) \supset \centerdot\, Z_{n+1}(y) \supset S(x, y)$ for $n = 0, 1, 2, \ldots$

PROOF. By 49.6

$$Z_n(x), S(z, y) \wedge Z_n(z) \vdash x = z$$

and so by substitutivity of equality (48.2)

$$Z_n(x), S(z, y) \wedge Z_n(z) \vdash S(x, y).$$

Now use 14.26 and the deduction theorem. ∎

49.9 $\vdash Z_n(x) \supset \centerdot\, Z_m(y) \supset x \neq y$ if $n \neq m$ $(n, m = 0, 1, 2, \ldots)$.

PROOF. Clearly it suffices to consider the case $n < m$. We proceed by induction on n. Suppose $n = 0$ and $m > 0$. As

$$Z_0(x) \vdash \forall z \sim S(z, x)$$

by D(14) and

$$Z_m(y) \vdash \exists z S(z, y)$$

by (D15) and first-order logic (details left to the reader) we obtain by substitutivity of equality (48.2) and propositional calculus

$$Z_0(x), Z_m(y), x = y \vdash \mathfrak{f}.$$

Now use the deduction theorem.

Next assume inductively that

$$\vdash Z_n(x) \supset . Z_m(y) \supset x \neq y.$$

By substitutivity of equality (48.2) and 49.3

$$S(x, x_1) \wedge Z_n(x), S(y, y_1) \wedge Z_m(y), x_1 = y_1 \vdash x = y.$$

These last two yield

$$S(x, x_1) \wedge Z_n(x), S(y, y_1) \wedge Z_m(y) \vdash x_1 \neq y_1$$

so by 14.26 twice and the deduction theorem

$$\vdash Z_{n+1}(x_1) \supset . Z_{m+1}(y_1) \supset x_1 \neq y_1$$

completing the proof of 49.9. ▮

§50 Primitive Recursive Functions

Unlike the formal language RA of Chapter 3, the formal language PA_2 has no names for the various primitive recursive functions. In this section we show how to overcome this difficulty. We shall construct for each n-place function constant **f** of RA (see §21) a wff $\mathbf{A}_\mathbf{f}(x_1, x_2, \ldots, x_n, y)$ of PA_2 (all free variables displayed) which (intuitively speaking) asserts that $\mathbf{f}(x_1, x_2, \ldots, x_n) = y$.

For each n-place function constant **f** of RA, the wff $\mathbf{A}_\mathbf{f}(x_1, x_2, \ldots, x_n, y)$ of PA_2 is defined by the following rules:

(f1) If **f** is the one-place function constant Z, then

$$\mathbf{A}_\mathbf{f}(x, y) \rightsquigarrow Z_0(y).$$

(f2) If $\mathbf{f}$ is the one-place function constant S, then

$$\mathbf{A_f}(x, y) \rightsquigarrow S(x, y).$$

(f3) If $\mathbf{f}$ is the n-place function constant I_i^n ($n = 1, 2, \ldots; i = 1, 2, \ldots, n$), then

$$\mathbf{A_f}(x_1, x_2, \ldots, x_n, y) \rightsquigarrow y = x_i.$$

(f4) If $\mathbf{f}$ is of the form $\mathbf{Chg}_1 \ldots \mathbf{g}_m$ where $\mathbf{h}$ is an m-place function constant and $\mathbf{g}_1, \ldots, \mathbf{g}_m$ are n-place function constants, then

$$\mathbf{A_f}(x_1, \ldots, x_n, y) \rightsquigarrow \exists z_1 \ldots \exists z_m \,\blacksquare\, \mathbf{A_h}(z_1, \ldots, z_m, y) \\ \wedge \mathbf{A}_{\mathbf{g}_1}(x_1, \ldots, x_n, z_1) \wedge \ldots \wedge \mathbf{A}_{\mathbf{g}_m}(x_1, \ldots, x_n, z_m).$$

(f5) If $\mathbf{f}$ is of the form $\mathbf{Rgh}$ where $\mathbf{g}$ is an n-place function constant and $\mathbf{h}$ is an $(n+2)$-place function constant, then

$$\mathbf{A_f}(x_1, \ldots, x_n, z) \rightsquigarrow \forall\alpha \,\blacksquare\, \Phi(\alpha) \supset \blacksquare\, \Psi(\alpha) \supset \alpha(x_1, \ldots, x_n, z)$$

where

$$\Phi(\alpha) \rightsquigarrow \forall x_1 \ldots \forall x_n \forall y \forall z \,\blacksquare\, Z_0(y) \\ \supset \blacksquare\, \mathbf{A_g}(x_1, \ldots, x_n, z) \supset \alpha(x_1, \ldots, x_n, z)$$

and

$$\Psi(\alpha) \rightsquigarrow \forall x_1 \ldots \forall x_n \forall y \forall y_1 \forall z\, z_1 \,\blacksquare\, \alpha(x_1, \ldots, x_n, y, z) \supset \blacksquare\, S(y, y_1) \\ \supset \blacksquare\, \mathbf{A_h}(x_1, \ldots, x_n, y, z, z_1) \supset \alpha(x_1, \ldots, x_n, y_1, z_1).$$

The idea of (f5) is this: $\Phi(\alpha)$ says that α is a set of $(n+2)$-tuples containing all $(n+2)$-tuples of form $(x_1, \ldots, x_n, 0, \mathbf{g}(x_1, \ldots, x_n))$; $\Phi(\alpha)$ corresponds to axiom schema 23.14. The wff $\Psi(\alpha)$ says that α is a set of $(n+2)$-tuples which contains $(x_1, \ldots, x_n, y+1, \mathbf{h}(x_1, \ldots, x_n, y, z))$ whenever it contains $(x_1, \ldots, x_n, y, z)$; the wff $\Psi(\alpha)$ corresponds to axiom schema 23.15. Now the set of all $(n+2)$-tuples of form $(x_1, \ldots, x_n, y, \mathbf{f}(x_1, \ldots, x_n, y))$ is the smallest set satisfying $\Phi(\alpha)$ and $\Psi(\alpha)$ and is hence also the intersection of all sets α satisfying $\Phi(\alpha)$ and $\Psi(\alpha)$. On the other hand, the wff $\mathbf{A_f}(x_1, \ldots, x_n, y, z)$ says that $(x_1, \ldots, x_n, y, z)$ is in this intersection—that $z = \mathbf{f}(x_1, \ldots, x_n, y)$.

We next prove the following theorem schema:

50.1 If $\mathbf{f}$ is an n-place function constant of RA, then

$$\vdash \exists! y \mathbf{A_f}(x_1, x_2, \ldots, x_n, y).$$

Proof. We prove 50.1 by induction (in the metalanguage) on the length of $\mathbf{f}$.

Case 1. Assume $\mathbf{f}$ is $\mathbf{Z}$ so that $\mathbf{A_f}(x, y)$ is $Z_0(y)$. Schema 50.1 is 49.1.

CASE 2. Assume **f** is S so that $\mathbf{A}_\mathbf{f}(x, y)$ is $S(x, y)$. Schema 50.1 is 49.2.

CASE 3. Assume **f** is I_i^n so that $\mathbf{A}_\mathbf{f}(x_1, \ldots, x_n, y)$ is $x_i = y$. By 14.9 $\vdash x_i = x_i \supset \exists y x_i = y$ and so by 48.1 and *modus ponens*

$$\vdash \exists y \mathbf{A}_\mathbf{f}(x_1, \ldots, x_n, y).$$

By 48.2 we get

$$\vdash x_i = y_1 \supset \centerdot\, x_i = y_2 \supset y_1 = y_2.$$

That is

$$\vdash \mathbf{A}_\mathbf{f}(x_1, \ldots, x_n, y_1) \supset \centerdot\, \mathbf{A}_\mathbf{f}(x_1, \ldots, x_n, y_2) \supset y_1 = y_2$$

Now generalize on y_1 and y_2 and use (D13) (and the propositional calculus).

CASE 4. Assume **f** is $\mathbf{Chg}_1 \ldots \mathbf{g}_m$ where **h** is m-place and $\mathbf{g}_1, \ldots, \mathbf{g}_m$ are n-place. To simplify the notation we consider only the case $m = n = 1$; the general case follows by what is essentially the same argument. We may assume as induction hypotheses that

$$\vdash \exists ! y \mathbf{A}_\mathbf{h}(z, y)$$

and

$$\vdash \exists ! z \mathbf{A}_\mathbf{g}(x, z).$$

By definition $\mathbf{A}_\mathbf{f}(x, y)$ is

$$\exists z \centerdot\, \mathbf{A}_\mathbf{h}(z, y) \wedge \mathbf{A}_\mathbf{g}(x, z).$$

By propositional calculus,

$$\mathbf{A}_\mathbf{g}(x, z), \mathbf{A}_\mathbf{h}(z, y) \vdash \mathbf{A}_\mathbf{h}(z, y) \wedge \mathbf{A}_\mathbf{g}(x, z)$$

so by 14.9 we get

$$\mathbf{A}_\mathbf{g}(x, z), \mathbf{A}_\mathbf{h}(z, y) \vdash \mathbf{A}_\mathbf{f}(x, y).$$

By 14.27 we get

$$\mathbf{A}_\mathbf{g}(x, z), \exists y \mathbf{A}_\mathbf{h}(z, y) \vdash \exists y \mathbf{A}_\mathbf{f}(x, y)$$

so by the deduction theorem, the induction hypotheses for **h**, and *modus ponens*

$$\mathbf{A}_\mathbf{g}(x, z) \vdash \exists y \mathbf{A}_\mathbf{f}(x, y).$$

Now use 14.26 (on z), the deduction theorem, the induction hypothesis for **g**, and *modus ponens* again to obtain

$$\vdash \exists y \mathbf{A}_\mathbf{f}(x, y).$$

Now we shall prove uniqueness. By the induction hypothesis for **g**

$$\mathbf{A_h}(z_1, y_1) \wedge \mathbf{A_g}(x, z_1), \mathbf{A_h}(z_2, y_2) \wedge \mathbf{A_g}(x, z_2) \vdash z_1 = z_2$$

whence by the substitutivity of equality (48.2) and the induction hypothesis for **g**, we find $y_1 = y_2$ can be proved from these same hypotheses. Then using 14.26 twice (on z_1 and z_2) we obtain

$$\mathbf{A_f}(x, y_1), \mathbf{A_f}(x, y_2) \vdash y_1 = y_2.$$

Now use the deduction theorem twice, generalize on y_1 and y_2, and use (D13) (and the propositional calculus).

CASE 5. Assume **f** is **Rgh** where **g** is n-place and **h** is $(n + 2)$-place. This is the most difficult case. The proof is simply a formalization in PA_2 of the informal proof justifying definition by primitive recursion given in the Appendix (see §A3). To simplify the notation, we only consider the case $n = 1$. As induction hypotheses we have

$$\exists ! z \mathbf{A_g}(x, z)$$

and

$$\exists ! z_1\, \mathbf{A_h}(x, y, z, z_1).$$

We shall need 50.2 and 50.3.

50.2 $\vdash Z_0(y) \supset_{\bullet} \mathbf{A_g}(x, z) \supset \mathbf{A_f}(x, y, z).$

50.3 $\vdash \mathbf{A_f}(x, y, z) \supset_{\bullet} S(y, y_1) \supset_{\bullet} \mathbf{A_h}(x, y, z, z_1) \supset \mathbf{A_f}(x, y_1, z_1).$

We leave the proofs of 50.2 and 50.3 to the reader; they require nothing more than the definition of $\mathbf{A_f}(x, y, z)$ and theorem schemas of second-order logic. (Schemas 50.2 and 50.3 are formalizations of Lemmas 1 and 2 of Appendix A3.)

We shall also need 50.4 and 50.5.

50.4 $\vdash Z_0(y) \supset_{\bullet} \mathbf{A_f}(x, y, z) \supset \mathbf{A_g}(x, z).$

50.5 $\vdash \mathbf{A_f}(x, y_1, z_1) \supset_{\bullet} S(y, y_1) \supset \exists z_{\bullet} \mathbf{A_f}(x, y, z) \wedge \mathbf{A_h}(x, y, z, z_1).$

The proofs of 50.4 and 50.5 are similar. We sketch the idea. (Schemas 50.4 and 50.5 are formalizations of Lemmas 3 and 4 of A3 in the Appendix.) Let $\mathbf{Q}(\alpha, x, y, z)$ be the wff defined by

$$\mathbf{Q}(\alpha, x, y, z) \rightsquigarrow \forall x_1\, \forall y_1\, \forall z_1 {}_{\bullet}\, \alpha(x_1, y_1, z_1)$$
$$\equiv_{\bullet} \mathbf{A_f}(x_1, y_1, z_1) \wedge [x \neq x_1 \vee y \neq y_1 \vee z \neq z_1]$$

Then $\exists \alpha \mathbf{Q}(\alpha, x, y, z)$ is an instance of the comprehension axiom schema (45.6).

Now recall that $\mathbf{A}_f(x, y, z)$ is given by

$$\mathbf{A}_f(x, y, z) \rightsquigarrow \forall\alpha \centerdot \Phi(\alpha) \supset \centerdot \Psi(\alpha) \supset \alpha(x, y, z)$$

where

$$\Phi(\alpha) \rightsquigarrow \forall x\, \forall y\, \forall z \centerdot \mathbf{Z}_0(y) \supset \centerdot \mathbf{A}_g(x, z) \supset \alpha(x, y, z)$$

and

$$\Psi(\alpha) \rightsquigarrow \forall x\, \forall y\, \forall y_1\, \forall z\, \forall z_1 \centerdot \alpha(x, y, z) \supset \centerdot \mathbf{S}(y, y_1) \supset \centerdot \mathbf{A}_h(x, y, z, z_1) \supset \alpha(x, y_1, z_1).$$

To prove 50.4 show that

$$\mathbf{Q}(\alpha, x, y, z), \mathbf{Z}_0(y), \sim \mathbf{A}_g(x, z) \vdash \Phi(\alpha) \wedge \Psi(\alpha).$$

It then follows that $\alpha(x, y, z)$ can be proved if $\mathbf{A}_f(x, y, z)$ is added as hypothesis and hence also $x \neq x \vee y \neq y \vee z \neq z$. Then by 48.1, propositional calculus, and the deduction theorem,

$$\mathbf{Q}(\alpha, x, y, z) \vdash \mathbf{Z}_0(y) \supset \centerdot \mathbf{A}_f(x, y, z) \supset \centerdot \mathbf{A}_g(x, z)$$

and the hypothesis $\mathbf{Q}(\alpha, x, y, z)$ can be eliminated by 14.26 and the comprehension axiom schema (45.6).

To prove 50.5 show

$$\mathbf{Q}(\alpha, x, y_1, z_1), \mathbf{S}(y, y_1), \sim \exists z \centerdot \mathbf{A}_f(x, y, z) \wedge \mathbf{A}_h(x, y, z, z_1) \vdash \Phi(\alpha) \wedge \Psi(\alpha)$$

and proceed in exactly the same way.

Now from 50.2 (for existence) and 50.4 (for uniqueness) and the induction hypothesis (for **g**) the reader may prove

(1) $\vdash \mathbf{Z}_0(y) \supset \exists! z \mathbf{A}_f(x, y, z).$

Similarly, from 50.3 (for existence) and 50.5 (for uniqueness) and the induction hypothesis (for **h**) follows

(2) $\vdash \exists! z \mathbf{A}_f(x, y, z) \wedge \mathbf{S}(y, y_1) \centerdot \supset \exists! z_1\, \mathbf{A}_f(x, y_1, z_1).$

Now let $\mathbf{B}(\alpha)$ be the wff defined by

$$\mathbf{B}(\alpha) \rightsquigarrow \forall y \centerdot \alpha(y) \equiv \exists! z \mathbf{A}_f(x, y, z).$$

Then by (1) and first-order logic

$$\mathbf{B}(\alpha) \vdash \mathbf{Z}_0(y) \supset \alpha(y)$$

and by (2)

$$\mathbf{B}(\alpha) \vdash \alpha(y) \wedge \mathbf{S}(y, y_1) \centerdot \supset \alpha(y_1)$$

so by the axiom of mathematical induction (49.4)

$$\mathbf{B}(\alpha) \vdash \alpha(y)$$

and hence

$$\mathbf{B}(\alpha) \vdash \exists! z \mathbf{A}_{\mathbf{f}}(x, y, z).$$

Now get rid of the hypothesis $\mathbf{B}(\alpha)$ by 14.26 and the comprehension axiom (45.6). This completes Case 5 and hence also the proof of 50.1. ▮

§51 Numeralwise Representability

In this section we continue the work begun in the last section. For each n-place function constant **f** of RA, $\mathbf{A}_{\mathbf{f}}(x_1, \ldots, x_n, y)$ is the wff of PA_2 defined in §50.

51.1 Theorem. Let **f** be an n-place function constant of RA and let f be the numerical function denoted by **f**. Suppose $a_1, \ldots, a_n$ are natural numbers, and $b = f(a_1, \ldots, a_n)$. Then

$$\vdash Z_{a_1}(x_1) \supset . \ldots \supset . Z_{a_n}(x_n) \supset . Z_b(y) \supset \mathbf{A}_{\mathbf{f}}(x_1, \ldots, x_n, y).$$

Proof. By induction (in the metalanguage on the length of **f**).

Case 1. Assume **f** is Z. Then $\mathbf{A}_{\mathbf{f}}(x, y)$ is $Z_0(y)$ and 51.1 follows from $\vdash Z_0(y) \supset Z_0(y)$.

Case 2. Assume **f** is S. Then $\mathbf{A}_{\mathbf{f}}(x, y)$ is $S(x, y)$ and 51.1 is 49.8.

Case 3. Assume **f** is I_i^n. Then $\mathbf{A}_{\mathbf{f}}(x_1, \ldots, x_n, y)$ is $x_i = y$ and 51.1 follows from 49.6.

Case 4. Assume **f** is $\mathbf{Chg}_1 \ldots \mathbf{g}_m$ where **h** is m-place and $\mathbf{g}_1, \ldots, \mathbf{g}_m$ are n-place. To illustrate the proof we suppose that $m = n = 1$. Then $\mathbf{A}_{\mathbf{f}}(x, y)$ is $\exists z . \mathbf{A}_{\mathbf{h}}(z, y) \wedge \mathbf{A}_{\mathbf{g}}(x, y)$. Choose a natural number a and let $c = g(a)$ and $b = h(c) = f(a)$ (where **g** denotes g and **h** denotes h). By the induction hypothesis

$$Z_a(x), Z_b(y), Z_c(z) \vdash \mathbf{A}_{\mathbf{h}}(z, y) \wedge \mathbf{A}_{\mathbf{g}}(x, z)$$

and so by 14.27

$$Z_a(x), Z_b(y), \exists z Z_c(z) \vdash \mathbf{A}_{\mathbf{f}}(x, y).$$

The hypotheses $\exists z Z_c(z)$ may be deleted by 49.5. Then the deduction theorem gives 51.1.

CASE 5. Assume $\mathbf{f}$ is $\mathbf{Rgh}$ where $\mathbf{g}$ is n-place and $\mathbf{h}$ is $(n+2)$-place. To simplify notation we assume $n = 1$. Choose natural numbers a and b and let $c = f(a, b)$. We shall prove

(*) $\quad \vdash Z_a(x) \supset . Z_b(y) \supset . Z_c(x) \supset \mathbf{A_f}(x, y, z)$

by induction (in the metalanguage) on b.

In case $b = 0$ we have (by the induction hypothesis of the whole proof) that

$$\vdash Z_a(x) \supset . Z_b(y) \supset . Z_c(z) \supset \mathbf{A_g}(x, z)$$

whence (*) follows by 50.2. Now assume (*) inductively and let $b_1 = b + 1$ and $c_1 = f(a, b_1) = h(a\ b, c)$. Then we have

$$Z_a(x), Z_b(y), Z_c(z), Z_{b_1}(y_1), Z_{c_1}(z_1) \vdash \mathbf{A_f}(x, y, z).$$

By the induction hypothesis (for $\mathbf{h}$) we can prove $\mathbf{A_h}(x, y, z, z_1)$ from these hypotheses and by 49.8 we can prove $S(y, y_1)$. Hence by 50.3 we obtain

$$Z_a(x), Z_b(y), Z_c(z), Z_{b_1}(y_1), Z_{c_1}(z_1) \vdash \mathbf{A_f}(x, y_1, z_1).$$

Use 14.26 and 48.5 to eliminate the hypotheses $Z_b(y)$ and $Z_c(z)$. Then by the deduction theorem

$$\vdash Z_a(x) \supset . Z_{b_1}(y_1) \supset . Z_{c_1}(z_1) \supset \mathbf{A_f}(x, y_1, z_1).$$

This completes Case 5 and the proof of 51.1. ▮

51.2 Corollary. With the notation of 51.1 we have

$$\vdash Z_{a_1}(x_1) \supset . \ldots \supset . Z_{a_n}(x_n) \supset . Z_b(y) \equiv \mathbf{A_f}(x_1, \ldots, x_n, y).$$

PROOF. Take $n = 1$ to simplify the notation. By 51.1

(†) $\quad Z_a(x) \vdash Z_b(y) \supset \mathbf{A_f}(x, y).$

For the same reason

$$Z_a(x), Z_b(y_1) \vdash \mathbf{A_f}(x, y_1).$$

Thus by 50.1 (uniqueness)

$$Z_a(x), Z_b(y_1), \mathbf{A_f}(x, y) \vdash y = y_1$$

so by substitutivity of equality and the deduction theorem

$$Z_a(x), Z_b(y_1) \vdash \mathbf{A_f}(x, y) \supset Z_b(y).$$

Now use 14.26 and 49.5 to get rid of the hypothesis $Z_b(y_1)$ obtaining

$$Z_a(x) \vdash \mathbf{A_f}(x, y) \supset Z_b(y)$$

which with (†), the propositional calculus, and the deduction theorem yields 51.2. ∎

Let R be an n-place relation on the natural numbers. The relation R is called **numeralwise representable** in PA_2 iff there is a wff $\mathbf{A}_R(x_1, \ldots, x_n)$ of PA_2 such that

$$\vdash Z_{a_1}(x_1) \supset . \ldots \supset . Z_{a_n}(x_n) \supset \mathbf{A}_R(x_1, \ldots, x_n) \quad \text{if} \quad R(a_1, \ldots, a_n)$$

and

$$\vdash Z_{a_1}(x_1) \supset . \ldots \supset . Z_{a_n}(x_n) \supset \sim \mathbf{A}_R(x_1, \ldots, x_n) \quad \text{if} \quad \text{not-}R(a_1, \ldots, a_n)$$

for all natural numbers $a_1, \ldots, a_n$. When this is the case, we say that the wff $\mathbf{A}_R(x_1, \ldots, x_n)$ **numeralwise represents the relation** R in PA_2.

Our next result gives us many examples of numeralwise-representable relations.

51.3 Theorem. Every primitive recursive relation is numeralwise representable in PA_2.

PROOF. Let R be an n-place primitive recursive relation. Then by definition its characteristic function K_R (see §27) is primitive recursive. Let $\mathbf{k}$ be a function constant of RA denoting K_R and define $\mathbf{A}_R(x_1, \ldots, x_n)$ by

$$\mathbf{A}_R(x_1, \ldots, x_n) \rightsquigarrow \exists y \,.\, Z_1(y) \wedge \mathbf{A}_{\mathbf{k}}(x_1, \ldots, x_n, y).$$

Let $a_1, \ldots, a_n$ be natural numbers. If $R(a_1, \ldots, a_n)$, then $K_R(a_1, \ldots, a_n) = 1$ and so by 51.1

$$Z_{a_1}(x_1), \ldots, Z_{a_n}(x_1), Z_1(y) \vdash Z_1(y) \wedge \mathbf{A}_{\mathbf{k}}(x_1, \ldots, x_n, y).$$

By 14.27

$$Z_{a_1}(x_1), \ldots, Z_{a_n}(x_1), \exists y Z_1(y) \vdash \mathbf{A}_R(x_1, \ldots, x_n).$$

Eliminate the hypothesis $\exists y Z_1(y)$ by 49.5 and use the deduction theorem to obtain

$$\vdash Z_{a_1}(x_1) \supset . \ldots \supset . Z_{a_n}(x_n) \supset \mathbf{A}_R(x_1, \ldots, x_n).$$

Now suppose not-$R(a_1, \ldots, a_n)$. Then $K_R(a_1, \ldots, a_n) = 0$. By 51.2

$$Z_{a_1}(x_1), \ldots, Z_{a_n}(x_n) \vdash Z_0(y) \equiv \mathbf{A}_{\mathbf{k}}(x_1, \ldots, x_n, y).$$

As $\vdash Z_0(y) \supset \sim Z_1(y)$ by 49.9 we obtain by propositional calculus

$$Z_{a_1}(x_1), \ldots, Z_{a_n}(x_n) \vdash \sim . Z_1(y) \wedge \mathbf{A}_{\mathbf{k}}(x_1, \ldots, x_n, y).$$

Generalizing on y and applying the deduction theorem yields

$$\vdash Z_{a_1}(x_1) \supset . \ldots \supset . Z_{a_n}(x_n) \supset \sim \mathbf{A}_R(x_1, \ldots, x_n).$$

Thus $\mathbf{A}_R(x_1, \ldots, x_n)$ numeralwise represents R. This completes the proof of 51.3. ∎

§52 Gödel's Theorem for PA_2

We may assign Gödel numbers to the formulas and sequences of formulas of PA_2 in such a way that the various syntactical functions are "encoded" as primitive recursive functions. We shall not present the details of this work as it is not much different from the work done in Chapter 4 for the language RA.

Let $ded(a, k)$ be the two-place relation which holds exactly when a is the Gödel number of a wff **A** of PA_2 and k is the Gödel number of a deduction of **A** (in PA_2). Let $sub(a, n)$ be the Gödel number of the wff

$$\forall \mathrm{x} \,\blacksquare\, \mathbf{Z}_n(\mathrm{x}) \supset \mathbf{A}$$

when a is the Gödel number of the wff **A** and let $sub(a, n) = 0$ if a is not the Gödel number of a wff of PA_2. Then $ded(a, k)$ is a primitive recursive relation in a and k and $sub(a, n)$ is primitive recursive function of a and n.

Let **Ded** (x, y) be a wff of PA_2 numeralwise representing $ded(a, k)$ according to 51.3. Then

$$(1) \qquad \vdash \mathbf{Z}_a(\mathrm{x}) \supset \blacksquare\, \mathbf{Z}_k(\mathrm{y}) \supset \mathbf{Ded}(\mathrm{x}, \mathrm{y})$$

whenever k is the Gödel number of a deduction of a wff whose Gödel number is a and

$$(2) \qquad \vdash \mathbf{Z}_a(\mathrm{x}) \supset \blacksquare\, \mathbf{Z}_k(\mathrm{y}) \supset {\sim}\, \mathbf{Ded}(\mathrm{x}, \mathrm{y})$$

in the contrary case.

Similarly let **sub** be a two-place function constant of RA denoting the primitive recursive function *sub* and let **Sub** (x, y, z) be the wff $\mathbf{A}_{\mathbf{sub}}(\mathrm{x}, \mathrm{y}, \mathrm{z})$. Then by 51.2

$$(3) \qquad \vdash \mathbf{Z}_a(\mathrm{x}) \supset \blacksquare\, \mathbf{Z}_n(\mathrm{y}) \supset \blacksquare\, \mathbf{Z}_b(\mathrm{z}) \equiv \mathbf{Sub}(\mathrm{x}, \mathrm{y}, \mathrm{z})$$

whenever $b = sub(a, n)$.

Now let **Th** (y) be the wff given by

$$\mathbf{Th}(\mathrm{y}) \rightsquigarrow \exists \mathrm{z}\, \mathbf{Ded}(\mathrm{y}, \mathrm{z}).$$

Let **I**(x) be the wff given by

$$\mathbf{I}(\mathrm{x}) \rightsquigarrow \forall \mathrm{y} \,\blacksquare\, \mathbf{Sub}(\mathrm{x}, \mathrm{x}, \mathrm{y}) \supset {\sim}\, \mathbf{Th}(\mathrm{y}).$$

Let i be the Gödel number of **I**(x) and let **J** be the wff given by

$$\mathbf{J} \rightsquigarrow \forall \mathrm{x} \,\blacksquare\, \mathbf{Z}_i(\mathrm{x}) \supset \mathbf{I}(\mathrm{x}).$$

Let j be the Gödel number of **J**.

The reader should compare these sentences with those of §37. Recall that PA_2 is **inconsistent** iff $\mathfrak{f}$ (and hence every wff) is a theorem and **consistent** otherwise.

52.1 Theorem. If PA_2 is consistent, then **J** is not a theorem of PA_2.

REMARK. Of course, PA_2 is consistent as it has a (standard) model. However, when the consistency of PA_2 is hypothesized, the proof of 52.1 (given below) is constructive.

PROOF. Suppose on the contrary that $\vdash \mathbf{J}$. We shall show (under this assumption) that PA_2 is inconsistent.

Let k be the Gödel number of a proof of **J**. Then by (1)

$$\mathbf{Z}_j(\mathrm{y}), \mathbf{Z}_k(\mathrm{z}) \vdash \mathbf{Ded}\,(\mathrm{y}, \mathrm{z})$$

so by 14.27

$$\mathbf{Z}_j(\mathrm{y}), \exists \mathrm{z} \mathbf{Z}_k(\mathrm{z}) \vdash \mathbf{Th}\,(\mathrm{y})$$

and by 49.7

$$(*) \qquad \mathbf{Z}_j(\mathrm{y}) \vdash \mathbf{Th}\,(\mathrm{y}).$$

Also by (3)

$$\mathbf{Z}_i(\mathrm{x}), \mathbf{Z}_j(\mathrm{y}) \vdash \mathbf{Sub}\,(\mathrm{x}, \mathrm{x}, \mathrm{y})$$

as $j = sub\,(i, i)$. We have assumed $\vdash \mathbf{J}$; that is,

$$\vdash \forall \mathrm{x} \centerdot \mathbf{Z}_i(\mathrm{x}) \supset \forall \mathrm{y} \centerdot \mathbf{Sub}\,(\mathrm{x}, \mathrm{x}, \mathrm{y}) \supset \sim \mathbf{Th}\,(\mathrm{y})$$

so by the last two steps

$$\mathbf{Z}_i(\mathrm{x}), \mathbf{Z}_j(\mathrm{y}) \vdash \sim \mathbf{Th}\,(\mathrm{y}).$$

By 14.26 (on x) and 49.7 we may eliminate the hypothesis $\mathbf{Z}_i(\mathrm{x})$ obtaining

$$\mathbf{Z}_j(\mathrm{y}) \vdash \sim \mathbf{Th}\,(\mathrm{y})$$

which together with (*), propositional calculus, and the deduction theorem yields $\vdash \sim \mathbf{Z}_j(\mathrm{y})$. Generalizing on y we obtain a wff whose negation is a theorem (by 49.5) and reach the conclusion that PA_2 is inconsistent. This establishes 52.1. ▮

52.2 Corollary. The sentence **J** holds in the standard model for PA_2 (see §49), but is not a theorem of PA_2.

Indeed, as in §37, **J** asserts of itself that it is not a theorem; as it is in fact not a theorem, it holds in the standard model.

The formal language PA_2 is called **ω inconsistent** iff there is a wff $\mathbf{A}(\mathbf{x})$ of PA_2 such that

$$\vdash \mathbf{Z}_n(\mathbf{x}) \supset \mathbf{A}(\mathbf{x})$$

for each $n = 0, 1, 2, \ldots$ and also

$$\vdash \exists \mathbf{x} \sim \mathbf{A}(\mathbf{x}).$$

The formal language PA_2 is **ω consistent** otherwise.

Of course, PA_2 is ω consistent as it is impossible that all the sentences $\forall \mathbf{x} \centerdot \mathbf{Z}_n(\mathbf{x}) \supset \mathbf{A}(\mathbf{x})$ (with $n = 0, 1, 2, \ldots$) and $\exists \mathbf{x} \sim \mathbf{A}(\mathbf{x})$ hold in the standard model. However, this proof of ω consistency is not constructive, and it is often useful to hypothesize in a theorem that PA_2 is ω consistent in order to emphasize that the proof of the theorem is constructive, as in the example that follows.

52.3 First Gödel Incompleteness Theorem for PA_2**.** If PA_2 is ω consistent, then neither **J** nor ~**J** is a theorem of PA_2.

Proof. Observe that ω consistency clearly implies consistency: if PA_2 is inconsistent, every wff is a theorem, and hence certainly PA_2 is ω inconsistent. Thus, under the hypothesis of ω consistency, **J** is not a theorem by 52.1.

As **J** is not a theorem $ded(j, n)$ is false for each $n = 0, 1, 2, \ldots$ and hence by (2) and generalization

$$(**) \quad \vdash \mathrm{Z}_n(\mathrm{z}) \supset \forall \mathrm{y} \centerdot \mathrm{Z}_j(\mathrm{y}) \supset \sim \mathbf{Ded}\,(\mathrm{y}, \mathrm{z})$$

for $n = 0, 1, 2, \ldots$. Now suppose $\vdash \sim \mathbf{J}$. Then by first-order logic

$$\vdash \exists \mathrm{z}\, \exists \mathrm{x}\, \exists \mathrm{y} \centerdot \mathrm{Z}_i(\mathrm{x}) \wedge \mathbf{Sub}\,(\mathrm{x}, \mathrm{x}, \mathrm{y}) \wedge \mathbf{Ded}\,(\mathrm{y}, \mathrm{z}).$$

By (3)

$$\mathrm{Z}_i(\mathrm{x}) \wedge \mathbf{Sub}\,(\mathrm{x}, \mathrm{x}, \mathrm{y}) \wedge \mathbf{Ded}\,(\mathrm{y}, \mathrm{z}) \vdash \mathrm{Z}_j(\mathrm{y}) \wedge \mathbf{Ded}\,(\mathrm{y}, \mathrm{z}).$$

Hence by 14.26 and 14.27 and the last two steps

$$\vdash \exists \mathrm{z}\, \exists \mathrm{y} \centerdot \mathrm{Z}_j(\mathrm{y}) \wedge \mathbf{Ded}\,(\mathrm{y}, \mathrm{z})$$

that is,

$$\vdash \exists \mathrm{z} \sim \forall \mathrm{y} \centerdot \mathrm{Z}_j(\mathrm{y}) \supset \sim \mathbf{Ded}\,(\mathrm{y}, \mathrm{z})$$

which with (**) contradicts ω consistency. Thus the assumption that $\vdash \sim \mathbf{J}$ was wrong and the proof of 52.3 is complete. ▌

§53 Church's Theorem for Second-Order Logic

In this section we prove that there is no decision procedure or algorithm for deciding if a wff of PA_2 is a theorem of PA_2. The proof is simply a modification of the proof for RA in §43. Since PA_2 has only finitely many nonlogical axioms we obtain Church's theorem for second-order logic as a corollary.

53.1 Church's Theorem for PA_2**.** There is no algorithm which, when applied to a wff of PA_2, decides if that wff is a theorem of PA_2. More precisely, the set of Gödel numbers of theorems of PA_2 is not recursive.

PROOF. (Compare with 43.1.) Suppose the theorem is false, that the set of Gödel numbers of theorems of PA_2 is recursive. Then the complement of this set is recursively enumerable (see §42); that is, there is a one-place primitive recursive function g with the following property:

> For every wff **B** of PA_2, **B** is not a theorem if and only if there is a natural number k such that $g(k)$ is the Gödel number of **B**.

Let **g** be a one-place function constant of RA denoting g and $\mathbf{A_g}(x, y)$ the wff of PA_2 which corresponds to **g** according to §50. Then by 51.2

(1) $\quad \vdash Z_k(x) \supset . Z_b(y) \equiv \mathbf{A_g}(x, y)$

for $k = 0, 1, 2, \ldots$ and $b = g(k)$.

Let **Sub** (x, y, z) be the wff of PA_2 introduced in §52. Then

(2) $\quad \vdash Z_a(x) \supset . Z_n(y) \supset . Z_b(z) \equiv \mathbf{Sub}\,(x, y, z)$

whenever a is the Gödel number of a wff **A** of PA_2 and b is the Gödel number of

$$\forall x \,.\, Z_n(x) \supset \mathbf{A}.$$

Let **I**(x) be the wff defined by

$$\mathbf{I}(x) \rightsquigarrow \forall y \,.\, \mathbf{Sub}\,(x, x, y) \supset \exists z \mathbf{A_g}(z, y).$$

Let i be the Gödel number of **I**(x) and let **J** be the wff defined by

$$\mathbf{J} \rightsquigarrow \forall x \,.\, Z_i(x) \supset \mathbf{I}(x).$$

Let j be the Gödel number of **J**.

Suppose that **J** is not a theorem. Then as g enumerates the nontheorems, there must be a natural number k such that $g(k) = j$. By (1) we obtain

$$\vdash Z_k(z) \supset . Z_j(y) \equiv \mathbf{A_g}(z, y).$$

But by (2) we obtain

$$\vdash Z_i(x) \supset . Z_j(y) \equiv \mathbf{Sub}\,(x, x, y).$$

These last two relations give

$$Z_i(x), \mathbf{Sub}\,(x, x, y), Z_k(z) \vdash \mathbf{A_g}(z, y)$$

so by 14.27

$$Z_i(x), \mathbf{Sub}\,(x, x, y), \exists z Z_k(z) \vdash \exists z \mathbf{A_g}(z, y).$$

By 49.5 the hypothesis $\exists z \mathbf{Z}_k(z)$ may be eliminated. Then by the deduction theorem and generalization we obtain $\vdash \mathbf{J}$, contradicting the assumption that $\mathbf{J}$ is not a theorem.

Very well then, assume $\vdash \mathbf{J}$. The reader easily can prove from this assumption that

$$\vdash \mathbf{Z}_j(y) \supset \exists z \mathbf{A}_g(z, y)$$

[use (2) with 14.26 and 49.5 to eliminate the hypothesis $\mathbf{Z}_i(x)$]. But as it is not the case that $\mathbf{J}$ is not a theorem, $j \neq g(k)$ for each $k = 0, 1, 2, \ldots$. Hence by (1) and 49.9

$$\vdash \mathbf{Z}_k(z) \supset . \mathbf{Z}_j(y) \supset \sim \mathbf{A}_g(z, y)$$

for $k = 0, 1, 2, \ldots$. Therefore, the wffs $\mathbf{Z}_j(y) \supset \exists z \mathbf{A}_g(z, y)$ and $\mathbf{Z}_k(z) \supset . \mathbf{Z}_j(y) \supset \sim \mathbf{A}_g(z, y)$ $(k = 0, 1, 2, \ldots)$ are all valid in the standard model which is clearly impossible. Thus the assumption $\vdash \mathbf{J}$ also leads to contradiction. Hence the original assumption that g exists must be wrong and 53.1 is proved. ▮

53.2 Corollary (Church's Theorem for Second-Order Logic). There is no algorithm which, when applied to a wff of second-order logic, decides if that wff is a theorem of second-order logic.

PROOF. Let $\mathbf{P}$ be the conjunction of the universal closures of the 4 axioms (49.1–49.4) of PA_2. Then a wff $\mathbf{B}$ of PA_2 is a theorem of PA_2 if and only if the wff $\mathbf{P} \supset \mathbf{B}$ is a theorem of second-order logic. Hence if we have an algorithm for deciding if a wff is a theorem of second-order logic, we have an algorithm for deciding if a wff $\mathbf{B}$ of PA_2 is a theorem of PA_2 (simply apply the first algorithm to $\mathbf{P} \supset \mathbf{B}$). As no algorithm for PA_2 exists (by 53.1), no algorithm for second-order logic exists. This proves 53.2. ▮

We remark here that the same sort of proof can be carried out for a first-order logic which has at least one n-place predicate letter with $n \geqslant 2$. This is because a finitely-axiomatizable fragment of first-order arithmetic can be given in which analogs of 50.2 and 50.3 hold. We shall not give the details.[1] For first-order logics containing only one-place predicate letters an algorithm can be given (see Exercise 22, §18).

EXERCISE

1. Remove the appeal to the standard model in the proof of 53.1 using instead the hypothesis that PA_2 is ω consistent.

---

[1] See Exercises 11–15, §56. For a somewhat different proof of Church's theorem for first-order logic, see Hans Hermes, *Enumerability, Decidability, and Computability* (Springer-Verlag, New York, 1961).

§54 Categoricity of PA_2

In this section we show that PA_2 has essentially only one full model (see §46), namely the standard model $\mathfrak{N}$ (see §49). This fact has interesting consequences for second-order logic.

Let D and D' be sets and $f\colon D \to D'$ a function. (The notation $f\colon D \to D'$ means that f is a function which assigns to each element a of D a unique element $f(a) = a'$ of D'.) Let $R \subseteq D^n$ be an n-place relation on D; that is, R is a set of n-tuples of elements of D. We define an n-place relation $f(R)$ on D' by

$$f(R) = \{(f(a_1), \ldots, f(a_n)) | a_1, \ldots, a_n \in R\}.$$

More precisely an n-tuple of elements $a'_1, \ldots, a'_n)$ of D' satisfies $f(R)$ if and only if there exists elements $a_1, \ldots, a_n$ of D such that $f(a_i) = a'_i$ for $i = 1, \ldots, n$ and $(a_1, \ldots, a_n)$ satisfies R.

Let $\mathfrak{S}$ be a set of relation constants and X be a set of individual constants. Two full second-order models (see §46) $\mathfrak{M} = \langle V, D, \mathfrak{D}_1, \mathfrak{D}_2, \ldots \rangle$ and $\mathfrak{M}' = \langle V', D', \mathfrak{D}'_1, \mathfrak{D}'_2, \ldots \rangle$ are **isomorphic** iff there exists a function $f\colon D \to D'$ with the following properties:

(Iso 1) The $f\colon D \to D'$ is a one-to-one correspondence; that is, for every $a' \in D'$ there is a unique $a \in D$ such that $f(a) = a'$;

(Iso 2) For each individual constant $\mathbf{a}$ of $X, f(V(\mathbf{a})) = V'(\mathbf{a})$;

(Iso 3) For each relation constant $\mathbf{P}$ of $\mathfrak{S}, f(V(\mathbf{P})) = V'(\mathbf{P})$; that is, for all elements $a'_1, \ldots, a'_n \in D'$ we have $(a'_1, \ldots, a'_n) \in f(V(\mathbf{P}))$ if and only if $(a'_1, \ldots, a'_n) \in V'(\mathbf{P})$.

A function $f\colon D \to D'$ satisfying (Iso 1)–(Iso 3) is called an **isomorphism** between $\mathfrak{M}$ and $\mathfrak{M}'$.

Of fundamental importance is the following theorem.

54.1 Isomorphism Theorem. Let $\mathfrak{M}$ and $\mathfrak{M}'$ be isomorphic full models of type $(\mathfrak{S}, X)$. Then for every sentence $\mathbf{A}$ of $L_2(\mathfrak{S}, X)$, $\mathfrak{M} \models \mathbf{A}$ if and only if $\mathfrak{M}' \models \mathbf{A}$.

PROOF. We shall prove a slightly more general theorem. Let $\mathbf{A}(\mathbf{v}_1, \ldots, \mathbf{v}_k)$ be a wff of $L_2(\mathfrak{S}, X)$ with all free variables displayed. For each $\mathbf{v}_i$ $(i = 1, 2, \ldots, k)$ let $\mathbf{v}_i$ be an element of the model $\mathfrak{M}$ of the same type as $\mathbf{v}_i$ (i.e., $v_i \in D$ if $\mathbf{v}_i$ is an individual variable, and $v_i \in \mathfrak{D}_n$ if $\mathbf{v}_i$ is an n-place relation variable). Then the notation

$$\mathfrak{M} \models \mathbf{A}(v_1, \ldots, v_k)$$

means that $\mathfrak{M}, E \models \mathbf{A}(\mathbf{v}_1, \ldots, \mathbf{v}_k)$ for some (and hence, by 46.1, every) evaluation E such that $E(\mathbf{v}_i) = v_i$ for $i = 1, \ldots, k$.

Now let $f: D \to D'$ be an isomorphism between $\mathfrak{M}$ and $\mathfrak{M}'$. We shall show that for every wff $\mathbf{A}(\mathbf{v}_1, \ldots, \mathbf{v}_k)$ (with all free variables displayed) of $L_2(\mathfrak{S}, X)$ and all elements $v_1, \ldots, v_k$ of the model $\mathfrak{M}$ of the same type as $\mathbf{v}_1, \ldots, \mathbf{v}_k$ respectively we have $\mathfrak{M} \models \mathbf{A}(v_1, \ldots, v_k)$ if and only if $\mathfrak{M}' \models \mathbf{A}(f(v_1), \ldots, f(v_k))$. (This last assertion reduces to 54.1 when $\mathbf{A}$ is a sentence.) To prove this simply use induction on the length of $\mathbf{A}(\mathbf{v}_1, \ldots, \mathbf{v}_k)$ and the definition of $\models$ [see (M1)–(M4), §46]. The details are straightforward and are left to the reader.

Now let $\mathbf{\Gamma}$ be a set of sentences of $L_2(\mathfrak{S}, X)$. The set $\mathbf{\Gamma}$ is called **categorical with respect to full models** iff any two full models of type $(\mathfrak{S}, X)$ both of which model all the sentences of $\mathbf{\Gamma}$ are isomorphic. For example

54.2 Categoricity of PA_2**.** Let $\mathbf{P}$ denote the conjunction of the universal closures of the four axioms of PA_2 (49.1–49.4). Then $\mathbf{P}$ (or more precisely $\{\mathbf{P}\}$) is categorical with respect to full models.

PROOF. It is obvious that if $\mathfrak{M}$ is isomorphic to $\mathfrak{M}_1$ and $\mathfrak{M}$ is isomorphic to $\mathfrak{M}_2$ then $\mathfrak{M}_1$ is isomorphic to $\mathfrak{M}_2$. Hence it will suffice to show that if $\mathfrak{M}$ is a full model of P and $\mathfrak{N}$ is the standard model of PA_2, then $\mathfrak{N}$ is isomorphic to $\mathfrak{M}$.

Let $\mathfrak{M} = \langle V, D, \mathfrak{D}_1, \mathfrak{D}_2, \ldots \rangle$ be a full model of P. As

$$\mathfrak{M} \models \forall \mathrm{x}\, \exists ! \mathrm{y} \mathrm{S}(\mathrm{x}, \mathrm{y})$$

(from 49.2) it follows that for every $a \in D$ there is a unique $b \in D$ such that $\mathfrak{M} \models \mathrm{S}(a, b)$; this b will be denoted by $\sigma(a)$. As

$$\mathfrak{M} \models \forall \mathrm{x}_1\, \forall \mathrm{x}_2\, \forall \mathrm{y} \,.\, \mathrm{S}(\mathrm{x}_1, \mathrm{y}) \supset .\, \mathrm{S}(\mathrm{x}_2, \mathrm{y}) \supset \mathrm{x}_1 = \mathrm{x}_2$$

(from 49.3) it follows that if a_1 and a_2 are elements of D such that $\sigma(a_1) = \sigma(a_2)$, then $a_1 = a_2$. Finally, as

$$\mathfrak{M} \models \exists ! \mathrm{x} \mathrm{Z}_0(\mathrm{x})$$

(from 49.1) it follows that there is a unique $\tilde{0} \in \mathrm{D}$ such that $\sigma(a) \neq \tilde{0}$ for all $a \in D$.

We now define $f: \mathbf{N} \to D$ inductively by

$$f(0) = \tilde{0}$$
$$f(n+1) = \sigma(f(n)).$$

More briefly,

$$f(n) = \underbrace{\sigma(\sigma(\ldots(\sigma}_{n}(\tilde{0}))\ldots))$$

for $n \in \mathbf{N}$.

Now if $f(n) = f(m)$ where $n < m$ then by repeated use of the fact that $\sigma(a_1) = \sigma(a_2)$ implies $a_1 = a_2$ we find that $f(0) = f(m-n)$; that is,

$\tilde{0} = \sigma(f(m-n-1))$ contradicting the fact that $\sigma(a) \neq \tilde{0}$ for all $a \in D$. Hence if $f(m) = f(n)$, then $m = n$. On the other hand $\tilde{0} = f(0) \in f(\mathbf{N}) \subseteq D$ then $\sigma(a) = f(n+1) \in f(\mathbf{N}) \subseteq D$. Thus

$$\mathfrak{M} \models \forall \mathrm{x} \,.\, \mathrm{Z}_0(\mathrm{x}) \supset \mathbf{M}(\mathrm{x})$$

and

$$\mathfrak{M} \models \forall \mathrm{x} \, \forall \mathrm{y} \,.\, \mathbf{M}(\mathrm{x}) \supset .\, \mathrm{S}(\mathrm{x}, \mathrm{y}) \supset \mathbf{M}(\mathrm{y})$$

where $\mathbf{M} = f(\mathbf{N})$. But as 49.4 is valid in $\mathfrak{M}$ it follows that

$$\mathfrak{M} \models \forall \mathrm{x} \mathbf{M}(\mathrm{x})$$

or $f(\mathbf{N}) = D$. Thus f is a one-to-one correspondence; that is, f satisfies (Iso 1).

As $f(n+1) = \sigma f(n)$, $\mathfrak{N} \models \mathrm{S}(n, m)$ if and only if $m = n+1$ which happens if and only if $f(m) = \sigma(f(n))$ which happens if and only if $\mathfrak{M} \models \mathrm{S}(f(n), f(m))$. Thus f satisfies (Iso 3). The condition (Iso 2) is vacuous as there are no individual constants in this language. We have thus shown that f is an isomorphism and this completes the proof of 54.2. ∎

Now again let **P** be the conjunction of the universal closures of the four axioms of PA_2 (49.1–49.4) and let $\mathbf{P}(\beta)$ be the wff which results from the sentence **P** by replacing each occurrence of the two-place relation constant S by the two-place relation variable β. Let **J** be the Gödel sentence of §52 so that **J** holds in the standard model $\mathfrak{N}$ of PA_2 but is not a theorem of PA_2. Let $\mathbf{J}(\beta)$ result from **J** by replacing each occurrence of S by β.

Now consider the sentence $\forall \beta \,.\, \mathbf{P}(\beta) \supset \mathbf{J}(\beta)$. It contains no constants. Furthermore, it holds in every full model, for if $\mathfrak{M} = \langle D, \mathfrak{D}_1, \mathfrak{D}_2, \ldots \rangle$ is a full model and $R \in \mathfrak{D}_2$ is such that $\mathfrak{M} \models \mathbf{P}(R)$, then the model $\mathfrak{M}' = \langle V, D, \mathfrak{D}_1, \mathfrak{D}_2, \ldots \rangle$ where $V(\mathrm{S}) = R$ is a full model for PA_2 and therefore by 54.2 is isomorphic to $\mathfrak{N}$. As $\mathfrak{N} \models \mathbf{J}$, $\mathfrak{M}' \models \mathbf{J}$ by 54.1; that is, $\mathfrak{M} \models \mathbf{J}(R)$. This shows that $\mathfrak{M} \models \forall \beta \,.\, \mathbf{P}(\beta) \supset \mathbf{J}(\beta)$. On the other hand, this sentence is not a theorem of second-order logic for if it were, **J** would be a theorem of PA_2, contradicting the Gödel incompleteness theorem (52.1). We have thus proved 54.3 which follows.

54.3 Theorem. The wff $\forall \beta \,.\, \mathbf{P}(\beta) \supset \mathbf{J}(\beta)$ is a sentence of second-order logic containing no constants and such that

(1) It holds in every full model.

(2) It is not provable in second-order logic. And hence

(3) Its negation holds in some second-order model (which is not full).

This theorem says that the axioms for second-order logic do not characterize validity in full models. But, as is always the case with the incompleteness arguments, it proves more; namely that it is impossible to characterize full models with a "recursive" set of axioms for second-order logic.

EXERCISES

1. Construct sentences $\mathbf{A}_n$ ($n = 1, 2, \ldots$) of second-order logic whose meaning is that the domain of individuals contains exactly n elements. Show that each such sentence is categorical with respect to full models.

2. Generalize the notion of isomorphism so that it makes sense for arbitrary (not necessarily full) second-order structures and so that an analog of 54.1 holds.

3. In a second-order language containing two individual constants (0 and 1), a one-place relation constant $\leqslant$, and two three-place relation constants $\sum$ and $\prod$ [where $\sum(\mathrm{x}, \mathrm{y}, \mathrm{z})$ is intended to mean $\mathrm{x} + \mathrm{y} = \mathrm{z}$ and $\prod(\mathrm{x}, \mathrm{y}, \mathrm{z})$ is intended to mean $\mathrm{xy} = \mathrm{z}$] give axioms for the real numbers. (Do not forget the axiom of least upper bounds.) It is a well-known result of real analysis that such an axiom system is categorical with respect to full models.

*4. Form a language PA_2' by adjoining an individual constant c to PA_2. In this language consider the set $\mathbf{\Gamma}$ consisting of all the sentences of PA_2 which hold in the standard model together with all the sentences $\sim\mathrm{Z}_n(\mathrm{c})$ (where $n = 0, 1, 2, \ldots$). Show that $\mathbf{\Gamma}$ is consistent and therefore has a model $\mathfrak{M}$. Does it have a full model? Suppose $\mathfrak{M} = \langle V, D, \mathfrak{D}_1, \mathfrak{D}_2, \ldots \rangle$ is a model for $\mathbf{\Gamma}$. Consider the map f: $\mathbf{N} \to D$ constructed in the proof of 54.2 (that same construction works here). Show that $f(\mathbf{N}) \notin \mathfrak{D}_1$. Are there any sentences of PA_2 which hold in $\mathfrak{M}$ but not in the standard model $\mathfrak{N}$ for PA_2?

§55 Skolem's Paradox

In this section we shall confine our remarks to the formal language PA_2: second-order Peano arithmetic. However, all the remarks which we make hold in more general contexts.

First we need some simple set theory. Recall that a set Q is **countable** iff it can be put in one to one correspondence with the natural numbers $\mathbf{N}$; that is, iff there is a function f: $\mathbf{N} \to Q$ such that for every $q \in Q$ there is a unique $n \in \mathbf{N}$ such that $f(n) = q$. An example of an infinite set which is not countable is given by the following.

Cantor's Theorem. The set of all subsets of $\mathbf{N}$ is not countable.

PROOF. Suppose the contrary and let $2^{\mathbf{N}}$ denote the set of all subsets of $\mathbf{N}$. Then there is a function f: $\mathbf{N} \to 2^{\mathbf{N}}$ such that for every $R \in 2^{\mathbf{N}}$ (i.e., $R \subseteq \mathbf{N}$) there is an $n \in \mathbf{N}$ with $f(n) = R$. Define a set $T \subseteq \mathbf{N}$ by

$$T = \{n \in \mathbf{N} \mid n \notin f(n)\}$$

that is, $n \in T$ if and only if $n \notin f(n)$. As $T \subseteq \mathbf{N}$, it follows that $T = f(n)$ for some $n \in \mathbf{N}$. Is $n \in T$? If $n \in T$, then $n \in f(n)$ and so by the definition of T, $n \notin T$. If $n \notin T$, then $n \notin f(n)$ and so $n \in T$. Either way we have a contradiction. Hence the assumption that $2^{\mathbf{N}}$ is countable is wrong. ∎

The result can be rephrased somewhat. Let R be a two-place relation on $\mathbf{N}$ (i.e. $R \subseteq \mathbf{N}^2$) and define for each $n \in \mathbf{N}$ a subset $R_n \subseteq \mathbf{N}$ by

$$R_n = \{k \in \mathbf{N} \mid (n, k) \in R\}.$$

Then Cantor's theorem can be rephrased as follows:

55.1 There is no $R \subseteq \mathbf{N}^2$ such that for every $T \subseteq \mathbf{N}$ there is an $n \in \mathbf{N}$ with $T = R_n$.

Now 55.1 can be expressed in second-order logic and the proof of Cantor's theorem may be translated into second-order logic (we leave this to the reader). We then have 55.2.

55.2 $\vdash \sim \exists \beta \, \forall \alpha \, \exists x \, \forall y \, . \, \alpha(y) \equiv \beta(x, y)$.

Thus we have a theorem of PA_2 whose meaning is that the set of all one-place relations is not countable.

Now let $\mathbf{\Gamma}$ be the set of all sentences of PA_2 which hold in the standard model $\mathfrak{N}$. This is a countable set of sentences and is consistent as it has a model $\mathfrak{N}$. But, as it is consistent, we also know it has a model $\mathfrak{M} = \langle V, D, \mathfrak{D}_1, \mathfrak{D}_2, \ldots \rangle$ by the completeness theorem (47.3). Now here's the rub. If the reader will examine the proof of 47.3 he will discover that the model $\mathfrak{M}$ constructed there is countable; more precisely D is countable and each $\mathfrak{D}_n$ (where $1, 2, \ldots$) is countable. (This is because the model $\mathfrak{M}$ is of form $\mathfrak{M}_{\mathbf{\Delta}}$ where $\mathbf{\Delta}$ is a countable set of sentences.) On the other hand, 55.2, being a theorem of PA_2 must hold in every model of PA_2. Thus we have the following situation:

(1) The set $\mathfrak{D}_1$ of one-place relations of the model $\mathfrak{M}$ is countable; and

(2) The sentence which says that the one-place relations are not countable holds in $\mathfrak{M}$.

This is Skolem's paradox. It is paradoxical indeed, but (1) and (2) are not mutually contradictory. The explanation is simple. According to (1) there is a two-place relation $R \subseteq \mathbf{N}^2$ such that the one-place relations $R_0, R_1, R_2, \ldots$ are precisely the elements of $\mathfrak{D}_1$. According to (2) this two-place relation is not in the model $\mathfrak{M}$; in other words, $R \notin \mathfrak{D}_2$.

§56 Formal Set Theory

In this section we describe a formal language into which virtually all extant mathematics can be translated. This language is called **formal set theory** and is denoted by Σ.

The wffs of Σ are those of $L_2(\mathfrak{S}_\Sigma, X_\Sigma)$ where $\mathfrak{S}_\Sigma$ is the system of relation constants consisting of a single two-place relation constant $\in$ and X_Σ is the set of individual constants consisting of a single constant 0. We introduce the abbreviations:

$$\mathbf{a} \in \mathbf{b} \rightsquigarrow \in(\mathbf{a}, \mathbf{b}),$$

$$\mathbf{a} \subseteq \mathbf{b} \rightsquigarrow \forall \mathbf{x} \centerdot \mathbf{x} \in \mathbf{a} \supset \mathbf{x} \in \mathbf{b}$$

and

$$S(\mathbf{a}, \mathbf{b}) \rightsquigarrow \forall \mathbf{x} \centerdot \mathbf{x} \in \mathbf{b} \equiv \centerdot \mathbf{x} \in \mathbf{a} \vee \mathbf{x} = \mathbf{a}.$$

(Here **a** and **b** are individual variables or constants and **x** is an individual variable distinct from **a** and **b**.)

The axioms and rules of Σ are those of $L_2(\mathfrak{S}_\Sigma, X_\Sigma)$ and in addition the following:

1. (extension) $\forall z[z \in x \equiv z \in y] \supset x = y$
2. (null set) $\forall x \sim x \in 0$
3. (unions) $\forall x\, \exists y\, \forall z \centerdot z \in y \equiv \exists z_1 \centerdot z \in z_1 \wedge z_1 \in x$
4. (pairs) $\forall x\, \forall y\, \exists z\, \forall z_1 \centerdot z_1 \in z \equiv \centerdot z_1 = x \vee z_1 = y$
5. (power set) $\forall x\, \exists y\, \forall z \centerdot z \in y \equiv z \subseteq x$
6. (infinity) $\exists x \centerdot 0 \in x \wedge \forall y\, \forall z \centerdot y \in x \supset \centerdot S(y, z) \supset z \in x$
7. (substitution) $\forall x\, \exists!y\alpha(x, y) \supset \forall z\, \exists z_1\, \forall y \centerdot y \in z_1 \equiv \exists x \centerdot x \in z \wedge \alpha(x, y)$
8. (foundation) $\exists x\alpha(x) \supset \exists x \centerdot \alpha(x) \wedge \forall y \centerdot \alpha(y) \supset \sim y \in x.$
9. (choice) $\exists \alpha\, \forall x \centerdot x \neq 0 \supset \exists!y \centerdot \alpha(x, y) \wedge y \in x.$

We shall not carry out the formal development of Σ nor shall we prove any metatheorems about Σ; this in itself is the subject of another book. We remark here that the formal language Σ is essentially the same as the semi-formal axiomatization of set theory given in the appendix of Kelley's book *General Topology* (Van Nostrand). If Σ is weakened by restricting the comprehension axiom schema (45.6) to those wffs **A** containing no bound relation variables then the resulting language is essentially Von Neumann–Gödel–Bernays set theory. The reader can find a smooth development of this theory in Gödel's monograph, *The Consistency of the Continuum Hypothesis* (Princeton University Press). This set theory is much the same (in a sense which can be made precise) as Zermelo–Fraenkel set theory. A good informal exposition of the latter is given in the book of Halmos entitled *Naive Set Theory* (Van Nostrand).

The reader who has completed this book and wants to continue his study of logic would do well to study set theory next. In addition to the mentioned books, the monograph of Paul Cohen entitled *Set Theory and the Continuum Hypothesis* provides a good exposition of recent developments in this area.

EXERCISES

*1. State and prove an analog of the Skolem–Lowenheim theorem for second-order logic (see Exercise 22, §18).

*2. Let D be a set and $R \subseteq D^2$ a two-place relation on D. For $a, b \in D$ the notation aRb shall mean $(a, b) \in R$. The relation R is *reflexive* iff aRa for all $a \in D$. The relation R is *antisymmetric* iff for all $a, b \in D$ if aRb and bRa, then $a = b$. The relation R is *transitive* iff for all $a, b, c \in D$ if aRb and bRc, then aRc. The relation R is *connex* iff for all $a, b \in D$ either aRb or bRa (or both). The relation R is a *partial ordering* iff R is reflexive antisymmetric, and transitive. The relation R is a *linear ordering* iff R is a partial ordering and R is connex. The relation R is a *well ordering* iff R is connex, and in addition for every nonempty subset X of D there is a unique element $a \in X$ such that aRb for all $b \in X$. (The usual order relation on the set of natural numbers is a well ordering; the usual order relation on the set of integers is a linear ordering but not a well ordering). Show that if R is a well ordering, then R is a linear ordering. *Hint:* If R is a well ordering, every nonempty set $X \subseteq D$ has a unique "least element." To show aRa apply this to $X = \{a\}$; to show aRb and bRa imply $a = b$ apply this to $X = \{a, b\}$ (use uniqueness of the least element and the fact that R is reflexive); and to show aRb and bRc imply aRc apply this to $\{a, b, c\}$ (there are three cases according as the least element if a, b, or c).

*3. Construct wffs $\mathbf{L}(\beta)$ and $\mathbf{W}(\beta)$ of second-order logic (where β is a two-place relation variable) expressing respectively that β is a linear ordering and β is a well ordering (on the domain of individuals), and prove $\mathbf{W}(\beta) \supset \mathbf{L}(\beta)$ in second-order logic. Show that $\exists\beta\mathbf{W}(\beta)$ holds in every second-order model $\mathfrak{M} = \langle D, \mathfrak{D}_1, \mathfrak{D}_2, \ldots\rangle$ where $\mathfrak{D}_1$ (the set of one-place relations of the model) is finite; hence it holds in every model $\mathfrak{M}$ where D (the domain of individuals of the model) is finite. *Hint:* A model in which $\mathfrak{D}_1$ is finite is essentially the same as a model in which D is finite.

*4. Let $\mathbf{N}$ be the set of natural numbers 0, 1, 2, . . . A *permutation* of $\mathbf{N}$ is a one-to-one correspondence $g\colon \mathbf{N} \to \mathbf{N}$ (that is, for every $b \in \mathbf{N}$ there is a unique $a \in \mathbf{N}$ with $b = g(a)$). Let G denote the set of all permutations of $\mathbf{N}$. For each $k = 0, 1, 2, \ldots$ let G_k denote the set of all $g \in G$ such that $g(i) = i$ for $i = 0, 1, 2, \ldots, k$. For $R \subseteq \mathbf{N}^n$ an n-place relation on $\mathbf{N}$ and $g \in G$, $g(R) \subseteq \mathbf{N}^n$ is defined by

$$g(R) = \{(g(a_1), \ldots, g(a_n)) \mid (a_1, \ldots, a_n) \in R\}$$

and R is g *invariant* iff $R = g(R)$. R is G_k *invariant* iff R is g invariant for all $g \in G_k$. For $n = 1, 2, \ldots$ and $k = 0, 1, 2, \ldots$ let $\mathfrak{D}_n^{(k)}$ denote the set of G_k invariant n-place relations on $\mathbf{N}$ and $\mathfrak{D}_n$ the set of n-place relations which are G_k invariant for some k; that is,

$$\mathfrak{D}_n = \bigcup_{k=0}^{\infty} \mathfrak{D}_n^{(k)}.$$

Let $\mathfrak{M}^{(k)}$ denote the second-order structure

$$\mathfrak{M}^{(k)} = \langle \mathbf{N}, \mathfrak{D}_1^{(k)}, \mathfrak{D}_2^{(k)}, \ldots \rangle$$

and $\mathfrak{M}$ denote the second order structure

$$\mathfrak{M} = \langle \mathbf{N}, \mathfrak{D}_1, \mathfrak{D}_2, \ldots \rangle.$$

Prove the following:

(1) $\mathfrak{D}_n^{(k)} \subseteq \mathfrak{D}_n^{(l)}$ if $k \leqslant l$.

(2) For each wff $\mathbf{A}(\mathrm{v}_1, \ldots, \mathrm{v}_p)$ of second-order logic (with all free variables displayed, $\mathrm{v}_1, \ldots, \mathrm{v}_p$ are variables of any type) and each k there is an l such that if $v_1, \ldots, v_p$ are any elements of $\mathfrak{M}^{(k)}$ (of the same type respectively as $\mathrm{v}_1, \ldots, \mathrm{v}_p$), then $\mathfrak{M}^{(m)} \models \mathbf{A}(v_1, \ldots, v_p)$ for all $m \geqslant l$ if and only if $\mathfrak{M} \models \mathbf{A}(v_1, \ldots, v_p)$.

(3) The second order structure $\mathfrak{M}$ is a second-order model (that is $\mathfrak{M}$ models the comprehension axiom schema 45.6).

★5. Let $\mathbf{L}(\beta)$ and $\mathbf{W}(\beta)$ be the wffs of Exercise 3 above and let $\mathfrak{M}$ be the second-order model of Exercise 4 above. Show that $\exists\beta\mathbf{L}(\beta)$ is false in $\mathfrak{M}$. Conclude that $\exists\beta\mathbf{W}(\beta)$ is also false in $\mathfrak{M}$ (see Exercise 2 above). Conclude that neither $\exists\beta\mathbf{L}(\beta)$, $\exists\beta\mathbf{W}(\beta)$ nor their negations are theorems of second-order logic.

★6. Show that $\exists\beta\mathbf{W}(\beta)$ (and hence $\exists\beta\mathbf{L}(\beta)$) is a theorem of PA_2. *Hint:* Let $\Phi(\alpha)$ be the wff given by

$$\Phi(\alpha) \rightsquigarrow \forall x \forall y \,\blacksquare\, Z_0(x) \supset \alpha(x, y)$$

and $\Psi(\alpha)$ be the wff given by

$$\Psi(\alpha) \rightsquigarrow \forall x \forall y \forall x_1 \forall y_1 \,\blacksquare\, S(x, x_1) \supset \blacksquare\, S(y, y_1) \supset \blacksquare\, \alpha(x, y) \supset \alpha(x_1, y_1).$$

Define the wff $x \leqslant y$ by

$$x \leqslant y \rightsquigarrow \forall\alpha \,\blacksquare\, \Phi(\alpha) \wedge \Psi(\alpha) \supset \alpha(x, y).$$

Show that

$$\forall x \forall y \,\blacksquare\, \beta(x, y) \equiv x \leqslant y \vdash \mathbf{W}(\beta)$$

and use the comprehension axiom schema.

★7. Modify the Rosser construction (see Exercise 1 of §43) to apply to PA_2 and thus show that the hypothesis ω consistency in 52.3 can be weakened to consistency without destroying the "constructiveness" of the proof. Of course, you will have to construct a different $\mathbf{J}$.

★8. In the formal language Σ of §56 let $\Phi(x)$ be the wff given by

$$\Phi(x) \rightsquigarrow 0 \in x \wedge \forall y \forall z \,.\, y \in x \supset .\, S(y, z) \supset z \in x.$$

Thus the axiom of infinity is $\exists x \Phi(x)$. Let $N(y)$ be the wff given by

$$N(y) \rightsquigarrow \forall x \,.\, \Phi(x) \supset y \in x.$$

Prove the following theorems in Σ:

(1) $\exists x \forall y \,.\, y \in x \equiv N(y)$

(2) $\exists ! x \,.\, N(x) \wedge Z_0(x)$

Here $Z_0(x)$ is the wff given by

$$Z_0(x) \rightsquigarrow \forall y \,.\, N(y) \supset \sim S(y, x).$$

(3) $\forall x \,.\, N(x) \supset \exists ! y \,.\, N(y) \wedge S(x, y)$

(4) $\forall x \forall y \forall z \,.\, N(x) \supset .\, N(y) \supset .\, N(z) \supset .\, S(x, z) \supset .\, S(y, z) \supset x = y$

(5) $\Psi(\alpha) \supset .\, \Omega(\alpha) \supset \forall x \,.\, N(x) \supset \alpha(x)$

where $\Psi(\alpha)$ is given by

$$\Psi(\alpha) \rightsquigarrow \forall x \,.\, N(x) \supset .\, Z_0(x) \supset \alpha(x)$$

and $\Omega(\alpha)$ is given by

$$\Omega(\alpha) \rightsquigarrow \forall x \forall y \,.\, N(x) \supset .\, N(y) \supset .\, \alpha(x) \supset .\, S(x, y) \supset \alpha(y).$$

★9. For each wff **A** of PA_2 define a wff **A*** of Σ as follows: first replace in **A** every well-formed part of **A** of form $S(\mathbf{x}, \mathbf{y})$ by the abbreviation $S(\mathbf{x}, \mathbf{y})$ given in §56; then replace every well-formed part of **A** of form $\forall \mathbf{x} \mathbf{B}$ by $\forall \mathbf{x} \,.\, N(\mathbf{x}) \supset \mathbf{B}$. Show that if **A** is a theorem of PA_2, then **A*** is a theorem of Σ. *Hint:* Compare (2)–(5) of Exercise 8 with 49.1–49.4.

★10. Show that if Σ is consistent, there is a sentence **J** of Σ such that neither **J** nor $\sim$**J** is a theorem of Σ. *Hint:* Use Exercise 9 and the proof of Exercise 7.

★11. In the following five exercises we outline a proof of Church's theorem for first-order logic. Let X_Q denote the set of individual constants consisting of a single individual constant 0. Let $\mathfrak{S}_Q$ denote the system of predicates consisting of four two-place predicate letters =, T, F, and S and two four-place predicate letters P and E. The wffs of Q are those of $L(\mathfrak{S}_Q, X_Q)$.

The *standard model* $\mathfrak{M}_Q$ of Q has as its domain of individuals the set consisting of all n-tuples of natural numbers and all n-place numerical functions ($n = 1, 2, \ldots$). We do not distinguish between the 1-tuple (b) of natural numbers and the natural number b. The values of the predicate letters of Q are given by:

(1) $\mathfrak{M}_Q \models a = b$ iff $a = b$;

(2) $\mathfrak{M}_Q \models T(n, a)$ iff $n = 1, 2, \ldots$ and a is an n-tuple of natural numbers;

(3) $\mathfrak{M}_Q \models F(n, f)$ iff $n = 1, 2, \ldots$ and f is an n-place numerical function;

(4) $\mathfrak{M}_Q \models S(a, b)$ iff a and b are natural numbers and $b = a + 1$;

(5) $\mathfrak{M}_Q \models P(n, i, a, b)$ iff $n = 1, 2, \ldots, i = 1, 2, \ldots, n$, a is an n-tuple of natural numbers, and $b = a_i$ where $a = (a_1, a_2, \ldots, a_n)$;

(6) $\mathfrak{M}_Q \models E(n, f, a, b)$ iff $n = 1, 2, \ldots, a$ is an n-tuple of natural numbers, f is an n-place numerical function, and $f(a) = b$.

Construct for each n-place function constant $\mathbf{f}$ of RA a wff $\mathbf{A_f}(x_1, x_2, \ldots, x_n, \mathrm{y})$ of Q such that where f is the n-place function denoted by $\mathbf{f}$ and $a_1, a_2, \ldots, a_n, b$ are individuals of $\mathfrak{M}_Q$ so that $\mathfrak{M}_Q \models \mathbf{A_f}(a_1, a_2, \ldots, a_n, b)$ if and only if $a_1, a_2, \ldots, a_n, b$ are natural numbers and $b = \mathbf{f}(a_1, a_2, \ldots, a_n)$.

*12. For each $n = 0, 1, 2, \ldots$ and each individual variable $\mathbf{x}$ construct a wff $Z_n(\mathbf{x})$ of Q such that

$\mathfrak{M}_Q \models Z_n(a)$ if and only if $a = n$.

Give a finite list of axioms for Q (in addition, of course, to the axioms for first-order logic) such that the following schema is a theorem schema of Q:

$$Z_{a_1}(\mathrm{x}_1) \wedge \ldots \wedge Z_{a_n}(\mathrm{x}_n) \,.\!\supset\!.\, \mathbf{A_f}(\mathrm{x}_1, \ldots, \mathrm{x}_n, \mathrm{y}) \equiv Z_b(\mathrm{y}).$$

[Here $\mathbf{f}$ is an n-place function constant of RA, $\mathbf{A_f}(\mathrm{x}_1, \ldots, \mathrm{x}_n, \mathrm{y})$ is the wff of the previous exercise, $\mathbf{f}$ denotes f, and $f(a_1, \ldots, a_n) = b$.]

*13. Prove Church's theorem for the formal language Q and derive Church's theorem for the first-order logic $L(\mathfrak{S}_Q, X_Q)$ as a corollary.

*14. Let $L(\mathfrak{S}, X)$ be a first-order language such that the system of predicates $\mathfrak{S}$ has a five-place predicate letter. Prove Church's theorem for $L(\mathfrak{S}, X)$. *Hint:* If $\mathbf{P}$ is a five-place predicate letter and $\mathbf{a}$ is an individual constant, then $\mathbf{P}(\mathbf{a}, \mathrm{x}_1, \mathrm{x}_2, \mathrm{x}_3, \mathrm{x}_4)$ behaves much like a four-place predicate and $\mathbf{P}(\mathbf{a}, \mathbf{a}, \mathbf{a}, \mathrm{x}_1, \mathrm{x}_2)$ is much like a two-place predicate. According to the previous exercise, Church's theorem holds for languages $L(\mathfrak{S}, X)$ having four two-place predicate letters and two four-place predicate letters.

*15. Let $L(\mathfrak{S}, X)$ be a first-order language such that the system of predicates $\mathfrak{S}$ has a two-place predicate letter. Show that Church's theorem holds for $L(\mathfrak{S}, X)$.

REMARK. This is the best possible result for if $\mathfrak{S}$ has only one-place predicate letters there is an algorithm for deciding if a wff is valid according to Exercise 22 of §18.

APPENDIX

§A1 Sets and Functions

All mathematics can be built up from two undefined notions: the notion of "set" and the notion of "being an element of a set." As these notions are undefined or primitive, we cannot define them precisely but must content ourselves with an intuitive description. In doing formal mathematics a list of axioms determining some properties of these notions would be given and then all mathematics would be derived from these axioms using only the laws of logic. We shall not give such an axiomatic development here, but instead give enough explanation of the properties of sets for the uninitiated to follow the simple set theory used in the text.[1]

Roughly speaking a set is a collection of objects and is thought to have an independent existence of its own; for example, the set of all even numbers is considered to be just as real as any particular even number such as 2 or 16. Given a set X and a mathematical object x either x is an element of X or x is not an element of X. In the former case we say x **belongs to** X and write $x \in X$; in the latter case we say x **does not belong to** X and write $x \notin X$. Thus, if E is the set of all even numbers, $4 \in E$ and $35 \notin E$.

If X is a set and $P(x)$ is a property which either holds or fails for each element $x \in X$, then $P(x)$ determines a new set Y of all those elements x of X for which $P(x)$ holds. The set Y is denoted by

$$Y = \{x \in X \mid P(x)\}.$$

For example, if $\mathbf{N}$ is the set of all natural numbers 0, 1, 2, . . . and

$$Y = \{x \in \mathbf{N} \mid 5x + 3 < x^2\},$$

then $2 \notin Y$ (as $5(2) + 3 = 13 \geqslant 4 = 2^2$) and $9 \in Y$ (as $5(9) + 3 = 48 < 81 = 9^2$).

[1] For a good semi-formal development of set theory see P. R. Halmos, *Naive Set Theory* (Van Nostrand, Princeton, New Jersey, 1960).

Let Y and X be two sets. Then Y is a **subset** of X, written $Y \subseteq X$, iff every element of Y is an element of X; that is, $Y \subseteq X$ iff for all x, if $x \in Y$, then $x \in X$. The Y is **equal to** X, written $Y = X$, iff $Y \subseteq X$ and $X \subseteq Y$.

One especially simple set is the **empty set** denoted by $\emptyset$. It has no elements; that is, $x \notin \emptyset$ for all x. A set X is **nonempty** iff it is not equal to $\emptyset$; namely iff there is at least one x such that $x \in X$. Clearly $\emptyset \subseteq X$ for every set X.

There are certain operations on sets called *Boolean operations* which may be applied to sets to give new sets. They are

(1) Intersection. The intersection of two sets X and Y is denoted by $X \cap Y$ and is the set of all elements which are in both X and Y; therefore, $x \in X \cap Y$ iff $x \in X$ and $x \in Y$.

(2) Union. The union of two sets X and Y is denoted by $X \cup Y$ and is the set of all elements which are in either X or Y (or both); therefore, $x \in X \cup Y$ iff $x \in X$ or $x \in Y$.

(3) Complement. The complement of a set Y in a set X is denoted by $X \backslash Y$ and is the set of all elements of X not in Y; therefore, $x \in X \backslash Y$ iff $x \in X$ and $x \notin Y$. This may be written

$$X \backslash Y = \{x \in X \mid x \notin Y\}.$$

(4) Infinite Unions and Intersections. Suppose for each $n = 0, 1, 2, \ldots$ X_n is a set. Then the intersection of the X_n's is the set of elements which are in each X_n and is denoted by $\bigcap_{n=0}^{\infty} X_n$; thus $x \in \bigcap_{n=0}^{\infty} X_n$ iff $x \in X_n$ for each $n = 0, 1, 2, \ldots$ The union of the X_n's is the set of elements belonging to at least one X_n and is denoted by $\bigcup_{n=0}^{\infty} X_n$ thus $x \in \bigcup_{n=0}^{\infty} X_n$ iff $x \in X_n$ for some $n = 0, 1, 2, \ldots$

If x is an element, we may form the **singleton** of x which is the set consisting of a single element x and is denoted by $\{x\}$. Thus $y \in \{x\}$ iff $y = x$. Note that $\{x\}$ and x are not the same; for instance, if $\emptyset$ is the empty set, then $\emptyset \in \{\emptyset\}$ but $\emptyset \notin \emptyset$. (In fact, it is always the case that $x \neq \{x\}$ but this can be proven only from an axiom of set theory called the "axiom of regularity" which we do not discuss here.) Similarly, if $x_1, x_2, \ldots, x_n$ is a finite sequence of elements, we may form the set $\{x_1, x_2, \ldots, x_n\}$; for each y, $y \in \{x_1, x_2, \ldots, x_n)$ iff $y = x_1$ or $y = x_2$ or ... or $y = x_n$. Note that $\{x_1, x_2\} = \{x_2, x_1\}$; for this reason $\{x_1, x_2\}$ is called the **unordered pair** consisting of x_1 and x_2.

Given elements x and y we may form the **ordered pair** (x, y); two pairs (x_1, y_1) and (x_2, y_2) are equal iff $x_1 = x_2$ and $y_1 = y_2$. If X and Y are two sets, we may form the **Cartesian product** $X \times Y$; the product $X \times Y$ consists of all ordered pairs (x, y) such that $x \in X$ and $y \in Y$. The product $X \times X$ is also denoted by X^2. Mathematicians usually do not distinguish between $((x, y), z)$

and $(x, (y, z))$, thus we may denote either by (x, y, z) and call it an **ordered triple**. Thus we consider $(X \times Y) \times Z$ and $X \times (Y \times Z)$ as being the same set. The set $(X \times X) \times X$ is denoted by X^3, and is the set of all ordered triples (x_1, x_2, x_3) with $x_1 \in X$, $x_2 \in X$, and $x_3 \in X$. More generally we may define for each $n = 1, 2, 3, \ldots$ and each set X the set X^n by

$$X^1 = X \qquad \text{and} \qquad X^{n+1} = X^n \times X.$$

A subset of X^n is called an **n-place relation on X**.

Let X and Y be sets. A **function from X to Y** is a rule which assigns to each $x \in X$ a unique $y \in Y$; more precisely a function from X to Y is a set f such that

(1) $f \subseteq X \times Y$

(2) For every $x \in X$ there is a unique $y \in Y$ such that $(x, y) \in f$.

The unique y such that $(x, y) \in f$ is denoted by $f(x)$; namely $(x, y) \in f$ iff $y = f(x)$. The notation

$$f: X \to Y$$

means f is a function from X to Y.

A function $f: X \to Y$ is usually defined by giving its value $f(x)$ by some formula involving $x \in X$. Thus we say

"Let $f: \mathbf{N} \to \mathbf{N}$ be the function defined by $f(x) = (x + 3)^2$ for each $x \in \mathbf{N}$"

rather than

"Let $f: \mathbf{N} \to \mathbf{N}$ be the function defined by $f = \{(x, y) \in \mathbf{N}^2 \mid y = (x + 3)^2\}$."

For example the set

$$\{(x, y) \in \mathbf{N}^2 \mid y = 3x + 1\}$$

is a function from $\mathbf{N}$ to $\mathbf{N}$. On the other hand

$$\{(x, y) \in \mathbf{N}^2 \mid x \leqslant y\}$$

is not a function as $(0, 1)$ and $(0, 2)$ are elements of this set (uniqueness of y is not satisfied) while

$$\{(x, y) \in \mathbf{N}^2 \mid x = y^2\}$$

is also not a function for there is no $y \in \mathbf{N}$ such that $(8, y)$ is in this set (existence of y is not satisfied).

A function $f: X \to Y$ is **one-to-one** iff $x_1 = x_2$ whenever $f(x_1) = f(x_2)$ and **onto** Y iff for every $y \in Y$ there is at least one $x \in X$ such that $f(x) = y$. Then f is **a one-one correspondence between X and Y** iff it is one-to-one and onto Y.

The function $f\colon \mathbf{N} \to \mathbf{N}$ defined by $f(x) = 2x$ is one-to-one but not onto $\mathbf{N}$. The function $g\colon \mathbf{N} \to \mathbf{N}$ defined by $g(x) = [x/2]$ (= the largest integer $\leqslant x/2$) is onto $\mathbf{N}$ (as $g(2y) = y$) but not one-to-one (as $g(4) = g(5)$). The function $h\colon \mathbf{N} \to \mathbf{N}$ defined by $h(x) = [x/2] + 3$ is neither one-to-one nor onto $\mathbf{N}$.

Finally, if X is any set, the **power set** of X is denoted by 2^X and is the set of all subsets of X; that is, $Y \in 2^X$ iff $Y \subseteq X$.

EXERCISES

1. Verify the following:

   (1) $X \cup Y = Y \cup X \qquad X \cap Y = Y \cap X$

   (2) $X \cap (Y \cup Z) = (X \cap Y) \cup (X \cap Z) \qquad X \cup (Y \cap Z) = (X \cup Y) \cap (X \cup Z)$

   (3) $X \cup (Y \cup Z) = (X \cup Y) \cup Z \qquad X \cap (Y \cap Z) = (X \cap Y) \cap Z$

   (4) $X \backslash (Y \cap Z) = (X \backslash Y) \cup (X \backslash Z) \qquad X \backslash (Y \cup Z) = (X \backslash Y) \cap (X \backslash Z)$

   (5) $X \cap \bigcup_{n=0}^{\infty} Y_n = \bigcup_{n=0}^{\infty} (X \cap Y_n) \qquad X \cup \bigcap_{n=0}^{\infty} Y_n = \bigcap_{n=0}^{\infty} (X \cup Y_n)$

   (6) $X \backslash \bigcup_{n=0}^{\infty} Y_n = \bigcap_{n=0}^{\infty} (X \backslash Y_n) \qquad X \backslash \bigcap_{n=0}^{\infty} Y_n = \bigcup_{n=0}^{\infty} (X \backslash Y_n)$

   Hint: To prove $X \backslash (Y \cap Z) = (X \backslash Y) \cup (X \backslash Z)$ you must, by the definition of set equality, show two things: if $x \in X \backslash (Y \cap Z)$, then $x \in (X \backslash Y) \cup (X \backslash Z)$ and also if $x \in (X \backslash Y) \cup (X \backslash Z)$, then $x \in X \backslash (Y \cap Z)$.

2. Verify the following:

   (1) $X \subseteq X \cup Y$

   (2) $X \cap Y \subseteq X$

   (3) If $Y \subseteq Z$, then $X \backslash Z \subseteq X \backslash Y$

   (4) $X \cup Y$ if and only if $X \subseteq Y$

   (5) $X \cap Y = Y$ if and only if $Y \subseteq X$

3. If X is a finite set let $|X|$ be the number of elements in X. Show that for all finite sets X and Y:

   (1) $|X| \leqslant |Y|$ if $X \subseteq Y$

   (2) $|Y \backslash X| = |Y| - |X|$ if $X \subseteq Y$

   (3) $|X \times Y| = |X|\,|Y|$

   (4) $|2^X| = 2^{|X|}$

   (5) $|X \cup Y| \leqslant |X| + |Y|$

   (6) $|X \cup Y| = |X| + |Y|$ if $X \cap Y = \emptyset$

   (7) $|\emptyset| = 0$

4. Let $f\colon X \to Y$ and $g\colon X \to Y$. Show that $f = g$ if and only if $f(x) = g(x)$ for all $x \in X$.

5. Give two (different) examples of functions f: $\mathbf{N} \to \mathbf{N}$ which are one-one correspondences.

6. For each set X, 1_X: $X \to X$ is the function defined by $1_X(x) = x$ for all $x \in X$. If f: $X \to Y$ and g: $Y \to Z$ the **composite** $g \circ f$: $X \to Z$ is defined by $g \circ f(x) = g(f(x))$ for all $x \in X$. If f: $X \to Y$ and g: $Y \to X$ g is a **right inverse** of f iff $f \circ g = 1_Y$ and a **left inverse** of f iff $g \circ f = 1_X$. The g is a **two-sided inverse** to f iff g is a left inverse to f and a right inverse to f. Prove

   (1) f: $X \to Y$ is one-to-one if and only if f has a left inverse.

   (2) f: $X \to Y$ is onto Y if and only if f has a right inverse (defined on Y).

   (3) f: $X \to Y$ is a one-one correspondence if and only if f has a two-sided inverse.

   Hint: (1) If f has a left inverse g and $f(x_1) = f(x_2)$, then $x_1 = 1_X(x_1) = g \circ f(x_1) = g \circ f(x_2) = 1_X(x_2) = x_2$ so f is one-to-one. (2) If f is onto Y, then for each $y \in Y$ the set

   $$f^{-1}(y) = \{x \in X \mid f(x) = y\}$$

   is nonempty. Let g: $Y \to X$ be any function such that $g(y) \in f^{-1}(y)$ for each $y \in Y$. (Unfortunately, it is not generally possible to specify one particular g having this property. To prove the existence of such a g in formal set theory, we would have to invoke an axiom known as the axiom of choice.)

§A2 Induction

Let $\mathbf{N}$ denote the set of natural numbers $0, 1, 2, \ldots$. The principle of induction says, that

> "If $X \subseteq \mathbf{N}$ is such that (1) $0 \in X$ and (2) $x + 1 \in \mathbf{N}$ whenever $x \in \mathbf{N}$, then $X = \mathbf{N}$."

It is often taken as an axiom in formal mathematics but may be informally justified as follows: By (1), we have $0 \in X$. But by (2), if $0 \in X$ then $0 + 1 = 1 \in X$. Hence $1 \in X$. By (2) again, if $1 \in X$, then $1 + 1 = 2 \in X$. Hence $2 \in X$. By (2) again, if $2 \in X$, then $2 + 1 = 3 \in X$. Hence $3 \in X$. Repeating n times, we may show that $n \in X$ for each $n = 0, 1, 2, \ldots$. Hence $X = \mathbf{N}$.

Taking $X = \{x \in \mathbf{N} \mid P(x)\}$ where $P(x)$ is any property of natural numbers, we see that the principle of mathematical induction may be reformulated as follows:

> "If $P(0)$ and $P(x)$ implies $P(x + 1)$ (for all $x \in \mathbf{N}$), then $P(x)$ (for all $x \in \mathbf{N}$)."

Now let us consider inductive definitions. The first example of this in the text is the definition of wff given in §1. We consider it again.

Recall that the primitive symbols of propositional calculus are the symbols

$$\mathrm{p}_1\ \mathrm{p}_2 \ldots,\ \mathfrak{f} \supset [\,].$$

Any finite sequence of these symbols was called a *formula*.

Consider the following:

Theorem 1. There is a unique set W of formulas having the following properties

(W1) Each $\mathrm{p}_n \in \mathrm{W}$ $(n = 1, 2, \ldots)$;

(W2) $\mathfrak{f} \in W$;

(W3) If $\mathbf{A} \in W$ and $\mathbf{B} \in W$, then $[\mathbf{A} \supset \mathbf{B}] \in W$;

(W4) If W' is any set of formulas satisfying (W1), (W2), and (W3), then $W \subseteq W'$.

(Then this unique set W is called the set of wffs. The theorem above is thus the "justification" for the definition of the set of wffs given in §1.)

We give two proofs of this theorem.

First Proof. Let Φ be the set of all subsets W' of the set of all formulas satisfying (W1), (W2), (W3); that is, $W' \in \Phi$ if and only if (1) $\mathrm{p}_n \in W'$ for each $n = 1, 2, \ldots$; (2) $\mathfrak{f} \in W'$; and (3) $[\mathbf{A} \supset \mathbf{B}] \in W'$ whenever $\mathbf{A} \in W'$ and $\mathbf{B} \in W'$. Let W be the intersection of all the elements of Φ; that is, $\mathbf{A} \in W$ if and only if $\mathbf{A} \in W'$ for every $W' \in \Phi$. Clearly, W satisfies (W1)–(W4).

Second Proof. A *formation sequence* is a sequence of formulas $\mathbf{A}_1$, $\mathbf{A}_2, \ldots, \mathbf{A}_m$ such that for each $k = 1, 2, \ldots, m$ *either* (1) $\mathbf{A}_k$ is p_n for some $n = 1, 2, \ldots$; *or* (2) $\mathbf{A}_k$ is $\mathfrak{f}$; *or* (3) $\mathbf{A}_k$ is $[\mathbf{A}_i \supset \mathbf{A}_j]$ where $i, j < k$. Let W be the set of formulas $\mathbf{A}$ such that $\mathbf{A}$ is $\mathbf{A}_m$ for some formation sequence $\mathbf{A}_1, \mathbf{A}_2, \ldots, \mathbf{A}_m$. Clearly, W satisfies (W1)–W4).

Now we give an example of a proof "by induction on the length of a wff." This method of proof is used frequently in the text.

Theorem 2. If $\mathbf{A}$ is any formula, let $F(\mathbf{A})$ be the number of occurrences of $\mathfrak{f}$ in $\mathbf{A}$ and $I(\mathbf{A})$ be the number of occurrences of $\supset$ in $\mathbf{A}$. Then, if $\mathbf{A}$ is a wff,

$$F(\mathbf{A}) \leqslant I(\mathbf{A}) + 1.$$

Proof. Method of proof is by induction on the length of $\mathbf{A}$.

Case 1. The wff $\mathbf{A}$ is a proposition letter p_n (for some $n = 1, 2, \ldots$). Then $F(\mathbf{A}) = I(\mathbf{A}) = 0$ and as $0 \leqslant 1$, $F(\mathbf{A}) \leqslant I(\mathbf{A}) + 1$.

CASE 2. The wff **A** is $\mathfrak{f}$. Then $I(\mathbf{A})=0$ and $F(\mathbf{A})=1$ and as $1 \leqslant 1$, $F(\mathbf{A}) \leqslant I(\mathbf{A})+1$.

CASE 3. The wff **A** is of the form $[\mathbf{A}_1 \supset \mathbf{A}_2]$. By induction hypothesis, $F(\mathbf{A}_1) \leqslant I(\mathbf{A}_1)+1$ and $F(\mathbf{A}_2) \leqslant I(\mathbf{A}_2)+1$. Adding the inequalities we obtain $F(\mathbf{A}_1)+F(\mathbf{A}_2) \leqslant I(\mathbf{A}_1)+1+I(\mathbf{A}_2)+1$. Clearly $F(\mathbf{A})=F(\mathbf{A}_1)+F(\mathbf{A}_2)$ and $I(\mathbf{A})=I(\mathbf{A}_1)+1+I(\mathbf{A}_2)$. Hence the last inequality may be rewritten as $F(\mathbf{A}) \leqslant I(\mathbf{A})+1$.

In the text, the proof would end here. However, it may be seen in two different ways that the proof is complete. First, we may let W' denote the set of all formulas **A** such that $F(\mathbf{A}) \leqslant I(\mathbf{A})+1$. According to Cases 1–3, W' satisfies clauses (W1)–(W3) of Theorem 1. Set W, the set of all wffs, is by (W4) the smallest set satisfying (W1)–(W3); hence $W \subseteq W'$; that is, if $\mathbf{A} \in W$, then $\mathbf{A} \in W'$; namely, if **A** is a wff, then $F(\mathbf{A}) \leqslant I(\mathbf{A})+1$.

Alternatively, Theorem 2 may be justified as follows. Let $P(n)$ be the property of a natural number n which holds exactly when $F(\mathbf{A}) \leqslant I(\mathbf{A})+1$ for every wff **A** having $n+1$ or fewer primitive symbols. According to Cases 1 and 2 above $P(0)$ is true (for the only wffs having one symbol are the proposition letters $p_1, p_2, \ldots$ and the falsity sign $\mathfrak{f}$. According to Case 3 if $P(n)$ is true, then $P(n+1)$ is true (for if **A** is a wff having $n+2$ symbols, then **A** is of the form $[\mathbf{A}_1 \supset \mathbf{A}_2]$ where $\mathbf{A}_1$ and $\mathbf{A}_2$ are wffs having fewer than $n+1$ symbols). Thus by induction on n, the assertion $P(n)$ is true for every $n=0, 1, 2, \ldots$. As every wff has length $\leqslant n+1$ for some n it follows that $F(\mathbf{A}) \leqslant I(\mathbf{A})+1$ for all wffs **A**.

Next we generalize Theorem 1; this generalization is sufficiently strong to justify all the inductive definitions used in the text.

Let X be any set and for each $n=1, 2, 3, \ldots$ let $M^n(X)$ be the set of all maps $f\colon X^n \to X$; that is, $f \in M^n(X)$ if and only if $f\colon X^n \to X$. Let $M(X)$ be the union of the $M^n(X)$; therefore,

$$M(X)=\bigcup_{n=1}^{\infty} M^n(X).$$

Theorem 3. Let X be any set, $Y \subseteq X$, and $F \subseteq M(X)$. Then there is a set $W \subseteq X$ with the following properties:

(1) $Y \subseteq W$;

(2) If $f \in F$ and $x_1, x_2, \ldots, x_n \in W$ (where $f \in M^n(X)$), then $f(x_1, x_2, \ldots, x_n) \in W$;

(3) If W' satisfies (1) and (2) then $W \subseteq W'$.

The proof of Theorem 3 is like the proof of Theorem 1 and is left to the reader. To derive Theorem 1 from Theorem 3 take $X =$ the set of all formulas, $Y =$ the set consisting of all the proposition letters $\mathrm{p}_0, \mathrm{p}_1, \mathrm{p}_2, \ldots$ and the symbol $\mathfrak{f}$, and F the set consisting of a single element $f \in M^2(X)$ defined by

$$f(\mathbf{A}_1, \mathbf{A}_2) = [\mathbf{A}_1 \supset \mathbf{A}_2]$$

for formulas $\mathbf{A}_1, \mathbf{A}_2 \in X$.

§A3 Primitive Recursion

In this section we will justify definition by primitive recursion (see §19) using only some very simple axioms for arithmetic. The proof is formalized in second-order arithmetic in §50.

Throughout, $\mathbf{N}$ is the set of natural numbers 0, 1, 2, . . . and $S\colon \mathbf{N} \to \mathbf{N}$ is the successor function; that is, $S(x) = x + 1$ (for $x \in \mathbf{N}$). The axioms which we use are

I. $S(x) \neq 0$ for all $x \in \mathbf{N}$.
II. If $S(x) = S(y)$, then $x = y$ for all $x, y \in \mathbf{N}$.
III. If $X \subseteq \mathbf{N}$ is such that $0 \in X$ and $S(x) \in X$ whenever $x \in X$, then $X = \mathbf{N}$.

(Axiom III is of course the axiom of induction.) Using Axioms I, II, and III we shall prove the next theorem.

Primitive Recursion Theorem. Let $g\colon \mathbf{N}^n \to \mathbf{N}$ and $h\colon \mathbf{N}^{n+2} \to \mathbf{N}$. Then there is a unique $f\colon \mathbf{N}^{n+1} \to \mathbf{N}$ such that for all $x_1, x_2, \ldots, x_n, y \in \mathbf{N}$:

$$f(x_1, x_2, \ldots, x_n, 0) = g(x_1, x_2, \ldots, x_n)$$

$$f(x_1, x_2, \ldots, x_n, S(y)) = h(x_1, x_2, \ldots, x_n, y, f(x_1, x_2, \ldots, x_n, y)).$$

Proof. To simplify the notation we take $n = 1$. Let Φ denote the set of all subsets of $\mathbf{N}^3$ which contain the set $\{(x, 0, y) \in \mathbf{N}^3 \mid y = g(x)\}$; that is, $\alpha \in \Phi$ if and only if $(x, 0, g(x)) \in \alpha$ for all $x \in \mathbf{N}$. Let Ψ denote the set of all subsets of $\mathbf{N}^3$ which contain $(x, S(y), h(x, y, z))$ whenever they contain (x, y, z); namely, $\alpha \in \Psi$ if and only if for all $x, y, z \in \mathbf{N}$ if $(x, y, z) \in \alpha$, then $(x, S(y), h(x, y, z)) \in \alpha$.

Let f be the intersection of all the classes $\alpha \in \Phi \cap \Psi$; that is, $(x, y, z) \in f$ if and only if $(x, y, z) \in \alpha$ for all $\alpha \in \Phi \cap \Psi$. We shall show that $f\colon \mathbf{N}^2 \to \mathbf{N}$; namely, for all $x, y \in \mathbf{N}$ there exists a unique $z \in \mathbf{N}$ with $(x, y, z) \in f$. Note that $\Phi \cap \Psi \neq \emptyset$; in particular $\mathbf{N}^3 \in \Phi \cap \Psi$.

Lemma 1. $f \in \Phi$.

PROOF. Choose $x \in \mathbf{N}$; we must show that $(x, 0, g(x)) \in f$; namely, $(x, 0, g(x)) \in \alpha$ for all $\alpha \in \Phi \cap \Psi$. Choose $\alpha \in \Phi \cap \Psi$. Then $\alpha \in \Phi$. By the definition of Φ, we have $(x, 0, g(x)) \in \alpha$. This proves Lemma 1. ▮

Lemma 2. $f \in \Psi$.

PROOF. Suppose $(x, y, z) \in f$; we must show that $(x, S(y), h(x, y, z)) \in f$; that is, that $(x, S(y), h(x, y, z)) \in \alpha$ for all $\alpha \in \Phi \cap \Psi$. Choose $\alpha \in \Phi \cap \Psi$. Then by the definition of f, we have $(x, y, z) \in \alpha$. But also, $\alpha \in \Psi$. So by the definition of Ψ, we have $(x, S(y), h(x, y, z)) \in \alpha$. This proves Lemma 2. ▮

Lemma 3. If $(x, 0, y) \in f$, then $y = g(x)$.

PROOF. Suppose not; that is, $y \neq g(x)$. Let $f' = f - \{(x, 0, y)\}$. Then $f' \in \Phi$ for if $y_1 = g(x_1)$ then $(x_1, 0, y_1) \in f$ (by Lemma 1) and hence $(x_1, 0, y_1) \in f'$ for in case $x_1 \neq x$ $(x_1, 0, y_1) \neq (x, 0, y)$ and in case $x_1 = x$, $y_1 = g(x_1) = g(x) \neq y$ and again $(x_1, 0, y_1) \neq (x, 0, y)$. Also $f' \in \Psi$ for if $(x_1, y_1, z) \in f'$, then $(x_1, y_1, z) \in f$ and hence $(x_1, S(y_1), h(x_1, y_1, z)) \in f$ (by Lemma 2) and as $S(y_1) \neq 0$ (by Axiom 1) it follows that $(x_1, S(y_1), h(x_1, y_1, z)) \neq (x, 0, y)$; i.e. $(x_1, S(y_1), h(x_1, y_1, z)) \in f'$.

Thus $f' \in \Phi$ and $f' \in \Psi$; that is, $f' \in \Phi \cap \Psi$. Then by the definition of f, we have $f \subseteq f'$. But $f' = f - \{(x, 0, y)\}$ so $(x, 0, y) \notin f'$. Hence $(x, 0, y) \notin f$. This contradiction proves Lemma 3. ▮

Lemma 4. If $(x, S(y), w) \in f$, then there exists $z \in \mathbf{N}$ such that $(x, y, z) \in f$ and $w = h(x, y, z)$.

PROOF. Suppose no such z exists; that is, $(x, S(y), w) \in f$ but for all z with $(x, y, z) \in f$ we have $w \neq h(x, y, z)$. Define f' by

$$f' = f - \{(x, S(y), w)\}.$$

$f' \in \Phi$ for if $x_1 \in \mathbf{N}$, $(x_1, 0, g(x_1)) \in f$ (by Lemma 1) and $(x_1, 0, g(x_1)) \neq (x, S(y), w))$ as $0 \neq S(y)$ (by Axiom I). Also $f' \in \Psi$. To see this suppose $(x_1, y_1, z) \in f'$. Then $(x_1, y_1, z) \in f$ and (by Lemma 2) $(x_1, S(y_1), h(x_1, y_1, z)) \in f$. Now if $x_1 \neq x$ or $y_1 \neq y$ (so that $S(y_1) \neq S(y)$ by Axiom II) then $(x_1, S(y_1), h(x_1, y_1, z)) \neq (x, S(y), w)$ and hence $(x_1, S(y_1), h(x_1, y_1, z)) \in f'$. On the other hand, if $x_1 = x$ and $y_1 = y$ then $w \neq h(x_1, y_1, z)$ by assumption, and so again $(x_1, S(y_1), h(x_1, y_1, z)) \in f'$. This proves $f' \in \Psi$.

We have shown $f' \in \Phi \cap \Psi$. Hence by the definition of f, we have $f \subseteq f'$. As $f' = f - \{(x, S(y), w)\}$ and $(x, S(y), w)$ is assumed to be in f we have a contradiction. This proves Lemma 4. ▮

Next we show that $f\colon \mathbf{N}^2 \to \mathbf{N}$; that is, for all $x \in \mathbf{N}$ and $y \in \mathbf{N}$ there exists a unique $z \in \mathbf{N}$ with $(x, y, z) \in f$. To prove this choose $x \in \mathbf{N}$. Let Y_x be the set of all $y \in \mathbf{N}$ such that there exists a unique $z \in \mathbf{N}$ such that $(x, y, z) \in f$. By Lemmas 1 and 3, $0 \in Y_x$; by Lemmas 2 and 4, $S(y) \in Y_x$ whenever $y \in Y_x$. Hence by the axiom of mathematical induction (Axiom III) we have shown that $Y_x = \mathbf{N}$; hence $f\colon \mathbf{N}^2 \to \mathbf{N}$. Now by Lemma 1,

$$f(x, 0) = g(x)$$

and by Lemma 2

$$f(x, S(y)) = h(x, y, f(x, y))$$

for all $x, y \in \mathbf{N}$. Thus f satisfies the requirements of the theorem. The uniqueness of f follows by a trivial application of axiom III: if $f'\colon \mathbf{N}^2 \to \mathbf{N}$ satisfies $f'(x, 0) = g(x)$ and $f'(x, S(y)) = h(x, y, f'(x, y))$, then define for each $x \in \mathbf{N}$ the set Z_x by

$$Z_x = \{y \in \mathbf{N} \mid f(x, y) = f'(x, y)\}.$$

Clearly $0 \in Z_x$ and $S(y) \in Z_x$ whenever $y \in Z_x$. Hence $Z_x = \mathbf{N}$ for each $x \in \mathbf{N}$; that is, $f(x, y) = f'(x, y)$ for all $x, y \in \mathbf{N}$; and hence $f = f'$. This completes the proof of the theorem. ▮

We now state a generalization of the above theorem the proof of which is left to the reader.

Theorem. Let X be a set, $a \in X$, and $\varphi\colon X \to X$. Then there exists a unique function $f\colon \mathbf{N} \to X$ such that

$$f(0) = a$$

$$f(S(y)) = \varphi(f(y))$$

for $y \in \mathbf{N}$. Furthermore, if $Z \subseteq X$ is such that $a \in Z$ and $\varphi(z) \in Z$ whenever $z \in Z$, then $f(y) \in Z$ for all $y \in \mathbf{N}$.

§A4 Countable Sets

A set X is **countable** (or **countably infinite**) iff there is a one-to-one correspondence $f\colon \mathbf{N} \to X$ where $\mathbf{N}$ is the set of natural numbers.

We leave the proofs of the following as exercises for the reader.

(1.) If X is countable and Y is either countable or finite, then $X \cup Y$ is countable.

(2.) If $f\colon \mathbf{N} \to X$ is surjective then X is either countable or finite.

(3.) If X is countable, and $Y \subseteq X$, then Y is countable or finite.

(4.) If X is countable and Y is countable or finite and nonempty, then $X \times Y$ is countable.

(5.) If each X_n ($n = 0, 1, 2, \ldots$) is countable, then so is $\bigcup_{n=0}^{\infty} X_n$.

(6.) If X is countable, then so is the set of finite sequences of elements of X.

In the proof of the completeness theorem (in particular in the proof of 16.1) it is tacitly assumed that the set of wffs of a language $\mathrm{L}(\mathfrak{S}, X)$ is countable when $\mathfrak{S}$ is a (finite or countable) system of predicate letters and X is a finite or countable set of individual constants. This, of course, follows from 1–6 above but can be more easily seen by putting the wffs in lexicographical (dictionary) order: each primitive symbol is represented by a natural number n in decimal notation and finite sequences of such numbers (adjoining elements being separated by a space) are simply arranged in alphabetical order and then enumerated to obtain the desired one-to-one correspondence with $\mathbf{N}$.

ANSWERS TO SELECTED EXERCISES

Chapter 1

Introduction

3. The traveler should ask, "Are you a peasant if and only if the left fork is the road to the capital?" An affirmative answer indicates that the left fork is the road to the capital; a negative answer the contrary. Note, however, that the answer does not reveal whether the citizen is peasant or prince.

5. "neither P nor Q" means "not P and not Q."

§1 Formation Rules for P

1. (1) and (4) are wffs. (2), (5), (6), and (11) are neither wffs nor correct abbreviations. The remaining are all correct abbreviations. (8) and (10) abbreviate the same wff. (14) and (15) abbreviate the same wff. (17) and (16) abbreviate the same wff.

2. Let R(**A**), L(**A**), and I(**A**) be respectively the number of right brackets, left brackets, and implication signs occurring in **A**. We prove that R(**A**) = L(**A**) = I(**A**) by induction on the length of **A**. If **A** is a proposition letter **p** or is the falsity sign $\mathfrak{f}$ then R(**A**) = L(**A**) = I(**A**) = 0. Otherwise, **A** has the form $[\mathbf{A}_1 \supset \mathbf{A}_2]$. By the induction hypothesis, $R(\mathbf{A}_1) = L(\mathbf{A}_1) = I(\mathbf{A}_1)$ and $R(\mathbf{A}_2) = L(\mathbf{A}_2) = I(\mathbf{A}_2)$. Clearly $L(\mathbf{A}) = 1 + L(\mathbf{A}_1) + L(\mathbf{A}_2)$ for the number of left brackets occurring in $[\mathbf{A}_1 \supset \mathbf{A}_2]$ is equal to 1 (for the leftmost left bracket) plus the number of left brackets occurring in $\mathbf{A}_1$ plus the number occurring in $\mathbf{A}_2$. Similarly, $R(\mathbf{A}) = 1 + R(\mathbf{A}_1) + R(\mathbf{A}_2)$ and $I(\mathbf{A}) = 1 + I(\mathbf{A}_1) + I(\mathbf{A}_2)$. Hence, L(**A**) = R(**A**) = I(**A**). (See the appendix A2 for more on induction.)

§2 Formal Semantics of P

1. (1) By truth table method:

$\sim$	$[\mathbf{A}$	$\supset$	$\mathbf{B}]$	$\supset$	$\mathbf{A}$
0	1	1	1	1	1
1	1	0	0	1	1
0	0	1	1	1	0
0	0	1	0	1	0

(4) Indirect method: Suppose $v(\mathbf{A} \supset [\mathbf{B} \supset \mathbf{C}] \,.\!\supset\!.\, [\mathbf{A} \supset \mathbf{B}] \supset [\mathbf{A} \supset \mathbf{C}]) = 0$ for some valuation v. Then $v(\mathbf{A} \supset [\mathbf{B} \supset \mathbf{C}]) = 1$ and $v([\mathbf{A} \supset \mathbf{B}] \supset [\mathbf{A} \supset \mathbf{C}]) = 0$; hence $v(\mathbf{A} \supset \mathbf{B}) = 1$ and $v(\mathbf{A} \supset \mathbf{C}) = 0$; hence $v(\mathbf{A}) = 1$ and $v(\mathbf{C}) = 0$. As $v(\mathbf{A} \supset \mathbf{B}) = 1$ and $v(\mathbf{A}) = 1$, $v(\mathbf{B}) = 1$. As $v(\mathbf{B}) = 1$ and $v(\mathbf{C}) = 0$, $v(\mathbf{B} \supset \mathbf{C}) = 0$. As $v(\mathbf{A}) = 1$ and $v(\mathbf{B} \supset \mathbf{C}) = 0$, $v(\mathbf{A} \supset [\mathbf{B} \supset \mathbf{C}]) = 0$ a contradiction.

4. By induction on the length of **A**. If **A** is either a proposition letter or the falsity sign then either **B** is **A** (replacement at zero places) or **A** is **p** and **B** is **q**. In the former case we obtain $\mathbf{p} \equiv \mathbf{q} \,.\!\supset\!.\, \mathbf{A} \equiv \mathbf{A}$ and in the latter $\mathbf{p} \equiv \mathbf{q} \,.\!\supset\!.\, \mathbf{p} \equiv \mathbf{q}$. Both are tautologies.

Suppose **A** has the form $\mathbf{A}_1 \supset \mathbf{A}_2$. Then **B** has the form $\mathbf{B}_1 \supset \mathbf{B}_2$ where B_i $(i = 1, 2)$ results from $\mathbf{A}_i$ by replacing zero or more occurrences of **p** by **q**. By the induction hypothesis $\mathbf{p} \equiv \mathbf{q} \,.\!\supset\!.\, \mathbf{A}_1 \equiv \mathbf{B}_1$ and $\mathbf{p} \equiv \mathbf{q} \,.\!\equiv\!.\, \mathbf{A}_2 \equiv \mathbf{B}_2$ are tautologies. Choose any valuation v. If $v(\mathbf{p} \equiv \mathbf{q}) = 0$, then $v(\mathbf{p} \equiv \mathbf{q} \,.\!\supset\!.\, \mathbf{A} \equiv \mathbf{B}) = 1$. If $v(\mathbf{p} \equiv \mathbf{q}) = 1$, then (by the induction hypothesis) $v(\mathbf{A}_i \equiv \mathbf{B}_i) = 1$ $(i = 1, 2)$. Hence $v(\mathbf{A}_1) = v(\mathbf{B}_1)$ and $v(\mathbf{A}_2) = v(\mathbf{B}_2)$ so $v(\mathbf{A}) = v(\mathbf{A}_1 \supset \mathbf{A}_2) = v(\mathbf{B}_1 \supset \mathbf{B}_2) = v(\mathbf{B})$. Thus $v(\mathbf{A} \equiv \mathbf{B}) = 1$ and $v(\mathbf{p} \equiv \mathbf{q} \,.\!\supset\!.\, \mathbf{A} \equiv \mathbf{B}) = 1$. Since v was arbitrary, $\mathbf{p} \equiv \mathbf{q} \,.\!\supset\!.\, \mathbf{A} \equiv \mathbf{B}$ is proved to be a tautology.

7. Use induction on the length of **A**.

§3 Axiomatization of P

3.5 $\vdash \mathbf{A} \supset \mathbf{A}$.

Proof:

(1)	$\vdash \mathbf{A} \supset [[\mathbf{A} \supset \mathbf{A}] \supset \mathbf{A}] \,.\!\supset\!.\, [\mathbf{A} \supset [\mathbf{A} \supset \mathbf{A}]] \supset [\mathbf{A} \supset \mathbf{A}]$	3.2
(2)	$\vdash \mathbf{A} \supset\!.\, [\mathbf{A} \supset \mathbf{A}] \supset \mathbf{A}$	3.1
(3)	$\vdash \mathbf{A} \supset [\mathbf{A} \supset \mathbf{A}] \,.\!\supset\!.\, \mathbf{A} \supset \mathbf{A}$	(1), (2), and 3.4
(4)	$\vdash \mathbf{A} \supset\!.\, \mathbf{A} \supset \mathbf{A}$	3.1
(5)	$\vdash \mathbf{A} \supset \mathbf{A}$	(3), (4), and 3.4 ∎

1. Suppose $\vdash \mathbf{A}$. Then there is a deduction $\mathbf{A}_1, \ldots, \mathbf{A}_n$ where $\mathbf{A}_n$ is $\mathbf{A}$. For each $i = 1, \ldots, n$ let $\mathbf{B}_i$ result from $\mathbf{A}_i$ by replacing each occurrence of $\mathbf{p}$ by $\mathbf{C}$. Then $\mathbf{B}_1, \ldots, \mathbf{B}_n$ is a deduction and $\mathbf{B}_n$ is $\mathbf{B}$; that is, $\vdash \mathbf{B}$.

§4 The Deduction Theorem

1. (1), (3)–(5), and (8)–(10) are always true. The others are not. For example (2) fails when $n = 1$ and $\mathbf{A}_1 = \mathbf{B} = \mathrm{p}$.

§5 Some Theorem Schemas of P

5.1 $\vdash \mathfrak{f} \supset \mathbf{A}$

Proof:

(1) $\mathfrak{f} \vdash \mathfrak{f} \supset . [\mathbf{A} \supset \mathfrak{f}] \supset \mathfrak{f}$	3.1
(2) $\mathfrak{f} \vdash \mathfrak{f}$	(DH1)
(3) $\mathfrak{f} \vdash \sim\sim \mathbf{A}$	(1), (2), 3.4, (D1)
(4) $\mathfrak{f} \vdash \sim\sim \mathbf{A} \supset \mathbf{A}$	3.3
(5) $\mathfrak{f} \vdash \mathbf{A}$	(3), (4), 3.4.

Now use the deduction theorem.

5.2 $\vdash \mathbf{A} \supset . \mathbf{B} \supset . \mathbf{A} \supset \mathbf{B}$

Proof:

$\mathbf{A}, \mathbf{B}, \mathbf{A} \vdash \mathbf{B}$	(DH1)
$\mathbf{A}, \mathbf{B} \vdash \mathbf{A} \supset \mathbf{B}$	deduction theorem
$\mathbf{A} \vdash \mathbf{B} \supset . \mathbf{A} \supset \mathbf{B}$	deduction theorem
$\vdash \mathbf{A} \supset . \mathbf{B} \supset . \mathbf{A} \supset \mathbf{B}$	deduction theorem ∎

5.3 $\vdash \mathbf{A} \supset . \sim \mathbf{B} \supset \sim [\mathbf{A} \supset \mathbf{B}]$

Proof:

$\mathbf{A}, \sim \mathbf{B}, \mathbf{A} \supset \mathbf{B} \vdash \mathbf{A}$	(DH1)
$\mathbf{A}, \sim \mathbf{B}, \mathbf{A} \supset \mathbf{B} \vdash \mathbf{A} \supset \mathbf{B}$	(DH1)
$\mathbf{A}, \sim \mathbf{B}, \mathbf{A} \supset \mathbf{B} \vdash \mathbf{B}$	3.4
$\mathbf{A}, \sim \mathbf{B}, \mathbf{A} \supset \mathbf{B} \vdash \mathbf{B} \supset \mathfrak{f}$	(DH1) and (D1)
$\mathbf{A}, \sim \mathbf{B}, \mathbf{A} \supset \mathbf{B} \vdash \mathfrak{f}$	3.4

Now use the deduction theorem.

5.4 $\vdash \sim \mathbf{A} \supset . \mathbf{B} \supset . \mathbf{A} \supset \mathbf{B}$

Proof:

$\sim \mathbf{A}, \mathbf{B}, \mathbf{A} \vdash \mathbf{B}$ by (DH1). Use the deduction theorem three times.

5.5 $\vdash \sim \mathbf{A} \supset . \sim \mathbf{B} \supset . \mathbf{A} \supset \mathbf{B}$

Proof:

$\sim \mathbf{A}, \sim \mathbf{B}, \mathbf{A} \vdash \mathbf{A}$	(DH1)
$\sim \mathbf{A}, \sim \mathbf{B}, \mathbf{A} \vdash \mathbf{A} \supset \mathfrak{f}$	(DH1) and (D1)
$\sim \mathbf{A}, \sim \mathbf{B}, \mathbf{A} \vdash \mathfrak{f}$	3.4
$\sim \mathbf{A}, \sim \mathbf{B}, \mathbf{A} \vdash \mathfrak{f} \supset \mathbf{B}$	5.1
$\sim \mathbf{A}, \sim \mathbf{B}, \mathbf{A} \vdash \mathbf{B}$	3.4

Now use the deduction theorem three times.

5.11 $\vdash \mathbf{A} \supset . \mathbf{B} \supset . \mathbf{A} \wedge \mathbf{B}$

Proof:

$\mathbf{A}, \mathbf{B}, \sim \sim \mathbf{A} \supset \sim \mathbf{B} \vdash \mathbf{A}$	(DH1)
$\mathbf{A}, \mathbf{B}, \sim \sim \mathbf{A} \supset \sim \mathbf{B} \vdash \mathbf{A} \supset \sim \sim \mathbf{A}$	5.10
$\mathbf{A}, \mathbf{B}, \sim \sim \mathbf{A} \supset \sim \mathbf{B} \vdash \sim \sim \mathbf{A}$	3.4
$\mathbf{A}, \mathbf{B}, \sim \sim \mathbf{A} \supset \sim \mathbf{B} \vdash \sim \sim \mathbf{A} \supset \sim \mathbf{B}$	(DH1)
$\mathbf{A}, \mathbf{B}, \sim \sim \mathbf{A} \supset \sim \mathbf{B} \vdash \sim \mathbf{B}$	3.4
$\mathbf{A}, \mathbf{B}, \sim \sim \mathbf{A} \supset \sim \mathbf{B} \vdash \mathbf{B}$	(DH1)
$\mathbf{A}, \mathbf{B}, \sim \sim \mathbf{A} \supset \sim \mathbf{B} \vdash \mathfrak{f}$	3.4

Now use the deduction theorem three times and definition (D3).

5.12 $\vdash \mathbf{A} \equiv \sim \sim \mathbf{A}$

Proof:

$\vdash \mathbf{A} \supset \sim \sim \mathbf{A}$	5.10
$\vdash \sim \sim \mathbf{A} \supset \mathbf{A}$	3.3
$\vdash [\mathbf{A} \supset \sim \sim \mathbf{A}] \supset . [\sim \sim \mathbf{A} \supset \mathbf{A}] \supset . \mathbf{A} \equiv \sim \sim \mathbf{A}$	5.11 and (D4)

Now use *modus ponens* (3.4) twice.

1. $\sim \mathbf{A} \supset \sim \mathbf{B} . \supset . \mathbf{B} \supset \mathbf{A}$ is a theorem schema of **P** by 5.9. To show that $\sim \sim \mathbf{A} \supset \mathbf{A}$ is a theorem schema of $\mathbf{P}^1$, note first that the deduction theorem holds in $\mathbf{P}^1$ (The proof given in §4 works for $\mathbf{P}^1$ as well as for **P**.) Let $\vdash_1 \mathbf{A}$ mean that **A** is a theorem of $\mathbf{P}^1$. Then:

Lemma: $\vdash_1 \sim \mathbf{B} \supset . \mathbf{B} \supset \mathbf{A}$

Proof:

$\sim \mathbf{B} \vdash_1 \sim \mathbf{B} \supset . \sim \mathbf{A} \supset \sim \mathbf{B}$	3.1
$\sim \mathbf{B} \vdash_1 \sim \mathbf{A} \supset \sim \mathbf{B}$	3.4 and (DH1)
$\sim \mathbf{B} \vdash_1 \sim \mathbf{A} \supset \sim \mathbf{B} . \supset . \mathbf{B} \supset \mathbf{A}$	Axiom
$\sim \mathbf{B} \vdash_1 \mathbf{B} \supset \mathbf{A}$	3.4

and use the deduction theorem. Now

$\sim\sim\mathbf{A} \vdash_1 \sim\sim\mathbf{A} \supset . \sim\mathbf{A} \supset \sim[p \supset p]$	lemma
$\sim\sim\mathbf{A} \vdash_1 \sim\mathbf{A} \supset \sim[p \supset p]$	(DH1) and 3.4
$\sim\sim\mathbf{A} \vdash_1 \sim\mathbf{A} \supset \sim[p \supset p] . \supset . [p \supset p] \supset \mathbf{A}$	axiom
$\sim\sim\mathbf{A} \vdash_1 [p \supset p] \supset \mathbf{A}$	3.4
$\sim\sim\mathbf{A} \vdash_1 [p \supset p]$	
$\sim\sim\mathbf{A} \vdash_1 \mathbf{A}$	

and use the deduction theorem.

§6 Completeness

1. If **A** contains no proposition letters, then $v(\mathbf{A})$ is independent of the choice of the valuation v; that is, either $v(\mathbf{A})=1$ for all v or $v(\mathbf{A})=0$ for all v. In the former case **A** is a tautology (so that $\vdash \mathbf{A}$ by 6.3) and in the latter, $\sim\mathbf{A}$ is a tautology (so that $\vdash \sim\mathbf{A}$). Note that neither p nor $\sim$p is a theorem.

2. A set of wffs $\mathbf{\Delta}$ of **P** is *complete* iff for every wff **A** of **P** either $\mathbf{A} \in \mathbf{\Delta}$ or $\sim\mathbf{A} \in \mathbf{\Delta}$. Suppose $\mathbf{\Gamma}$ is consistent. By an argument similar to the proof of 16.1 (but simpler) there is a complete consistent set $\mathbf{\Delta}$ extending $\mathbf{\Gamma}$. Define a valuation v by setting $v(\mathbf{p})=1$ iff $\mathbf{p} \in \mathbf{\Delta}$ (for each proposition letter **p**). By an argument similar to the proof of 17.1 we have $v(\mathbf{A})=1$ if and only if $\mathbf{A} \in \mathbf{\Delta}$ (for each wff **A**). Hence $v(\mathbf{A})=1$ for every $\mathbf{A} \in \mathbf{\Gamma}$.

Chapter 2

Introduction

1. (1)–(4), (6)–(9), and (11) are true; (5) and (10) are false. To see that (6) is true note that a natural number $x \in \mathbf{N}$ satisfies

   $$\forall y \in \mathbf{N} x \leqslant y$$

   exactly when $x=0$.

2. (5), (10), and (11) are false; the rest are true. To see that (6) is true note that there is no $x \in \mathbf{Z}$ which satisfies

   $$\forall y \in \mathbf{Z} x \leqslant y.$$

   Thus (6) has the form "$\forall x \in \mathbf{Z}$ if $P(x)$, then $x=0$" where $P(x)$ is always false.

§7 Formation Rules for L($\mathfrak{S}$, X)

1. (3) and (9)–(11) are correct abbreviations for wffs.

2. (1) The well-formed parts of $\forall xP(x) \supset Q(x)$ are $P(x)$, $Q(x)$, $\forall xP(x)$, and $\forall xP(x) \supset Q(x)$.

   (2) The well-formed parts of $\forall x[P(x) \supset Q(x)]$ are $P(x)$, $Q(x)$, $[P(x) \supset Q(x)]$, and $\forall x[P(x) \supset Q(x)]$.

§8 Free and Bound Variables

1. (1) In $\forall xP(x) \supset Q(x)$ the first two occurrences of x are bound, the third is free, and $P(x)$ is the scope of the quantifier.

   (2) In $\forall x[P(x) \supset Q(x)]$ all three occurrences of x are bound and $[P(x) \supset Q(x)]$ is the scope of the quantifier.

2. Yes, yes, no.
3. y is free for x in (2), (3), (5)–(7).
4. $S_y^x P(x) \supset \forall xQ(x, y)|$ is $P(y) \supset \forall xQ(x, y)$.

§9 Models

1. (1), (2), (4)–(6), (8), and (10)–(18) hold in $\mathfrak{M}$; (3), (7), and (9) fail in $\mathfrak{M}$.

   Examples:

   (2) $\mathfrak{M} \models \forall x \forall y \centerdot Q(x, x, y) \supset P(x, y)$

   Proof:

   Choose $a, b \in \mathbf{N}$. If $\mathfrak{M} \models Q(a, a, b)$, then $a + a = b$ which implies $a \leqslant b$ so that $\mathfrak{M} \models P(a, b)$. Hence $\mathfrak{M} \models Q(a, a, b) \supset P(a, b)$. As this is true for all $b \in \mathbf{N}$, then $\mathfrak{M} \models \forall y \centerdot Q(a, a, y) \supset P(a, y)$ and as this is true for all $a \in \mathbf{N}$, then $\mathfrak{M} \models \forall x \forall y \centerdot Q(x, x, y) \supset P(x, y)$.

   (3) $\mathfrak{M} \not\models \forall x \forall y \centerdot P(x, y) \supset Q(x, x, y)$.

   Proof:

   $\mathfrak{M} \models P(3, 5)$ as $3 \leqslant 5$ and $\mathfrak{M} \not\models Q(3, 3, 5)$ as $3 + 3 \neq 5$. Hence $\mathfrak{M} \not\models P(3, 5) \supset Q(3, 3, 5)$. Hence $\mathfrak{M} \not\models \forall y \centerdot Q(3, y) \supset P(3, 3, y)$. Hence $\mathfrak{M} \not\models \forall x \forall y \centerdot Q(x, y) \supset P(x, x, y)$.

   (4) $\mathfrak{M} \models \exists x \forall yQ(x, y, y)$.

   Proof:

   For $b \in \mathbf{N}$, we have $\mathfrak{M} \models Q(0, b, b)$ as $0 + b = b$. Hence, as b is arbitrary, $\mathfrak{M} \models \forall yQ(0, y, y)$. Hence $\mathfrak{M} \models \exists x \forall yQ(x, y ,y)$.

   (7) $\mathfrak{M} \not\models \exists y \forall xP(x, y)$.

   Proof:

   Suppose $\mathfrak{M} \models \exists y \forall xP(x, y)$. Then there exists $b \in \mathbf{N}$ such that $\mathfrak{M} \models \forall xP(x, b)$. Hence $\mathfrak{M} \models P(a, b)$ for each $a \in \mathbf{N}$. In particular, taking $a = b + 1$, we get $\mathfrak{M} \models P(b + 1, b)$ or $b + 1 \leqslant b$ which is a contradiction.

(8) $\mathfrak{M} \models \forall x\, \exists y P(x, y)$.

Proof:

For each $a \in \mathbf{N}$, we have $a \leqslant a+3$. Hence $\mathfrak{M} \models P(a, a+3)$. Hence $\mathfrak{M} \models \exists y P(a, y)$. As $a \in \mathbf{N}$ was arbitrary, $\mathfrak{M} \models \forall x\, \exists y P(x, y)$.

(17) $\mathfrak{M} \models \forall z \,.\, \forall x\, \exists y \sim P(x, y) \supset \exists y \sim P(z, y)$.

Proof:

For each $b \in \mathbf{N}$ we have $0 \leqslant b$ so that $\mathfrak{M} \models P(0, b)$ or $\mathfrak{M} \not\models \sim P(0, b)$. Hence $\mathfrak{M} \not\models \exists y \sim P(0, y)$ and thus $\mathfrak{M} \not\models \forall x\, \exists y \sim P(x, y)$. Thus for each $c \in \mathbf{N}$, we get $\mathfrak{M} \models \forall x\, \exists y \sim P(x, y) \supset \exists y \sim P(c, y)$ (whether or not $\mathfrak{M} \models \exists y \sim P(c, y)$) and as c is arbitrary, $\mathfrak{M} \models \forall z \,.\, \forall x\, \exists y \sim P(x, y) \supset \exists y \sim P(z, y)$.

2. (1), (4), (6), (8), (13), (14), (16), and (17) hold in $\mathfrak{M}$; (2), (3), (5), (7), (9)–(12), (15), and (18) fail in $\mathfrak{M}$.

§10 Validity

1. (1)–(4), (7), (9), (11)–(13), and (16) are valid; (5), (6), (8), (10), (14), and (15) are not valid.

Examples:

(4) $\exists y\, \forall x P(x, y) \supset \forall x\, \exists y P(x, y)$ is valid.

Proof:

Let $\mathfrak{M} = (X, V)$ be any model. If $\mathfrak{M} \not\models \exists y\, \forall x P(x, y)$, then $\mathfrak{M} \models \exists y\, \forall x (Px, y) \supset \forall x\, \exists y P(x, y)$. Suppose $\mathfrak{M} \models \exists y\, \forall x P(x, y)$. Then there exists $b \in X$ such that $\mathfrak{M} \models \forall x P(x, b)$. Hence for every $a \in X$, we have $\mathfrak{M} \models P(a, b)$. Thus $\mathfrak{M} \models \exists y P(a, y)$ and as a was arbitrary, $\mathfrak{M} \models \forall x\, \exists y P(x, y)$. Hence $\mathfrak{M} \models \exists y\, \forall x P(x, y) \supset \forall x\, \exists y P(x, y)$.

(5) $\forall x\, \exists y P(x, y) \supset \exists y\, \forall x P(x, y)$ is not valid.

Proof:

Define a model $\mathfrak{M} = (X, V)$ where $X = \{0, 1\}$ is a set of two elements and for $a, b \in X$, we have $\mathfrak{M} \models P(a, b)$ iff $a \neq b$. Then $\mathfrak{M} \models \forall x\, \exists y P(x, y)$ but $\mathfrak{M} \not\models \exists y\, \forall x P(x, y)$. Hence $\mathfrak{M} \not\models \forall x\, \exists y P(x, y) \supset \exists y\, \forall x P(x, y)$.

2. $\forall \mathbf{x} \mathbf{A} \supset \mathbf{S}_{\mathbf{y}}^{\mathbf{x}} \mathbf{A}|$ is valid if $\mathbf{y}$ is free for $\mathbf{x}$ in $\mathbf{A}$. If $\mathbf{A}$ is $\exists y P(x, y)$, then y is not free for x in $\mathbf{A}$ and $\forall \mathbf{x} \mathbf{A} \supset \mathbf{S}_{\mathbf{y}}^{\mathbf{x}} \mathbf{A}|$ is $\forall x\, \exists y P(x, y) \supset \exists y P(y, y)$ which is not valid. If $\mathbf{A}$ is $\forall y P(x, y)$, then y is not free for x in $\mathbf{A}$, and $\forall x \mathbf{A} \supset \mathbf{S}_{\mathbf{y}}^{\mathbf{x}} \mathbf{A}|$ is $\forall x\, \forall y P(x, y) \supset \forall y P(y, y)$ which is valid.

§11 Axiomatization of L($\mathfrak{S}$, X)

1. Suppose $\mathbf{A}$ is a theorem of L($\mathfrak{S}_1$, X_1). Then there is a deduction $\mathbf{A}_1, \mathbf{A}_2, \ldots, \mathbf{A}_n$ of $\mathbf{A}$ ($\mathbf{A}_n$ is $\mathbf{A}$) where each $\mathbf{A}_i$ (where $i = 1, \ldots, n$) is a wff of L($\mathfrak{S}_1$, X_1). Let $\mathbf{x}$ be some individual variable not appearing in $\mathbf{A}_1, \ldots, \mathbf{A}_n$ and $\mathbf{C}$ be some sentence

of $L(\mathfrak{S}_2, X_2)$. For each $i = 1, 2, \ldots, n$ let $\mathbf{B}_i$ result from $\mathbf{A}_i$ be replacing each individual constant of X_1 which is not in X_2 by $\mathbf{x}$ and each well-formed part $\mathbf{P}(\mathbf{a}_1, \ldots, \mathbf{a}_n)$ where $\mathbf{P}$ is a predicate letter of $\mathfrak{S}_1$ which is not in $\mathfrak{S}_2$ by $\mathbf{C}$. Then $\mathbf{A}_n$ is unchanged and $\mathbf{B}_1, \ldots, \mathbf{B}_n$ is a deduction of $\mathbf{A}$ in $L(\mathfrak{S}_2, X_2)$.

2. Suppose $\vdash \mathbf{A}$. Then $\vdash \forall \mathbf{x}\mathbf{A}$ by 11.7. By 11.4 $\vdash \forall \mathbf{x}\mathbf{A} \supset \mathbf{S}_{\mathbf{a}}^{\mathbf{x}}\mathbf{A}|$ and so by 11.6 $\vdash \mathbf{S}_{\mathbf{a}}^{\mathbf{x}}\mathbf{A}|$.

§14 Some Theorems of First-Order Logic

14.1

$\forall \mathbf{x}\mathbf{A} \vdash \forall \mathbf{x}\mathbf{A} \supset \mathbf{S}_{\mathbf{y}}^{\mathbf{x}}\mathbf{A}|$	11.4
$\forall \mathbf{x}\mathbf{A} \vdash \forall \mathbf{x}\mathbf{A}$	(DHL1)
$\forall \mathbf{x}\mathbf{A} \vdash \mathbf{S}_{\mathbf{y}}^{\mathbf{x}}\mathbf{A}|$	11.6
$\forall \mathbf{x}\mathbf{A} \vdash \forall \mathbf{y}\mathbf{S}_{\mathbf{y}}^{\mathbf{x}}\mathbf{A}|$	11.7
$\vdash \forall \mathbf{x}\mathbf{A} \supset \forall \mathbf{y}\mathbf{S}_{\mathbf{y}}^{\mathbf{x}}\mathbf{A}|$	13.2

14.2

$\vdash \forall \mathbf{x}\mathbf{A} \supset \forall \mathbf{y}\mathbf{S}_{\mathbf{y}}^{\mathbf{x}}\mathbf{A}|$ 14.1

As $\mathbf{S}_{\mathbf{y}}^{\mathbf{x}}\mathbf{S}_{\mathbf{y}}^{\mathbf{x}}\mathbf{A}||$ and $\mathbf{A}$ are the same,

$\vdash \forall \mathbf{y}\mathbf{S}_{\mathbf{y}}^{\mathbf{x}}\mathbf{A}| \supset \forall \mathbf{x}\mathbf{A}$ 14.1

Substitute $\forall \mathbf{x}\mathbf{A}$ for p and $\forall \mathbf{y}\mathbf{S}_{\mathbf{y}}^{\mathbf{x}}\mathbf{A}|$ for q in the tautology $p \supset q \,.\!\supset\!.\, [q \supset p] \supset [p \equiv q]$ and use 11.6 twice to obtain 14.2.

14.3

$\forall \mathbf{x}\, \forall \mathbf{y}\mathbf{A} \vdash \forall \mathbf{y}\mathbf{A}$	11.4, (DHL1), 11.6 (note that $\forall \mathbf{y}\mathbf{A}$ is $\mathbf{S}_{\mathbf{x}}^{\mathbf{x}}\forall \mathbf{y}\mathbf{A}$).
$\forall \mathbf{x}\, \forall \mathbf{y}\mathbf{A} \vdash \mathbf{A}$	11.4 and 11.6 (note that $\mathbf{A}$ is $\mathbf{S}_{\mathbf{y}}^{\mathbf{y}}\mathbf{A}|$).
$\forall \mathbf{x}\, \forall \mathbf{y}\mathbf{A} \vdash \forall \mathbf{x}\mathbf{A}$	11.7
$\forall \mathbf{x}\, \forall \mathbf{y}\mathbf{A} \vdash \forall \mathbf{y}\, \forall \mathbf{x}\mathbf{A}$	11.7
$\vdash \forall \mathbf{x}\, \forall \mathbf{y}\mathbf{A} \supset \forall \mathbf{y}\, \forall \mathbf{x}\mathbf{A}$	13.2

Interchanging x and y we obtain

$\vdash \forall \mathbf{y}\, \forall \mathbf{x}\mathbf{A} \supset \forall \mathbf{x}\, \forall \mathbf{y}\mathbf{A}.$

Now use propositional calculus.

14.4

$\forall \mathbf{x} \sim\sim \forall \mathbf{y} \sim \mathbf{A} \vdash \sim\sim \forall \mathbf{y} \sim \mathbf{A}$	11.4, (DHL1), 11.6
$\forall \mathbf{x} \sim\sim \forall \mathbf{y} \sim \mathbf{A} \vdash \forall \mathbf{y} \sim \mathbf{A}$	prop. calc.
$\forall \mathbf{x} \sim\sim \forall \mathbf{y} \sim \mathbf{A} \vdash \sim \mathbf{A}$	11.4, 11.6
$\forall \mathbf{x} \sim\sim \forall \mathbf{y} \sim \mathbf{A} \vdash \forall \mathbf{x} \sim \mathbf{A}$	11.7
$\forall \mathbf{x} \sim\sim \forall \mathbf{y} \sim \forall \vdash \sim\sim \forall \mathbf{x} \sim \mathbf{A}$	prop. calc.
$\forall \mathbf{x} \sim\sim \forall \mathbf{y} \sim \mathbf{A} \vdash \forall \mathbf{y} \sim\sim \forall \mathbf{x} \sim \mathbf{A}$	11.7
$\vdash \forall \mathbf{x} \sim\sim \forall \mathbf{y} \sim \mathbf{A} \supset \forall \mathbf{y} \sim\sim \forall \mathbf{x} \sim \mathbf{A}$	13.2
$\vdash \sim \forall \mathbf{y} \sim\sim \forall \mathbf{x} \sim \mathbf{A} \supset \sim \forall \mathbf{x} \sim\sim \forall \mathbf{y} \sim \mathbf{A}$	prop. calc.

This last abbreviates to $\vdash \exists \mathbf{y}\, \exists \mathbf{x} \mathbf{A} \supset \exists \mathbf{x}\, \exists \mathbf{y} \mathbf{A}$. Interchanging **x** and **y** gives $\vdash \exists \mathbf{x}\, \exists \mathbf{y} \mathbf{A} \supset \exists \mathbf{y}\, \exists \mathbf{x} \mathbf{A}$. Now use propositional calculus.

14.5

$\mathbf{A} \supset \forall \mathbf{x} \mathbf{B}, \mathbf{A} \vdash \forall \mathbf{x} \mathbf{B}$	(DHL1), 11.6
$\mathbf{A} \supset \forall \mathbf{x} \mathbf{B}, \mathbf{A} \vdash \mathbf{B}$	11.4, 11.6
$\mathbf{A} \supset \forall \mathbf{x} \mathbf{B} \vdash \mathbf{A} \supset \mathbf{B}$	13.2
$\mathbf{A} \supset \forall \mathbf{x} \mathbf{B} \vdash \forall \mathbf{x}[\mathbf{A} \supset \mathbf{B}]$	11.7

Now use 13.2.

14.6

$\forall \mathbf{x}[\mathbf{A} \supset \mathbf{B}], \forall \mathbf{x} \mathbf{A} \vdash \mathbf{A} \supset \mathbf{B}$	11.4, (DHL1), 11.6
$\forall \mathbf{x}[\mathbf{A} \supset \mathbf{B}], \forall \mathbf{x} \mathbf{A} \vdash \mathbf{A}$	11.4, (DHL1), 11.6
$\forall \mathbf{x}[\mathbf{A} \supset \mathbf{B}], \forall \mathbf{x} \mathbf{A} \vdash \mathbf{B}$	11.6
$\forall \mathbf{x}[\mathbf{A} \supset \mathbf{B}], \forall \mathbf{x} \mathbf{A} \vdash \forall \mathbf{x} \mathbf{B}$	11.7

Now use 13.2 twice.

14.7

$\forall \mathbf{x}[\mathbf{A} \equiv \mathbf{B}], \forall \mathbf{x} \mathbf{A} \vdash \mathbf{A} \equiv \mathbf{B}$	11.4, (DHL1), 11.6
$\forall \mathbf{x}[\mathbf{A} \equiv \mathbf{B}], \forall \mathbf{x} \mathbf{A} \vdash \mathbf{A}$	11.4, (DHL1), 11.6
$\forall \mathbf{x}[\mathbf{A} \equiv \mathbf{B}], \forall \mathbf{x} \mathbf{A} \vdash \mathbf{B}$	prop. calc.
$\forall \mathbf{x}[\mathbf{A} \equiv \mathbf{B}], \forall \mathbf{x} \mathbf{A} \vdash \forall \mathbf{x} \mathbf{B}$	11.6
$\forall \mathbf{x}[\mathbf{A} \equiv \mathbf{B}] \vdash \forall \mathbf{x} \mathbf{A} \supset \forall \mathbf{x} \mathbf{B}$	13.2

Similarly

$$\forall \mathbf{x}[\mathbf{A} \equiv \mathbf{B}] \vdash \forall \mathbf{x} \mathbf{B} \supset \forall \mathbf{x} \mathbf{A}.$$

By propositional calculus

$$\forall \mathbf{x}[\mathbf{A} \equiv \mathbf{B}] \vdash \forall \mathbf{x} \mathbf{A} \equiv \forall \mathbf{x} \mathbf{B}.$$

Now use 13.2.

14.8 We first prove two special cases:

Case 1. The replacement is at zero places. Then **B** is **A** and the theorem is $\vdash [\mathbf{M} \equiv \mathbf{N}]' \supset . \mathbf{A} \equiv \mathbf{A}$ which is a substitution instance of the tautology $p \supset . q \equiv q$.

Case 2. **M** is **A** and **N** is **B**. Then the theorem is $\vdash [\mathbf{M} \equiv \mathbf{N}]' \supset . \mathbf{M} \equiv \mathbf{N}$. This is a special case of a more general assertion: if **C** is any wff and **C′** is the universal closure of **C**, then $\vdash \mathbf{C}' \supset \mathbf{C}$. This is proved as follows:

$\mathbf{C}'$ is $\forall \mathbf{x}_1 \forall \mathbf{x}_2 \ldots \forall \mathbf{x}_n \mathbf{C}$	
$\mathbf{C}' \vdash \forall \mathbf{x}_1 \forall \mathbf{x}_2 \ldots \forall \mathbf{x}_n \mathbf{C}$	(DHL1)
$\mathbf{C}' \vdash \forall \mathbf{x}_1 \forall \mathbf{x}_2 \ldots \forall \mathbf{x}_n \mathbf{C} \supset \forall \mathbf{x}_2 \ldots \forall \mathbf{x}_n \mathbf{C}$	11.4
$\mathbf{C}' \vdash \forall \mathbf{x}_2 \ldots \forall \mathbf{x}_n \mathbf{C}$	11.6
$\mathbf{C}' \vdash \forall \mathbf{x}_2 \forall \mathbf{x}_3 \ldots \forall \mathbf{x}_n \mathbf{C} \supset \forall \mathbf{x}_3 \ldots \forall \mathbf{x}_n \mathbf{C}$	11.4
$\mathbf{C}' \vdash \forall \mathbf{x}_3 \ldots \forall \mathbf{x}_n \mathbf{C}$	11.6
$\vdots$	
$\mathbf{C}' \vdash \forall \mathbf{x}_n \mathbf{C}$	
$\mathbf{C}' \vdash \forall \mathbf{x}_n \mathbf{C} \supset \mathbf{C}$	11.4
$\mathbf{C}' \vdash \mathbf{C}$	11.6
$\vdash \mathbf{C}' \supset \mathbf{C}$	13.2

We now prove the general case of 14.8 by induction on the length of **A**.

(i) If **A** has the form $\mathbf{P}(\mathbf{a}_1, \ldots, \mathbf{a}_n)$, where **P** is a predicate letter and each $\mathbf{a}_i$ (where $i = 1, \ldots, n$) is either an individual variable or constant, then one of the two special cases above obtains.

(ii) If **A** is $\mathfrak{f}$ one of the two special cases above obtains.

(iii) If **A** has the form $[\mathbf{A}_1 \supset \mathbf{A}_2]$, then either case 2 above obtains, or **B** has the form $[\mathbf{B}_1 \supset \mathbf{B}_2]$ where $\mathbf{B}_i$ (where $i = 1, 2$) results from $\mathbf{A}_i$ by replacing zero or more occurrences of **M** by **N**. By the induction hypothesis

$$\vdash [\mathbf{M} \equiv \mathbf{N}]' \supset . \mathbf{A}_1 \equiv \mathbf{B}_1$$
$$\vdash [\mathbf{M} \equiv \mathbf{N}]' \supset . \mathbf{A}_1 \equiv \mathbf{B}_2.$$

Hence

$$[\mathbf{M} \equiv \mathbf{N}]' \vdash \mathbf{A}_1 \equiv \mathbf{B}_1$$
$$[\mathbf{M} \equiv \mathbf{N}]' \vdash \mathbf{A}_2 \equiv \mathbf{B}_2.$$

Substitute into the tautology

$$[p_1 \equiv q_1] \supset . [p_2 \equiv q_2] \supset . [p_1 \supset p_2] \equiv [q_1 \supset q_2]$$

and apply *modus ponens* to obtain

$$[\mathbf{M} \equiv \mathbf{N}]' \vdash \mathbf{A} \equiv \mathbf{B}$$

from which 14.8 follows by the deduction theorem.

(iv) If $\mathbf{A}$ has the form $\forall \mathbf{x} \mathbf{A}_1$, then either case 2 above obtains or $\mathbf{B}$ has the form $\forall \mathbf{x} \mathbf{B}_1$ where the induction hypothesis applies to $\mathbf{A}_1$ and $\mathbf{B}_1$. As in case 3,

$$[\mathbf{M} \equiv \mathbf{N}]' \vdash \mathbf{A}_1 \equiv \mathbf{B}_1.$$

Then

$[\mathbf{M} \equiv \mathbf{N}]' \vdash \forall \mathbf{x}[\mathbf{A}_1 \equiv \mathbf{B}_1]$	11.7
$[\mathbf{M} \equiv \mathbf{N}]' \vdash \forall \mathbf{x}[\mathbf{A}_1 \equiv \mathbf{B}_1] \supset . \forall \mathbf{x} \mathbf{A}_1 \equiv \forall \mathbf{x} \mathbf{B}_1$	14.7
$[\mathbf{M} \equiv \mathbf{N}]' \vdash \mathbf{A} \equiv \mathbf{B}$	11.6

Now use the deduction theorem. This completes the proof.

14.12 Note that it suffices to prove the two following:

(i) $\vdash \forall \mathbf{x}[\mathbf{A} \supset \mathbf{B}] \supset . \exists \mathbf{x} \mathbf{A} \supset \mathbf{B}$

(ii) $\vdash \exists \mathbf{x} \mathbf{A} \supset \mathbf{B} . \supset \forall \mathbf{x}[\mathbf{A} \supset \mathbf{B}]$.

For (i)

$\forall \mathbf{x}[\mathbf{A} \supset \mathbf{B}], \exists \mathbf{x} \mathbf{A}, \sim \mathbf{B} \vdash \mathbf{A} \supset \mathbf{B}$	11.4, (DHL1), 11.6
$\forall \mathbf{x}[\mathbf{A} \supset \mathbf{B}], \exists \mathbf{x} \mathbf{A}, \sim \mathbf{B} \vdash \sim \mathbf{B}$	(DHL1)
$\forall \mathbf{x}[\mathbf{A} \supset \mathbf{B}], \exists \mathbf{x} \mathbf{A}, \sim \mathbf{B} \vdash \sim \mathbf{A}$	prop. calc.
$\forall \mathbf{x}[\mathbf{A} \supset \mathbf{B}], \exists \mathbf{x} \mathbf{A}, \sim \mathbf{B} \vdash \forall \mathbf{x} \sim \mathbf{A}$	11.7
$\forall \mathbf{x}[\mathbf{A} \supset \mathbf{B}], \exists \mathbf{x} \mathbf{A}, \sim \mathbf{B} \vdash \sim \forall \mathbf{x} \sim \mathbf{A}$	(DHL1), (D5)
$\forall \mathbf{x}[\mathbf{A} \supset \mathbf{B}], \exists \mathbf{x} \mathbf{A}, \sim \mathbf{B} \vdash \mathfrak{f}$	11.6
$\forall \mathbf{x}[\mathbf{A} \supset \mathbf{B}], \exists \mathbf{x} \mathbf{A}, \vdash \sim \sim \mathbf{B}$	13.2
$\forall \mathbf{x}[\mathbf{A} \supset \mathbf{B}], \exists \mathbf{x} \mathbf{A}, \vdash \mathbf{B}$	prop. calc.

and use the deduction theorem (13.2).

For (ii)

$\exists \mathbf{x} \mathbf{A} \supset \mathbf{B}, \mathbf{A}, \sim \mathbf{B} \vdash \exists \mathbf{x} \mathbf{A} \supset \mathbf{B}$	(DHL1)
$\exists \mathbf{x} \mathbf{A} \supset \mathbf{B}, \mathbf{A}, \sim \mathbf{B} \vdash \sim \mathbf{B}$	(DHL1)
$\exists \mathbf{x} \mathbf{A} \supset \mathbf{B}, \mathbf{A}, \sim \mathbf{B} \vdash \forall \mathbf{x} \sim \mathbf{A}$	prop. calc. (D5)
$\exists \mathbf{x} \mathbf{A} \supset \mathbf{B}, \mathbf{A}, \sim \mathbf{B} \vdash \sim \mathbf{A}$	11.4, 11.6
$\exists \mathbf{x} \mathbf{A} \supset \mathbf{B}, \mathbf{A}, \sim \mathbf{B} \vdash \mathbf{A}$	(DHL1)
$\exists \mathbf{x} \mathbf{A} \supset \mathbf{B}, \mathbf{A}, \sim \mathbf{B} \vdash \mathfrak{f}$	11.6
$\exists \mathbf{x} \mathbf{A} \supset \mathbf{B}, \mathbf{A}, \vdash \sim \sim \mathbf{B}$	13.2
$\exists \mathbf{x} \mathbf{A} \supset \mathbf{B}, \mathbf{A} \vdash \mathbf{B}$	prop. calc.
$\exists \mathbf{x} \mathbf{A} \supset \mathbf{B} \vdash \mathbf{A} \supset \mathbf{B}$	13.2
$\exists \mathbf{x} \mathbf{A} \supset \mathbf{B} \vdash \forall \mathbf{x}[\mathbf{A} \supset \mathbf{B}]$	11.7

and use the deduction theorem.

14.14 Let $\mathbf{Q}'$ be $\exists\mathbf{x}$ if $\mathbf{Q}$ is $\forall\mathbf{x}$ and let $\mathbf{Q}'$ be $\forall\mathbf{x}$ if $\mathbf{Q}$ is $\exists\mathbf{x}$. Then 14.10 and 14.11 may be expressed by

(i) $\vdash \mathbf{Q}[\mathbf{A} \supset \mathbf{B}] \equiv \centerdot\, \mathbf{A} \supset \mathbf{QB}$

and 14.12 and 14.13 may be expressed by

(ii) $\vdash \mathbf{Q}[\mathbf{A} \supset \mathbf{B}] \equiv \centerdot\, \mathbf{Q}'\mathbf{A} \supset \mathbf{B}$.

We prove 14.14 by induction on the length of **A**. If **A** contains no quantifiers, **B** is **A** and 14.14 results from substitution in the tautology $p \equiv p$. Suppose **A** has the form $\forall\mathbf{x}\mathbf{A}_1$. By the induction theorem there is a wff $\mathbf{B}_1$ in prenex normal form such that $\vdash \mathbf{A}_1 \equiv \mathbf{B}_1$. Then by 11.7 $\vdash \forall\mathbf{x} \centerdot \mathbf{A}_1 \equiv \mathbf{B}_1$ and by 14.7 and 11.6 $\vdash \mathbf{A} \equiv \mathbf{B}$ where **B** is $\forall\mathbf{x}\mathbf{B}_1$ and is in prenex normal form.

Suppose **A** has the form $\mathbf{A}_1 \supset \mathbf{A}_2$. By the induction hypothesis there are wffs $\mathbf{B}_1$ and $\mathbf{B}_2$ in prenex normal form such that $\vdash \mathbf{A}_1 \equiv \mathbf{B}_1$ and $\vdash \mathbf{A}_2 \equiv \mathbf{B}_2$. By 14.8 it suffices to find a wff **B** in prenex normal form with $\vdash [\mathbf{B}_1 \supset \mathbf{B}_2] \equiv \mathbf{B}$. Now $\mathbf{B}_1$ has the form $\mathbf{Q}_1\mathbf{Q}_2 \ldots \mathbf{Q}_n\, \mathbf{M}_1$ and $\mathbf{B}_2$ has the form $\mathbf{Q}_{n+1}\,\mathbf{Q}_{n+2} \ldots \mathbf{Q}_{n+m}\,\mathbf{M}_2$ where $\mathbf{M}_1$ and $\mathbf{M}_2$ contain no quantifiers. By 14.2 and 14.8. we may, by changing some of the bound variables if necessary, assume that for $i = 1, \ldots, n$ the variable in $\mathbf{Q}_i$ does not appear in $\mathbf{M}_2$ and for $i = n+1, \ldots, n+m$ the variable in $\mathbf{Q}_i$ does not appear in $\mathbf{M}_1$.

By repeated application (ii) above and 14.8

$$\vdash \mathbf{B}_1 \supset \mathbf{B}_2 \equiv \mathbf{Q}_1'\,\mathbf{Q}_2' \ldots \mathbf{Q}_n' \centerdot \mathbf{M}_1 \supset \mathbf{B}_2.$$

By repeated application of (i) above and 14.8

$$\vdash \mathbf{Q}_1'\,\mathbf{Q}_2' \ldots \mathbf{Q}_n'[\mathbf{M}_1 \supset \mathbf{B}_2] \equiv \mathbf{B}$$

where **B** is $\mathbf{Q}_1'\,\mathbf{Q}_2' \ldots \mathbf{Q}_n'\,\mathbf{Q}_{n+1}\,\mathbf{Q}_{n+2} \ldots \mathbf{Q}_{n+m} \centerdot \mathbf{M}_1 \supset \mathbf{M}_2$. Then by propositional calculus

$$\vdash [\mathbf{B}_1 \supset \mathbf{B}_2] \equiv \mathbf{B}$$

and as **B** is in prenex normal form, this completes the proof.

14.17

$\exists\mathbf{x} \centerdot \mathbf{A} \wedge \mathbf{B}, \forall\mathbf{x} \sim \mathbf{A} \vdash \sim \mathbf{A}$	11.4, (DHL1), 11.6
$\exists\mathbf{x} \centerdot \mathbf{A} \wedge \mathbf{B}, \forall\mathbf{x} \sim \mathbf{A} \vdash \sim \centerdot\, \mathbf{A} \wedge \mathbf{B}$	prop. calc.
$\exists\mathbf{x} \centerdot \mathbf{A} \wedge \mathbf{B}, \forall\mathbf{x} \sim \mathbf{A} \vdash \forall\mathbf{x} \sim \centerdot\, \mathbf{A} \wedge \mathbf{B}$	11.7
$\exists\mathbf{x} \centerdot \mathbf{A} \wedge \mathbf{B}, \forall\mathbf{x} \sim \mathbf{A} \vdash \exists\mathbf{x} \centerdot \mathbf{A} \wedge \mathbf{B}$	(DHL1)
$\exists\mathbf{x} \centerdot \mathbf{A} \wedge \mathbf{B}, \forall\mathbf{x} \sim \mathbf{A} \vdash \mathfrak{f}$	11.6, (D5)
$\exists\mathbf{x} \centerdot \mathbf{A} \wedge \mathbf{B} \vdash \exists\mathbf{x}\mathbf{A}$	13.2

Similarly

$$\exists\mathbf{x} \centerdot \mathbf{A} \wedge \mathbf{B} \vdash \exists\mathbf{x}\mathbf{B}.$$

Hence by the propositional calculus

$$\exists \mathbf{x} \centerdot \mathbf{A} \wedge \mathbf{B} \vdash \exists \mathbf{x}\mathbf{A} \wedge \exists \mathbf{x}\mathbf{B}.$$

Now use the deduction theorem.
The converse is not a theorem schema for if it were the sentence

$$\exists \mathrm{x}\mathrm{P}(\mathrm{x}) \wedge \exists \mathrm{x}\mathrm{Q}(\mathrm{x}) \supset \exists \mathrm{x} \centerdot \mathrm{P}(\mathrm{x}) \wedge \mathrm{Q}(\mathrm{x})$$

would be a theorem. This sentence is not a theorem as it is not valid, and every theorem is valid. (The fact that every theorem is valid is proved in §15.)

§18 First-Order Logic with Equality

3. Let $\mathfrak{M} = (Y, V)$ be any model such that $\mathfrak{M} \vDash a = b$ for all $a, b \in Y$. If Y has more than one element, $\mathfrak{M}$ does not respect equality. The model $\mathfrak{M}' = (Y', V')$ constructed from $\mathfrak{M}$ as in 18.7 has only one element. (More precisely, Y' has only one element.)

4. $\mathbf{B}_n$ is

$$\exists \mathrm{x}_1 \, \exists \mathrm{x}_2 \ldots \exists \mathrm{x}_n \centerdot \mathrm{x}_1 \neq \mathrm{x}_2 \wedge \ldots \wedge \mathrm{x}_1 \neq \mathrm{x}_n \wedge \ldots \wedge \mathrm{x}_{n-1} \neq \mathrm{x}_n.$$

23. Let X_0 be the empty set and assuming X_n has been defined, define X_{n+1} as follows: for each sentence of $\mathrm{L}(\mathfrak{S}, X_n)$ of form $\exists \mathbf{x}\mathbf{A}$ which holds in $\mathfrak{M}$ let $b \in X$ be a constant such that $\mathfrak{M} \vDash \mathbf{S}_b^{\mathbf{x}} \mathbf{A}|$. Let X_{n+1} be the set formed from X_n by adding exactly one such b for each such sentence $\exists \mathbf{x}\mathbf{A}$ of $\mathrm{L}(\mathfrak{S}, X_n)$. Each X_n is countable and hence so is $X' = \bigcup_{n=0}^{\infty} X_n$. The model $\mathfrak{M}' = (X', V')$ (where V' is defined so that $\mathfrak{M}'$ is a submodel of $\mathfrak{M}$) is an elementary submodel of $\mathfrak{M}$.

Chapter 3

§19 Primitive Recursive Functions

1. $f(2, 0) = g(2) = (2 + 1)^2 = 9$

   $f(2, 1) = h(2, 0, 9) = 11$

   $f(2, 2) = h(2, 1, 11) = 16$

   $f(2, 3) = h(2, 2, 16) = 24$

   $f(3, 2) = 25$

2. $f(3, 4, 2) = 15$

$$\begin{aligned} f(x_1, x_2, y) &= x_1 \, x_2 + \textstyle\sum_{k=0}^{y} k \\ &= x_1 \, x_2 + \tfrac{1}{2}(y + 1) \, y \end{aligned}$$

3. $g_1(3, 2) = 5$
   $g_2(3, 2) = 6$
   $g_3(3, 2) = 16$
   $f(3, 2) = h(5, 6, 16) = 5 \cdot 6 + 5 \cdot 16 + 6 \cdot 16 = 206$
   $f(\mathrm{x}, \mathrm{y}) = (\mathrm{x}+\mathrm{y})\,\mathrm{xy} + (\mathrm{x}+\mathrm{y})(\mathrm{x}+1)^{\mathrm{y}} + \mathrm{xy}(\mathrm{x}+1)^{\mathrm{y}}$

§20 Some Primitive Recursive Functions

1. Let H be the three-place function defined by $H(x, y, z) = h(y, z)$. H is primitive recursive as $H(x, y, z) = h(I_2^3(x, y, z), I_3^3(x, y, z))$. Let F be the two-place function defined from Z_a and H by primitive recursion; i.e. $F(x, 0) = Z_a(x) = a$ and $F(x, y+1) = H(x, y, F(x, y)) = h(y, F(x, y))$. F is primitive recursive. But $f(y) = F(0, y) = F(Z(y), I_1^1(y))$ and so f is primitive recursive.

2. $0! = 1$, $(\mathrm{x}+1)! = (\mathrm{x}+1)\,\mathrm{x}!$

3. $e(0) = 0$, $e(\mathrm{x}+1) = 1 \dot{-} e(\mathrm{x})$

4. $[0/2] = 0$, $[(\mathrm{x}+1)/2] = [\mathrm{x}/2] + e(\mathrm{x})$.

§21 Formation Rules for RA

1–3. (1) Z is a one-place function constant. (2) Z(0) is a term. (3) (||I|) abbreviates to I_1^2 and is a two-place function constant. (4) (|I||) is not a well-formed function constant (I_i^n is well formed only if $n \geqslant 1$ and $1 \leqslant i \leqslant n$). (8) and (10) are correct abbreviations for (different) four-place function constants. (11) (CZS) is a one-place function constant and (12) CZS is a correct abbreviation for (CZS). (13) RCZSI_1^3 is a correct abbreviation for a two-place function constant. (14) is not (a correct abbreviation for) a function constant. (15), (16) and (17) are terms, and (16) and (17) abbreviate the same term. (19) is an abbreviation for the two-place function constant (18). (21) is an abbreviation for the three-place function constant (20). (23), (24), and (28) are correct abbreviations for terms, but (25)–(27) are not.

4. (1) is an index. (2)–(5) are individual variables and therefore also terms. (6) is a term. (13) is a three-place function constant. The remaining are wffs.

§22 Semantics

1. Let S_3 stand for the function CSI_3^3 so that $\boldsymbol{\sigma}$ is $\mathrm{RI}_1^1\mathrm{S}_3$. Then $val\,(\mathrm{S}_3)(a, b, c) = val\,(\mathrm{S})(val\,(\mathrm{I}_3^3)(a, b, c)) = val\,(\mathrm{S})(c) = c+1$. As $val\,(\boldsymbol{\sigma})(a, 0) = val\,(\mathrm{I}_1^1)(a) = a$ and $val\,(\boldsymbol{\sigma})(a, b+1) = val\,(\mathrm{S}_3)(a, b, val\,(\boldsymbol{\sigma})(a, b)) = val\,(\boldsymbol{\sigma})(a, b) + 1$ it follows that $val(\boldsymbol{\sigma})$ satisfies the recursion equations defining σ (see 20.2) so that $val\,(\boldsymbol{\sigma}) = \sigma$.

3. Take $\boldsymbol{\epsilon}$ to be $\mathrm{R(CSZ)(C\pi I_1^3 I_3^3)}$.

4. Either $\mathrm{C}\boldsymbol{\sigma}(\mathrm{C}\boldsymbol{\sigma}\mathrm{I}_1^3\mathrm{I}_2^3)\mathrm{I}_3^3$ or $\mathrm{R}\boldsymbol{\sigma}(\mathrm{CSI}_4^4)$ will do. (Note that the problem has infinitely many solutions.)

5. (1) $v(\sigma(\mathbf{k}_3, \mathbf{k}_2)) = val\,(\sigma)(v(\mathbf{k}_3), v(\mathbf{k}_2)) = 5$

   (2) $v(\pi(\sigma(\mathbf{k}_3, \mathbf{k}_2), \mathrm{I}_2{}^3(\mathbf{k}_4, \mathbf{k}_5, \mathbf{0})) = val\,(\pi)(v(\sigma(\mathbf{k}_3, \mathbf{k}_2)), v(\mathrm{I}_2{}^3(\mathbf{k}_4, \mathbf{k}_5, \mathbf{0})) = 25$

   (3) $v(\mathrm{I}_3{}^4(\mathbf{k}_2, \sigma(\mathbf{k}_3, \mathbf{k}_2), \mathbf{k}_4, \sigma(\mathbf{k}_2, \mathbf{k}_3))) = 4$

   (4) $val\,(\mathrm{C}\sigma\pi\mathrm{I}_1{}^2(\sigma(\mathbf{k}_1, \mathbf{k}_2), \mathrm{I}_1{}^3(\mathbf{k}_4, \mathbf{k}_5, \mathbf{k}_5)) = 15$

6. (1) $v(\mathrm{RSI}_3{}^3(\mathbf{k}_1, \mathbf{0})) = val\,(\mathrm{RSI}_3{}^3)(1, 0) = val\,(\mathrm{S})(1) = 2$

   (2) $v(\mathrm{RSI}_3{}^3(\mathbf{k}_1, \mathbf{k}_1) = val\,(\mathrm{RSI}_3{}^3)(1, 1) = val\,(\mathrm{I}_3{}^3)(1, 0, val\,(\mathrm{RSI}_3{}^3)(1, 0))$
   $= val\,(\mathrm{RSI}_3{}^3)(1, 0) = val\,(\mathrm{S})(1) = 2.$

   (3) $v(\mathrm{RSI}_3{}^3(\mathbf{k}_1, \mathbf{k}_2)) = val\,(\mathrm{RSI}_3{}^3)(1, 2) = val\,(\mathrm{I}_3{}^3)(1, 1, val\,(\mathrm{RSI}_3{}^3)(1, 1)) = 2$

   (4) $v(\mathrm{RSI}_3{}^3(\mathbf{0}, \mathbf{k}_3)) = 1$

   (5) $v(\mathrm{CSI}_3{}^3(\mathbf{k}_4, \mathrm{S}(\mathrm{Z}(\mathbf{k}_2)), \mathrm{Z}(\mathrm{S}(\mathbf{0}))) = 1$

7. (3)–(5) and (8)–(10) hold in **N**; the rest do not.

Chapter 4

§28 Definition by Cases and the Least Number Operation

1. $x|y \Leftrightarrow \exists z \leqslant y[zx = y]$

2. $[x/y] = \mu z \leqslant x[zy \leqslant x \text{ and } x < (z+1)y]$

3. $q(x, y) = [x/y]$
   $r(x, y) = x \dot{-} [x/y]y \quad \text{if } \; y \neq 0;$
   $\qquad\;\; = 0 \quad \text{if } \; y = 0.$

4. $(x, y) = \mu z \leqslant x[z|x \text{ and } z|y \text{ and } [z_1 \leqslant x\; z_1|x \text{ and } z_2|y \text{ implies } z_1 \leqslant z]]$.

§29 Prime numbers

1. $p_5 = 11, p_7 = 17$

2. $90 = 2\cdot3^2\cdot5, 210 = 2\cdot3\cdot5\cdot7, 200 = 2^3\cdot5^2$

3. $(90)_1 = 1, (90)_2 = 2, (90)_3 = 1, (90)_4 = 0$

4. $(200)_1 = 3, (200)_2 = 0, (200)_3 = 2, (200)_4 = 0.$

5. $\langle 2, 1, 1\rangle = 2^2\cdot3\cdot5 = \langle 2, 1, 1, 0\rangle.$

6. $2 * 3 = \langle 1\rangle * \langle 0, 1\rangle = \langle 1, 0, 1\rangle = 2\cdot5 = 10$
   $3 * 2 = \langle 0, 1\rangle * \langle 1\rangle = \langle 0, 1; 1\rangle = 3\cdot5 = 15$
   $10 * 5 = \langle 1, 0, 1\rangle * \langle 0, 0, 1\rangle = \langle 1, 0, 1, 0, 0, 1\rangle = 2\cdot5\cdot13 = 130$

7. $200 * 900 = \langle 3, 0, 2\rangle * \langle 2, 2, 2\rangle = 2^3\, 5^2\, 7^2\, 11^2\, 13^2$

§31 Gödel Numbers

1. (3) $''\mathrm{S}(\mathrm{x}_0)'' = ''\mathrm{S}((\mathrm{v}))'' = \langle 2, 13, 13, 8, 14, 14\rangle$

2. (3) The Gödel number of the sequence $\supset\supset$, **0**, **0** is $\langle a, b, c\rangle = 2^a 3^b 5^c$ where $a = ''\supset\supset'' = \langle 10, 10\rangle = 2^{10}3^{10}$ and $b = c = ''\mathbf{0}'' = \langle 7\rangle = 2^7$.

§32 Primitive Recursiveness of the Notion of Function Content

1. (1) Z, S, CZS
   (3) $\mathrm{S}, \mathrm{I}_3^{\,3}, (\mathrm{CSI}_3^{\,3}), \mathrm{I}_1^{\,1}, (\mathrm{RI}_1^{\,1}(\mathrm{CSI}_3^{\,3})), \mathrm{I}_1^{\,3}, (\mathrm{C}(\mathrm{RI}_1^{\,1}(\mathrm{CSI}_3^{\,3}))\mathrm{I}_1^{\,3}\mathrm{I}_3^{\,3}), \mathrm{Z}$, $\mathrm{RZ}(\mathrm{C}(\mathrm{RI}_1^{\,1}(\mathrm{CSI}_3^{\,3}))\mathrm{I}_1^{\,3}\mathrm{I}_3^{\,3})$.

§33 Primitive Recursiveness of the Notion of Term

1. (1) **0**, CZS(**0**)
   (2) **0**, S(**0**), S(S(**0**)), $\mathrm{RI}_1^{\,1}\mathrm{CSI}_3^{\,3}$(S(**0**), S(S(**0**))).

§34 Primitive Recursiveness of the Notion of Wff

1. (2) **0** = **0**, S(**0**) = **0**, [**0** = **0** ⊃ S(**0**) = **0**], f, [[**0** = **0** ⊃ S(**0**) = **0**] ⊃ f].

SUGGESTED READING

No attempt at completeness has been made in compiling the following bibliography. I have attempted to include books which either would make good collateral reading for readers of the present book or would provide good introductions to more specialized or advanced topics in mathematical logic.

Good general textbooks on mathematical logic are

[1] Alonzo Church, *Introduction to Mathematical Logic* (Princeton University Press, Princeton, New Jersey, 1956).

[2] S. C. Kleene, *Introduction to Mathematics* (Van Nostrand, Princeton, New Jersey, 1952).

[3] J. R. Schoenfield, *Mathematical Logic* (Addison-Wesley, Reading, Massachusetts, 1967).

Reference [1] overlaps with Chapters 1 and 2 of the present book, but it treats certain syntactical questions in greater detail. In particular, other formulations of the various formal languages are given (using substitution rules rather than schemata) and are shown to be equivalent to the formulations given in the present book. An important feature of [1] is the introduction which gives a clear exposition of a philosophy of mathematics called *Fregean realism.* Reference [2] is a classic. It overlaps considerably with Chapters 3–5 and also has much material on recursive function theory and intuitionism. Reference [3] is a modern, advanced introduction to mathematical logic. It has advanced material on recursive function theory, model theory, and set theory, and is a "must" for anyone interested in specializing in mathematical logic.

Recursive function theory is a mathematical theory which deals with the capabilities and limitations of computing machines and algorithms. My favorite introduction to it is

[4] Hans Hermes, *Enumerability, Decidability, Computability: An Introduction to the Theory of Recursive Functions* (Springer-Verlag, New York, 1965).

Also good is

[5] Martin Davis, *Computability and Unsolvability* (McGraw-Hill, New York, 1958).

As mentioned above, [2] has good introductory material on this subject. A good advanced book is

[6] Hartley Rogers, Jr., *Theory of Recursive Functions and Effective Computability* (McGraw-Hill, New York, 1967).

Model theory is a branch of mathematical logic which has many applications to algebra and analysis as well as great intrinsic interest. A good introduction is

[7] Abraham Robinson, *Introduction to Model Theory and to the Metamathematics of Algebra* (North Holland, Amsterdam, 1963).

An interesting application of model theory to analysis is explained in

[8] Abraham Robinson, *Non-Standard Analysis* (North Holland, Amsterdam, 1966).

Every mathematician should learn set theory. A good informal exposition is given in

[9] P. R. Halmos, *Naive Set Theory* (Van Nostrand, Princeton, New Jersey, 1960).

One of the first and most important metatheorems in set theory was proved by Gödel and deals with the consistency of the axiom of choice and the continuum hypothesis. An exposition of this metatheorem together with a good formal development of set theory may be found in

[10] K. Gödel, *The Consistency of the Generalized Continuum Hypothesis* (Princeton University Press, Princeton, New Jersey, 1940).

Before reading this monograph, the reader would do well to consult Gödel's original papers:

[11] K. Gödel, "The consistency of the axiom of choice and of the generalized continuum hypothesis," *Proc. Natl. Acad. Sci. U.S.* **24** (1938), pp. 556–557.

[12] K. Gödel, "Consistency-proof for the generalized continuum-hypothesis," *Proc. Natl. Acad. Sci. U.S.* **25** (1939), pp. 220–224.

and also

[13] K. Gödel, "What is Cantor's Continuum Problem?" *Am. Math. Monthly* **54** (1947), pp. 515–525.

The related question of the independence of the continuum hypothesis was solved recently by Cohen. An exposition of this is given in

[14] Paul Cohen, *Set Theory and the Continuum Hypothesis* (W. A. Benjamin, New York, 1966).

Formal intuitionism was treated in the exercises of the present book. The interested reader should consult [2]. An intuitionistic development of mathematics as well as a philosophical defense of intuitionism is given in

[15] A. Heyting, *Intuitionism: An Introduction* (North Holland, Amsterdam, 1956).

Kripke models were introduced in

[16] S. A. Kripke, "Semantical analysis of intuitionistic logic I," in V. N. Crossley and M. A. E. Dummett (eds.), *Formal Systems and Recursive Functions* (North Holland, Amsterdam, 1965), pp. 92–130.

The completeness proofs outlined in the exercises may be found in

[17] P. H. G. Aczel, "Some results in intuitionistic predicate logic" (to appear in the proceedings of an international Colloquium on Logic and the Foundations of Mathematics held in Hanover, Germany in 1966).

and

[18] R. H. Thomason, "Strong semantical completeness of intuitionistic predicate calculus," *J. Symbolic Logic* **33**, 1 (1968), pp. 1–7.

Second-order intuitionistic logic is discussed in

[19] S. C. Kleene and R. E. Vesley, *The Foundations of Intuitionistic Mathematics* (North Holland, Amsterdam, 1965).

Those interested in the history of mathematical logic will want to consult

[20] Martin Davis (ed.), *The Undecidable* (Raven Press, Hewlett, Long Island, New York, 1965).

and

[21] Jean Van Heijenoort, *From Frege to Gödel: A Source Book in Mathematical Logic* 1879–1931 (Harvard University Press, Cambridge, Massachusetts, 1967).

Reference [20] contains the original papers on undecidable propositions, unsolvable problems and computable functions by Gödel, Church, Turing, Rosser, Kleene, and Post. Reference [21] contains a good selection of original papers from the period which gave birth to modern mathematical logic. The papers have been translated into English and an explanatory introduction is given for each paper.

Finally, for those interested in the philosophy of mathematics, a good anthology, containing papers representing virtually every point of view, is

[22] Paul Benaceraf and Hilary Putnam (eds.), *Philosophy of Mathematics, Selected Readings* (Prentice-Hall, Englewood Cliffs, New Jersey, 1964).

INDEX OF SYMBOLS

Notational Conventions

The following notational conventions have been (more or less) consistently followed (the page number refers to the first page where the notational convention is used).

CHAPTER 1

		Page
$p_1, p_2, \ldots$	the proposition letters	4
$\mathbf{p}, \mathbf{q}, \ldots$	arbitrary proposition letters	13
p, q, r	particular proposition letters	7
A, B, C, . . .	arbitrary wffs	5, 7

CHAPTER 2

P_i^k	the ith k-place predicate letter	34
$x_0, x_1, x_2, \ldots$	the individual variables	35
a, b, c, . . .	arbitrary individual variables or individual constants	35
x, y, z, . . .	arbitrary individual variable	35
x, y, z	particular individual variables	36
a, b, c, . . .	arbitrary individual constants	39
P, Q, . . .	arbitrary predicate letters	35
P, Q, R	particular predicate letters	36
A, B, C	arbitrary wffs	35

CHAPTERS 3, 4, 5

		Page
$x, y, a, b, \ldots$	arbitrary natural numbers	66
$f, g, h, \ldots$	arbitrary numerical functions	66
Z	the zero function	67
S	the successor function	67
I_i^m	a projection function	67
x_m	m^{th} individual variable	73
x, y, z	particular individual variables	85
f, **g**, **h**, ...	arbitrary function constants	73
Z	the zero function letter	72
S	the successor function letter	72
I_i^m	a projection function letter	73
t, **s**, ...	arbitrary terms	74
A, **B**, **C**, ...	arbitrary wffs	74

CHAPTER 6

$\mathrm{x}, \mathrm{y}, \mathrm{z}, \mathrm{x}_1, \mathrm{y}_1, \mathrm{z}_1, \ldots$	the individual variables	133
$\alpha, \beta, \gamma, \ldots$	particular relation variables	133
$\boldsymbol{\varphi}, \boldsymbol{\psi}, \ldots$	arbitrary relation variable or relation constant	133
v, **u**, ...	arbitrary variable	134
x, **y**, ...	arbitrary individual variable	138
$\boldsymbol{\alpha}, \boldsymbol{\beta}, \ldots$	arbitrary relation variable	134
a, **b**, ...	usually an arbitrary individual variable or individual constant; occasionally an arbitrary variable or constant	138
P, **Q**, ...	arbitrary relation constant	137
$\varphi, \psi, \ldots$	arbitrary relation	137
$a, b, \ldots$	arbitrary individual	138
A, **B**, **C**, ...	arbitrary wffs	134

Names of Formal Languages

P	the propositional calculus	4
P_I	implication propositional calculus	24

Syntactical Notations

Semantical Notations

Notations for Primitive Recursive Function Theory

Standard Mathematical Notations

iff	if and only if
▮	end of proof
$\Leftrightarrow$	if and only if

The following notations are explained in Appendix A1:

$$x \in X, \qquad \{x\}$$

$$x \notin X \qquad \bigcup_{m=0}^{\infty} X_m$$

$X \subseteq Y$	$\bigcap_{m=0}^{\infty} X_m$
$X = Y$	$f\colon X \to Y$
$X \cap Y$	$\{x \mid P(x)\}$
$X \cup Y$	$\{x \in X \mid P(x)\}$
$X \setminus Y$	
X^k	

The notation $\{f(x) \mid x \in X\}$ is occasionally used in place of the more cumbersome $\{y \mid \text{ there exists } x \in X \text{ with } f(x) = y\}$.

INDEX